PRENTICE-HALL SERIES IN
ENGINEERING OF THE PHYSICAL SCIENCES

James B. Reswick and Warren M. Rohsenow, *editors*

PRENTICE-HALL INTERNATIONAL SERIES
IN ENGINEERING OF THE PHYSICAL SCIENCES

PRENTICE-HALL, INC.
PRENTICE-HALL INTERNATIONAL, INC.,
UNITED KINGDOM AND EIRE
PRENTICE-HALL OF CANADA, LTD., CANADA

VOLUME I

AUTOMATIC
CONTROL SYSTEMS
ENGINEERING

CONTROL SYSTEMS ENGINEERING

A. W. Langill, Jr.

Technical Specialist
Aerojet-General Corporation
Sacramento, California

Prentice-Hall, Inc., Englewood Cliffs, N.J.

PRENTICE-HALL INTERNATIONAL, INC., *London*
PRENTICE-HALL OF AUSTRALIA, PTY., LTD., *Sydney*
PRENTICE-HALL OF CANADA, LTD., *Toronto*
PRENTICE-HALL OF INDIA (PRIVATE) LTD., *New Delhi*
PRENTICE-HALL OF JAPAN, INC., *Tokyo*

Current printing (last digit):

11   10   9   8   7   6   5   4   3   2

Library of Congress Catalog Card Number 65-14988

Printed in the United States of America
C-05506

To Jeanette

PREFACE

One of the most difficult tasks facing the newly graduated control systems engineer is that of adapting his analytical training to a highly sophisticated industrial environment. Upon graduation, the engineer is suddenly thrust into a real-life world of complex multiple loop autopilots and nonlinear process controllers in which electronic computer programming is often substituted for the more classical and direct paper and pencil analysis approach. The success of the emerging designer can often be measured directly in terms of his ability to cope with these surroundings.

In addition, many control systems engineers have simply been born of necessity and not cultivated through any prior systematic training. Not so many years ago, the terms "servomechanism" and "Laplace transformation" were considered in the same general category with "witchcraft" or "black magic" by a majority of graduate engineers. In recent years, however, massive emphasis has been placed upon all types of intricate military control systems, while industrial automation has evolved into an important economic as well as technological expression. Because of this dramatic and continuing expansion, more and more engineers are becoming directly involved with control systems design.

As the title signifies, *Automatic Control Systems Engineering* attempts to present a comprehensive introduction to those bodies of knowledge required of the controls designer. The book is practical from the standpoint of providing information relevant to the industrial environment, but simultaneously maintains a high degree of academic rigor. When possible, concepts are explained through both theoretical and intuitive approaches. Analog simulation is introduced early and employed liberally throughout the remainder of the text; this appreciation of automatic machine simulation is in keeping with general industrial practices.

Automatic Control Systems Engineering is written two volumes, containing a total of twenty-three individual chapters. Volume I consists of an introduction followed by two main sections: (1) Dynamic Systems Analysis (Chapters 2 through 6), and (2) Basic Control Systems Theory (Chapters 7 through 13).

Two appendices complete the text. Volume II, *Advanced Control Systems Engineering*, comprises ten chapters devoted primarily to the subject of nonlinear control systems theory.

The purpose of Part I, Dynamic Systems Analysis, is to equip the reader with a sufficient but not overpowering amount of prerequisite information. This section presents the essentials of complex-variable theory, operational calculus, engineering circuit theory, and linear analog simulation techniques in a concise and integrated form. The multiplicity of theorems, lemmas, postulates, etc., that characterizes pure mathematics have been drastically reduced in favor of a continuous engineering type of presentation. The only prerequisite to a full understanding of Part I is a previous course in integral and differential calculus. For those having a prior knowledge of the subject material, the preliminary section provides an excellent opportunity for review. An extensive problem set is included at the end of each chapter; partial problem solutions follow Appendix B.

Part I begins with an introduction to complex variable theory (Chapter 2), in which the fundamental complex number is derived and various complex variable operations and concepts formalized. Chapter 3 reviews the processes by which differential equations can be determined from corresponding linear passive and active electrical, mechanical, and electromechanical systems. The differential equation is solved, in Chapter 4, by the application of Laplace transformation techniques to yield the corresponding physical-system transient and steady-state response characteristics. The subject of system frequency-response calculations is introduced in Chapter 5. Part I concludes with a discussion of analog simulation and programming as applied to the arbitrary linear system.

Part II, Basic Control Systems Theory, builds upon the preliminary considerations previously mentioned, a consistent and self-sufficient procedure for the analysis and design of linear control systems. The root-locus is presented prior to historical frequency response methods because of the clear insight into systems behavior afforded by this technique. Chapter 7 illustrates the transfer function and block diagram representation of linear control processes; first- and second-order systems are characterized in Chapter 8; and Chapter 9 is devoted to a study of steady-state system errors. The root-locus is formulated in Chapter 10 and employed in a number of practical sample problem analyses. Frequency response methods are discussed in Chapters 11, 12, and 13 as follows: Chapter 11 derives the Nyquist stability criterion through conventional methods and, in addition, illustrates a simplified approach; polar plots and polar frequency response methods are presented in Chapter 12; Chapter 13 summarizes the well-known log frequency plot analysis.

Two appendices complete the text: Appendix A consists of an extensive table of Laplace transform pairs; Appendix B illustrates the Routh stability criterion and defines through typical examples the determination of conditions existing at the point of marginal stability.

The material covered in Volume I can be integrated into an engineering curriculum in a variety of ways. Accelerated but comprehensive 18-week courses in Dynamic Systems Analysis and Control Systems Theory, based upon the format as derived in the text, have been offered at the Aerojet-General Corporation with excellent results. The text is compatible with the requirements for a one-year course of instruction at the senior year under-graduate level. Further, the book should be acceptable to those desiring a reference text for individual study. In this regard, the fact that partial solutions are provided should tend to encourage completion of the problems. The entire text has been cleared for public release by the Department of Defense.

I would like to express my appreciation to the students of Aerojet Course Numbers 38–50 and 38–60 for their thorough review and constructive criticism of the course syllabus, which formed the forerunner of this text, and to the Aerojet-General Corporation for providing facilities for the course presentations. In addition, particular thanks are due to Drs. Walter J. Karplus, Leonard Pode, Theodore A. Savo, and John M. Salzer of the University of California at Los Angeles, whose excellent class notes and homework problems form the basis for a significant portion of the text. Finally, I wish to express sincere appreciation to Mrs. Adella Phillips and Mrs. Gloria Burns, Aerojet-General Corporation, for their outstanding assistance in the preparation of the manuscript.

A. W. LANGILL, JR.

CONTENTS

INTRODUCTION TO AUTOMATIC CONTROL SYSTEMS ENGINEERING

1

1-1 ELEMENTS OF A CONTROL SYSTEM

Broadly speaking, a control system can be defined as an element or series of elements that implement the transformation of a physical input excitation into a corresponding physical output response in some deterministic manner. To illustrate, both the high-speed missile-steering autopilot and the conventional automobile power-steering mechanism steer vehicles in accordance with a set of input commands. In the latter case, the input takes the form of manually directed position signals generated by the driver; for the former, the missile autopilot is excited through electrical voltages generated by the guidance system. In either case, however, the net result is identical; the vehicle is adjusted into a new frame of reference by the steering systems. Further, the mechanisms through which the transformation from input variable (steering signal) to output variable (change in position) is accomplished is perfectly predictable.

Although both qualify as control systems under the basic definition, the missile and automobile steering systems differ significantly. As its name implies, the power steering controller performs only as a power converter, i.e., there are no built-in safeguards to prevent oversteering into the ditch. Conversely, the missile designer takes many elaborate precautions to insure automatically that at no time will the missile flight become erratic. This automatic vehicle-control feature is realized principally through the application of feedback techniques. Assume, for the sake of illustration, that the electrical guidance command signals are to be transformed, by the steering autopilot, into corresponding missile angular pitch rate characteristics. Now, if the desired or controlled variable is measured by a suitable transducer (in this case a rate gyroscope would be appropriate) and this output response compared directly to the system excitation (electrical guidance unit command), a new variable is formed that relates the instantaneous error between the desired response and the actual response. Further, if the newly formed error variable is employed to drive the missile steering mechanism in a direction that continually reduces the error, then the possibility of marked oversteering or understeering is greatly minimized. In practice, a number of feedback loops would be provided to insure optimum system performance under widely varying physical environments; nonlinear elements quite possibly could be inserted within the system to improve the response characteristics and an in-flight digital computer might afford a rapid and accurate numerical calculation capability. However, regardless of the degree of complexity, the steering system is based upon an error signal minimization criterion.

I-2 OPEN- AND CLOSED-LOOP FUNCTIONAL DIAGRAMS

In the previous section, two common steering assemblies were considered. It was observed that the primary difference between these systems was the existence or nonexistence of stabilizing feedback. The power-steering assembly, without feedback, was easily capable of directing the vehicle into the nearest telephone pole. A system in which the power-actuator output is not influenced by the response variable is referred to as an *open-loop* system. Figure 1-2.1 illustrates a typical open-loop system, consisting of an input signal, a power converter, and an output signal.

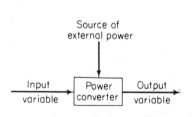

Figure I-2.1 Open-loop system.

This form of flow chart, specifying the paths of information (action and reaction) and identifying qualitatively each system component, is defined as a *functional diagram*.

As discussed previously, the closed-loop control system is one in which the power converter drive signal is affected by the instantaneous state of the output variable. In particular, a simplified functional diagram corresponding to the high-speed missile pitch rate autopilot of Section 1-1, illustrated in Fig. 1-2.2, consists of three principal components: (1) a power converter, (2) an output-variable sensor, and (3) a symbolic subtracting element. Thus, the output variable is subtracted from the input signal to form the power converter driving function (error signal). Negative (subtractive) feedback is employed for a variety of very practical reasons, among which are included: (a) the stabilization of systems response against variations in the power converter, (b) the minimization of steady-state errors, and (c) the elimination of a precision calibration requirement. While the closed-loop control system has very marked advantages over the open-loop form of mechani-

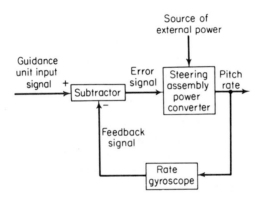

Figure 1-2.2 Closed-loop system.

zation, two very significant disadvantages are inherently present. First, by definition, the closed-loop system is more difficult to mechanize because of increased structural complexity. In addition, the closed-loop system is subject to instability phenomena. Whereas the properly designed and constructed closed-loop control system may function according to specification under practically any combination of operational environment and component parameter variations, the improperly designed or constructed system will react in an altogether different manner. In the unstable system, the output variable can oscillate with a constantly increasing amplitude, or increase exponentially until total destruction or a form of saturation occurs. In the unstable system, the output variable bears no resemblance to the input variable, i.e., an input comprised exclusively of random noise causes the system to enter a regenerative mode. Needless to say, the primary objective of any closed-loop system design is to insure absolute stability for all expected, and many unexpected, operating conditions.

I-3 ANALYSIS VS. SYNTHESIS

In any problem of dynamic analysis, three quantities are invariably present within the problem formulation, i.e., an input function or set of functions, a dynamic system, and an output function or set of functions. The conventional engineering problem can be formulated as follows: Given two of the three quantities, compute the third. Strictly speaking, *analysis* involves a process of calculating a known system's response to a given input excitation. *Synthesis* is the process of defining a system to generate some specified input-output relationship. And finally, the process of eliminating the dynamical content of a response variable so as to define more adequately the true input forcing function is termed dynamic compensation or *reconstruction*.

Although many texts concerned with control systems theory contain the word "synthesis" in the title, the author has observed that few practical systems can be designed by rigorous synthesis procedures, principally because no powerful or universally applicable synthesis techniques have been developed to date. Unlike network design, which perhaps represents the most advanced state of synthesis, control systems are designed by a repetitive trial-and-error analysis. The engineer begins the design procedure with a group of fixed or invariant components often called the *plant*, a group of variable elements containing design parameters, and a set of over-all system specifications. To illustrate, the plant might consist of a particular control motor and a feedback transducer; these elements must be employed in the design. The selection of the summing amplifier gain is, however, a variable and thus represents a design parameter. In addition, any reasonable amount of passive network compensation can be inserted. The specifications normally relate to minimum or maximum standards associated with either time or frequency domains, e.g., "the system shall have a step function response with a rise time of less than 1 second and a maximum overshoot of less than 15 per cent."

To initiate the system design, the engineer would usually choose a specific value of amplifier gain, assuming no network compensation, thus fixing all elements contained within the loop. At this point, then, the problem has been reduced to one of analysis, i.e., given the system and the input function (step), compute the output response. Once the analysis has been accomplished, the resulting system step-function response is evaluated according to the specification requirements. If the specifications are satisfied, the design is completed; usually, however, it could be expected that the initial system configuration would be somewhat less than totally satisfactory. Thus, in the general case, a second system is assumed, a corresponding analysis completed, and the results again compared to the loop requirements. This process of choosing a system, analyzing the system response to an assumed excitation, and comparing to the specified response is repeated until a suitable design has been generated. At this point, the system is frozen and the engineer must await the results of field testing.

Thus, the control system design is nothing more complicated than a conventional trial-and-error analysis. A majority of the subjects discussed in subsequent chapters of this text deal directly with the problem of generating accurate and rapid methods of analysis.

I-4 CONTROL COMPONENTS

A complete listing of all components or elements that could conceivably be utilized in a control system would include practically every electrical, mechanical, electromechanical, electronic, thermal, pneumatic, hydraulic, and nuclear device ever invented. Although the servomotor, the hydraulic servovalve, the rate gyroscope and other devices are normally associated with control systems engineering, the list could be extended practically to infinity. Because of the mass of available equipment and the very excellent coverage extended to componentry by a variety of trade catalogs and manufacturer brochures, this text will consider physical elements only in passing, or in order to demonstrate a point in theory by a practical example. To see how easily huge amounts of commercial technical information can be gathered, try circling each item on a trade magazine "reader's reply" sheet.

I-5 ANALOG SIMULATION IN CONTROL SYSTEMS DESIGN

The electronic differential analyzer or *analog computer* represents perhaps the most highly satisfactory engineering tool available for the design, optimization, and analysis of linear or nonlinear control systems. Because of the universal acceptance of this device by practically all dynamic systems designers, and with the advent of the small transistorized computer capable of fitting easily into an undersized shoe box, it is becoming more and more essential that the control systems engineer be appreciative of analog simulation techniques. A knowledge of analog simulation allows the controls designer to personally check (if not actually mechanize) an analog schematic, therefore reducing his dependence upon the computer programming specialist normally responsible for generating the simulation. In this manner, the designer can personally verify that the schematic is indeed correct.

An understanding of computer processes also equips the design engineer with a technique for analytically manipulating mathematical models of physical systems. For example, a nonfeedback system can be converted into a totally analogous model containing feedback. Special techniques for the analysis of nonlinear control systems are developed in subsequent chapters. These methods are based upon a preliminary paper-and-pencil analog computer mechanization of certain linear portions of the loop. Thus, a knowledge of analog simulation is desirable from the standpoint of providing an insight into basic loop processes; the technique will be viewed in this context throughout the remainder of the text.

COMPLEX VARIABLE THEORY[1,2,3]

2

2-1 INTRODUCTION

Complex-variable theory provides a firm foundation upon which are constructed many of the techniques employed in the analysis and design of automatic control systems. Although it is not necessary for the controls designer to be a master mathematician, an appreciation of at least the rudiments of complex-variable theory is essential to a clear understanding of many of the more important concepts to follow. Such topics as the Laplace transformation, frequency-response calculations, root-locus theory, and Nyquist's stability criterion are derived directly from this branch of mathematics. The author must apologize for beginning an engineering-oriented text with a purely mathematical introduction (the normal procedure is to relegate this type of information to some obscure appendix). However, although the subject is surely of a mathematical nature, an engineering presentation is employed whenever possible, and only that material necessary for a clear comprehension of later topics is included. It is strongly recommended that Chapter 2 be thoroughly reviewed before additional chapters are considered.

2-2 COMPLEX NUMBERS AND BASIC OPERATIONS

The complex-number system can be interpreted as a mathematical generalization of the real-number system described in elementary arithmetic, and it arises naturally in the solution to the quadratic equation

$$as^2 + bs + c = 0 \qquad (2\text{-}2.1)$$

If the discriminant, $b^2 - 4ac$ is positive, then the corresponding roots are real quantities with values $-b/2a \pm \sqrt{b^2 - 4ac}/2a$. For a negative discriminant, however, an operation is required that is not compatible with real-number theory, i.e., obtaining the square root of a negative number. The complex number was invented to provide a solution to this and similar type problems.

If we define a complex indicator j such that $j^2 = -1$, the solution to Eq. (2-2.1), for negative discriminants, becomes

$$s = -\frac{b}{2a} \pm j\,\frac{\sqrt{4ac - b^2}}{2a} \qquad (2\text{-}2.2)$$

A number of the form shown in Eq. (2-2.2) can be represented by the position of a point situated upon a plane surface, just as the real number N corresponds to a point situated upon a line. By definition, the complex number $s_i = \sigma_i + j\omega_i$ consists of two independent portions: a real part σ_i and an imaginary part ω_i. Furthermore, this number is expressed geometrically by a point in a complex plane referenced to a pair of orthogonal axes, where the numbers σ_i and ω_i correspond to the abscissa and ordinate coordinates of the point respectively. As illustrated in Fig. 2-2.1, the complex number $s_i = \sigma_i + j\omega_i$ represents only one of an infinite number of possible points lying upon the complex s-plane.

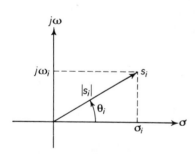

Figure 2-2.1 The complex s-plane.

This particular method for geometrically describing a complex number is consistent with the conventional method of picturing real-number systems. If all imaginary parts of Fig. 2-2.1 are identically zero, the complex plane degenerates into a real-number axis. Thus, this mode of representing the complex-number system encompasses, as a special case, all real numbers.

A particular complex number s_i, when illustrated in terms of real and imaginary components, is said to be expressed in rectangular coordinates. The point $\sigma_i + j\omega_i$ may also be defined by the length and direction of a vector, originating at the origin $(0 + j0)$ and terminating upon the point $s = s_i$. The scalar length of the resulting vector illustrated in Fig. 2-2.1, denoted as $|s_i|$, is referred to as the magnitude, modulus, or absolute value of s_i, and is expressed as

$$|s_i| = |\sigma_i + j\omega_i| = \sqrt{\sigma_i^2 + \omega_i^2} \qquad (2\text{-}2.3)$$

The vector direction angle θ_i through which the positive real axis must be rotated to coincide with this vector (positive for a counterclockwise real axis rotation) is referred to as the phase, phase angle, angle, or argument of s_i

$$\theta_i = \arg s_i = \angle s_i \qquad (2\text{-}2.4)$$

Although there is but one absolute value associated with any s-plane point location, an infinite number of arguments exist. Thus, while $\theta_i = \tan^{-1} \omega_i/\sigma_i$ is the principal phase angle, additional arguments of the form $\theta_i + k2\pi$ (where $k = 1, 2, 3, \ldots$) also occur, and they are all equivalent. Except as specifically noted, the remainder of this chapter will consider only principal phase angles lying between the limits of $\pm\pi$.

If A_i and θ_i denote the polar coordinates of the s-plane point (σ_i, ω_i), then

$$\sigma_i = A_i \cos \theta_i \qquad (2\text{-}2.5)$$

and

$$\omega_i = A_i \sin \theta_i \qquad (2\text{-}2.6)$$

so that

$$s_i = \sigma_i + j\omega_i = A_i(\cos \theta_i + j \sin \theta_i) \qquad (2\text{-}2.7)$$

The final expression of Eq. (2-2.7) describes a point s_i by means of trigonometric polar coordinates. One additional polar from exists, however, and it is intuitively derived as follows: Consider the infinite series expansions for the trigonometric functions $\sin \theta_i$ and $\cos \theta_i$.

$$\sin \theta_i = \theta_i - \frac{\theta_i^3}{3!} + \frac{\theta_i^5}{5!} - \cdots \qquad (2\text{-}2.8)$$

$$\cos \theta_i = 1 - \frac{\theta_i^2}{2!} + \frac{\theta_i^4}{4!} - \cdots \qquad (2\text{-}2.9)$$

Combining Eqs (2-2.8) and (2-2.9) into the final expression of Eq. (2-2.7), and remembering that $j^2 = -1$

$$s_i = A_i\left[1 - \frac{\theta_i^2}{2!} + \frac{\theta_i^4}{4!} - \cdots + j\left(\theta_i - \frac{\theta_i^3}{3!} + \cdots\right)\right] \qquad (2\text{-}2.10)$$

$$= A_i\left[1 + j\theta_i + \frac{(j\theta_i)^2}{2!} + \frac{(j\theta_i)^3}{3!} + \frac{(j\theta_i)^4}{4!} + \cdots\right] \qquad (2\text{-}2.11)$$

But the series expansion for $e^{j\theta_i}$ is

$$e^{j\theta_i} = 1 + j\theta_i + \frac{(j\theta_i)^2}{2!} + \frac{(j\theta_i)^3}{3!} + \cdots \qquad (2\text{-}2.12)$$

Since the series of Eqs. (2-2.11) and (2-2.12) are identical, it follows directly that

$$s_i = \sigma_i + j\omega_i = A_i(\cos\theta_i + j\sin\theta_i) = A_i e^{j\theta_i} \qquad (2\text{-}2.13)$$

Thus, the point $s = s_i$ can be described in either a rectangular, trigonometric polar, or exponential polar coordinate form. The basic operations of complex addition, subtraction, multiplication, and division are now

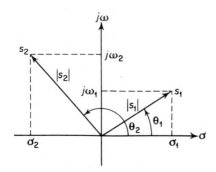

Figure 2-2.2 Complex numbers s_1 and s_2 expressed in rectangular and polar coordinates.

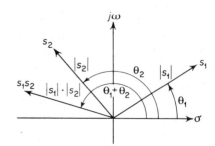

Figure 2-2.3 Multiplication of two complex numbers in polar coordinates.

examined by considering the two complex numbers illustrated in Fig. 2-2.2

$$s_1 = \sigma_1 + j\omega_1 = A_1 e^{j\theta_1} \qquad (2\text{-}2.14)$$

$$s_2 = \sigma_2 + j\omega_2 = A_2 e^{j\theta_2} \qquad (2\text{-}2.15)$$

Multiplication: The multiplication of two complex numbers is most easily visualized in the exponential polar form, i.e.

$$s_1 s_2 = (A_1 e^{j\theta_1})(A_2 e^{j\theta_2}) = A_1 A_2 e^{j(\theta_1 + \theta_2)} \qquad (2\text{-}2.16)$$

Hence, as described in Fig. 2-2.3, the product of two complex numbers is a complex number whose magnitude is the product of the component vector lengths, and whose phase is the sum of the component arguments. Although not nearly as convenient, complex multiplication can also be carried out in rectangular coordinates to yield

$$s_1 s_2 = (\sigma_1 + j\omega_1)(\sigma_2 + j\omega_2) = (\sigma_1\sigma_2 - \omega_1\omega_2) + j(\sigma_1\omega_2 + \sigma_2\omega_1) \qquad (2\text{-}2.17)$$

Division: Complex division is most simply generated by the exponential polar format. Thus

$$\frac{s_1}{s_2} = \frac{A_1 e^{j\theta_1}}{A_2 e^{j\theta_2}} = \frac{A_1}{A_2} e^{j(\theta_1 - \theta_2)} \tag{2-2.18}$$

In rectangular coordinates

$$\frac{s_1}{s_2} = \frac{\sigma_1 + j\omega_1}{\sigma_2 + j\omega_2} = \frac{(\sigma_1 + j\omega_1)(\sigma_2 - j\omega_2)}{(\sigma_2 + j\omega_2)(\sigma_2 - j\omega_2)} \tag{2-2.19}$$

$$= \frac{(\sigma_1\sigma_2 + \omega_1\omega_2) + j(\sigma_2\omega_1 - \sigma_1\omega_2)}{\sigma_2^2 + \omega_2^2} \tag{2-2.20}$$

In Eq. (2-2.19), the divisor is made real (such that the final result will appear as a complex number with real and imaginary parts) by multiplying both the numerator and the denominator by the complex conjugate of the divisor.

As stated earlier and illustrated in Fig. 2-2.4, $\bar{s}_2 = \sigma_2 - j\omega_2$ is defined as the complex conjugate of $s_2 = \sigma_2 + j\omega_2$. Complex-conjugate pairs are of special interest to the physical systems analyst. It will be shown later that, should a physical system give rise to a complex root, a complex-conjugate root must also be present. Thus, some of the principles concerned with complex conjugates will now be discussed, together with additional complex algebraic manipulations.

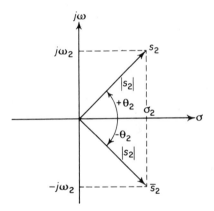

2-3 ALGEBRA OF COMPLEX NUMBERS

Figure 2-2.4 Complex conjugate quantities.

In this section, a few of the more important consequences of complex algebra are stated and, as required, justified intuitively. Returning to the complex conjugate, we can state that the sum of a complex number and its conjugate is equal to twice the real part of the complex number (or complex conjugate). Thus

$$s_1 + \bar{s}_1 = (\sigma_1 + j\omega_1) + (\sigma_1 - j\omega) = 2\sigma_1 = 2\,\text{Re}\,s_1 \tag{2-3.1}$$

Similarly, the difference between a complex number and its conjugate is a purely imaginary number, equal in magnitude to twice the imaginary part of the complex number.

$$s_1 - \bar{s}_1 = (\sigma_1 + j\omega_1) - (\sigma_1 - j\omega_1) = j2\omega_1 = j2 \text{ Im } s_1 \qquad (2\text{-}3.2)$$

And finally, the product of a complex number and its complex conjugate is a real number, equal in magnitude to the square of the vector length of the complex number. In investigating this relationship, one makes use of the exponential form. Thus, if $s_1 = A_1 e^{j\theta_1}$, then $\bar{s}_1 = A_1 e^{-j\theta_1}$. Hence

$$s_1 \bar{s}_1 = (A_1 e^{j\theta_1})(A_1 e^{-j\theta_1}) = A_1^2 e^{j(\theta_1 - \theta_1)} = A_1^2 \qquad (2\text{-}3.3)$$

The equality or inequality of two complex quantities is slightly more complicated than in the case of real numbers. Since a complex quantity can be expressed by means of independent real and imaginary parts, two complex numbers are identical if, and only if, their real parts and their imaginary parts are equal. Similarly, when expressed in polar coordinates, a necessary and sufficient criterion for equality is that both the vector magnitudes and phase angles must be equal. Thus, $A_1 e^{j\theta_1}$ and $A_2 e^{j\theta_2}$ are equal if, and only if, $A_1 = A_2$ and $\theta_1 = \theta_2$.

An interesting process that can be investigated through complex number theory is the determining of roots of a complex number. Initially, let us calculate the n distinct nth roots of unity. For this application, one invokes the fact that a complex number has associated with it an infinite number of phase angles, each separated by 2π radians. Thus, unity is defined in exponential coordinates as

$$1 = e^{j0} = e^{j(0+2\pi k)} = e^{j2\pi k} \qquad (2\text{-}3.4)$$

where $k = 0, 1, 2, \ldots$.

Hence

$$1^{1/n} = e^{j(2\pi k/n)} = \cos \frac{2\pi k}{n} + j \sin \frac{2\pi k}{n} \qquad (2\text{-}3.5)$$

As an illustrative example, consider the three cube roots of unity. Using Eq. (2-3.5) for $k = 0, 1,$ and 2

$$1^{1/3}_{k=0} = \cos 0 + j \sin 0 = 1$$

$$1^{1/3}_{k=1} = \cos \frac{2\pi}{3} + j \sin \frac{2\pi}{3} = -\frac{1}{2} + j\frac{\sqrt{3}}{2}$$

$$1^{1/3}_{k=2} = \cos \frac{4\pi}{3} + j \sin \frac{4\pi}{3} = -\frac{1}{2} - j\frac{\sqrt{3}}{2}$$

The results of the preceding calculations are pictured geometrically in Fig. 2-3.1. Note that the three roots of unity are symmetrically disposed upon a circle of unit radius and centered at the origin. This outcome is general, and it is similarly true for the nth roots of unity.

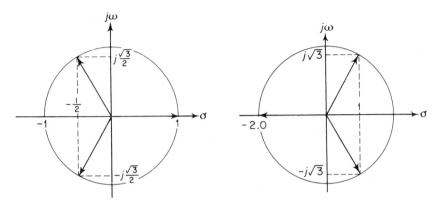

Figure 2-3.1   The cube roots of unity.   Figure 2-3.2   The cube roots of -8.

Now consider the generalized complex quantity, $Ae^{j\theta}$. The n distinct nth roots of this number are described as

$$(Ae^{j\theta})^{1/n} = A^{1/n}e^{j(\theta+2\pi k/n)} = A^{1/n}\left(\cos\frac{\theta + 2\pi k}{n} + j\sin\frac{\theta + 2\pi k}{n}\right) \qquad (2\text{-}3.6)$$

Hence, the three cube roots of $-8 = 8e^{j180°}$ are computed as

$$-8_{k=0}^{1/3} = 8^{1/3}\left(\cos\frac{\pi}{3} + j\sin\frac{\pi}{3}\right) = 1 + j\sqrt{3}$$

$$-8_{k=1}^{1/3} = 8^{1/3}(\cos\pi + j\sin\pi) = -2$$

$$-8_{k=2}^{1/3} = 8^{1/3}\left(\cos\frac{5\pi}{3} + j\sin\frac{5\pi}{3}\right) = 1 - j\sqrt{3}$$

The cube roots of -8 are illustrated in Fig. 2-3.2.

2-4 FUNCTIONS OF A COMPLEX VARIABLE

A complex quantity, $s = \sigma + j\omega$, in which σ and ω are real variables, is denoted as a complex variable. A complex variable differs from a complex number in that, the latter is characterized by specific real and imaginary parts, e.g., $\sigma_1 + j\omega_1$, whereas the former is allowed to take on all values of σ and ω If in some region of the s-plane, for each $s_i = \sigma_i + j\omega_i$, a corresponding complex number $G_i = \text{Re } G_i + j \text{ Im } G_i$ is defined, we say that G is a function of the complex variable s; it is thus designated as $G(s)$. A complex function $G(s)$ is single valued if, for each s_i, a unique $G(s_i)$ arises. If more than one value of $G(s_i)$ corresponds to s_i, the function $G(s)$ is multiple valued. The great majority of all $G(s)$ functions encountered in control systems theory consist of ratios of polynomials in s, e.g.

$$G(s) = \frac{K(s^n + a_1 s^{n-1} + a_2 s^{n-2} + \cdots + a_n)}{s^m + b_1 s^{m-1} + b_2 s^{m-2} + \cdots + b_m} \qquad (2\text{-}4.1)$$

which are single-valued functions of s. An example of a multivalued function, which will be encountered again in Chapter 13, is

$$W(s) = \log_e s \qquad (2\text{-}4.2)$$

Since the logarithm of a complex number is defined in an identical manner as in real-variable theory, it follows that

$$s = e^{W(s)} \qquad (2\text{-}4.3)$$

Substituting $W(s) = \text{Re } W(s) + j \text{ Im } W(s)$ into Eq. (2-4.3)

$$s = e^{\text{Re } W(s) + j \text{ Im } W(s)}$$
$$A e^{j(\theta + 2\pi k)} = e^{\text{Re } W(s)} e^{j \text{ Im } W(s)} \qquad (2\text{-}4.4)$$

Equation (2-4.4) expresses an equality between two complex variables. Thus

$$A = e^{\text{Re } W(s)} \qquad (2\text{-}4.5)$$

and

$$\theta + 2\pi k = \text{Im } W(s) \qquad (2\text{-}4.6)$$

where $k = 0, \pm 1, \pm 2, \ldots$.

Since $\text{Re } W(s)$ and $\text{Im } W(s)$ are real variables, it follows from Eq. (2-4.5) that

$$\text{Re } W(s) = \text{Log}_e A \qquad (2\text{-}4.7)$$

where Log is employed to denote the natural logarithm encountered in real variable theory. Hence

$$W(s) = \text{Re } W(s) + j \text{ Im } W(s) = \log_e s = \text{Log}_e A + j(\theta + 2\pi k) \qquad (2\text{-}4.8)$$

Thus, $\log_e s$ has infinitely many values corresponding to all possible integer values of k in Eq. (2-4.8). If $k = 0$ and θ is constrained to lie between zero and 2π, then

$$\log_e s = \text{Log}_e A + j\theta \qquad (2\text{-}4.9)$$

Equation (2-4.8) serves to illustrate the procedure used to evaluate irrational and complex powers of the complex variable s. To demonstrate, consider the function

$$W(s) = s^p \qquad (2\text{-}4.10)$$

Taking the log of Eq. (2-4.10)

$$\log_e W(s) = \log_e s^p = p \log_e s \qquad (2\text{-}4.11)$$

from which

$$W(s) = e^{p \log_e s} \qquad (2\text{-}4.12)$$

Substituting the expression for $\log_e s$ developed in Eq. (2-4.8)

$$W(s) = e^{p[\text{Log}_e A + j(\theta + 2\pi k)]} \qquad (2\text{-}4.13)$$

Equation (2-4.13) can be utilized to compute $W(s)$ for complex or irrational exponents p.

2-5 ANALYTIC FUNCTIONS

From differential calculus, the derivative of a function of real variable, with respect to that variable, is defined in terms of a limiting process. Thus

$$\frac{df(x)}{dx} = f'(x) = \lim_{\Delta x \to 0} \frac{f(x + \Delta x) - f(x)}{\Delta x} \qquad (2\text{-}5.1)$$

Similarly, the derivative of a function of a complex variable $G(s)$ is

$$\frac{dG(s)}{ds} = G'(s) = \lim_{\Delta s \to 0} \frac{G(s + \Delta s) - G(s)}{\Delta s} \qquad (2\text{-}5.2)$$

Hence, the definitions denoted by Eqs. (2-5.1) and (2-5.2) are physically analogous, implying that the limiting process of real-variable theory is equally valid in the case of complex variables. One difficulty arises, however, that has no counterpart in real-variable theory. The complex increment, $\Delta s = \Delta\sigma + j\,\Delta\omega$, may approach zero, as required in Eq. (2-5.2), along an infinite number of separate paths. Thus, for the complex function $G(s)$ to possess a derivative $G'(s)$, it is necessary that the value of $G'(s)$ be independent of the particular path by which Δs approaches zero. Fortunately, the great majority of all $G(s)$ functions that arise in the study of feedback control systems are differentiable.

It now remains to determine a criterion for the existence of a derivative. Consider the arbitrary function $G(s)$ of Eq. (2-5.3), which consists of both real and imaginary parts, G_R and G_I. In general, G_R and G_I are functions of both σ and ω as shown.

$$G(s) = G_R(\sigma, \omega) + jG_I(\sigma, \omega) \tag{2-5.3}$$

From Eq. (2-5.2)

$$G'(s) = \lim_{\substack{\Delta\sigma \to 0 \\ \Delta\omega \to 0}} \frac{[G_R(\sigma + \Delta\sigma, \omega + \Delta\omega) + jG_I(\sigma + \Delta\sigma, \omega + \Delta\omega)] - [G_R(\sigma, \omega) + jG_I(\sigma, \omega)]}{\Delta\sigma + j\,\Delta\omega} \tag{2-5.4}$$

In this equation, both $\Delta\sigma$ and $\Delta\omega$ must approach zero. In particular, assume the sequence in which $\Delta\omega$ goes to zero first, followed next by $\Delta\sigma$. For these conditions, Eq. (2-5.4) becomes

$$G'(s) = \lim_{\Delta\sigma \to 0} \left[\frac{G_R(\sigma + \Delta\sigma, \omega) - G_R(\sigma, \omega)}{\Delta\sigma} + j\,\frac{G_I(\sigma + \Delta\sigma, \omega) - G_I(\sigma, \omega)}{\Delta\sigma} \right] \tag{2-5.5}$$

The two components of Eq. (2-5.5) are, however, nothing more than definitive expressions for the partial derivatives of $G_R(\sigma, \omega)$ and $G_I(\sigma, \omega)$ with respect to σ, i.e.

$$G'(s) = \frac{\partial G_R(\sigma, \omega)}{\partial \sigma} + j\,\frac{\partial G_I(\sigma, \omega)}{\partial \sigma} \tag{2-5.6}$$

If Eq. (2-5.4) is computed by allowing $\Delta\sigma$ to approach zero first, followed by $\Delta\omega$

$$G'(s) = \lim_{\Delta\omega \to 0} \left[\frac{G_R(\sigma, \omega + \Delta\omega) - G_R(\sigma, \omega)}{j\,\Delta\omega} + j\,\frac{G_I(\sigma, \omega + \Delta\omega) - G_I(\sigma, \omega)}{j\,\Delta\omega} \right] \tag{2-5.7}$$

This reduces to

$$G'(s) = \frac{\partial G_I(\sigma, \omega)}{\partial \omega} - j\,\frac{\partial G_R(\sigma, \omega)}{\partial \omega} \tag{2-5.8}$$

If the derivative $G'(s)$ exists, then the value is unique and is independent of

only. Thus, let us render R_1 simply connected by inserting a slice or crosscut between A and B of C_1 to D and E of C_2. Cauchy's theorem now applies to the simply connected closed contour, i.e.

$$\int_{AD} G(s)\,ds + \int_{DP_2E} G(s)\,ds + \int_{EB} G(s)\,ds + \int_{BP_1A} G(s)\,ds = 0 \qquad (2\text{-}6.5)$$

Since the lines AD and EB are arbitrarily close, and since $G(s)$ is analytic over both paths, the line integrals $\int_{AD} G(s)\,ds$ and $\int_{BE} G(s)\,ds$ are equal. Hence

$$\int_{AD} G(s)\,ds + \int_{EB} G(s)\,ds = 0 \qquad (2\text{-}6.6)$$

Substituting Eq. (2-6.6) into (2-6.5)

$$\oint_{C_2} G(s)\,ds + \oint_{C_1} G(s)\,ds = 0 \qquad (2\text{-}6.7)$$

If the direction of integration around C_2 is reversed

$$\oint_{C_2} G(s)\,ds = \oint_{C_1} G(s)\,ds \qquad (2\text{-}6.8)$$

Note that the results of Eq. (2-6.8) do not require that $G(s)$ be analytic in R_2. Hence, it follows that the value of an integral of an analytic function over any closed contour, C_1, remains unchanged as C_1 is deformed into any new closed contour, C_2, provided that no singular points lie between C_1 and C_2. These results are generalized further in that the closed exterior contour, C_1, can be deformed into a great many simply connected regions enclosed by C_{2a}, C_{2b}, . . . , so long as no singular points lie in the area between C_{2a}, C_{2b}, . . . , and C_1.

It is now possible to derive, through Cauchy's theorem, the fact that every analytic function $G(s)$ is completely determined in the interior of a closed region R when $G(s)$ is specified on the boundary. If $G(s)$ is analytic within a simply connected region R, and s_i is an interior point of R, then the function $G(s)/s - s_i$ is analytic in R, with the possible exception of the point $s = s_i$. Under these constraints, the exterior contour C may be replaced by a circle of radius γ, with its center located at s_i, i.e.

$$\oint_C \frac{G(s)}{s - s_i}\,ds = \oint_\gamma \frac{G(s)}{s - s_i}\,ds \qquad (2\text{-}6.9)$$

where the directions of rotation of C and γ are the same. Adding and subtracting the expressions $\oint_{\gamma} G(s_i)/s - s_i\, ds$ to the right side of Eq. (2-6.9)

$$\oint_{\gamma} \frac{G(s)}{s - s_i}\, ds = \oint_{\gamma} \frac{G(s) - G(s_i)}{s - s_i}\, ds + G(s_i) \oint_{\gamma} \frac{ds}{s - s_i} \qquad \text{(2-6.10)}$$

The second term of Eq. (2-6.10) is now simply evaluated. As illustrated in

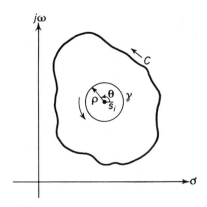

Figure 2-6.3 An example of the deformation-of-contour principle.

Fig. 2-6.3, $s - s_i = \rho e^{j\theta}$ and $ds = \rho e^{j\theta} j\, d\theta$. Substituting into the second term of Eq. (2-6.10)

$$G(s_i) \oint_{\gamma} \frac{ds}{s - s_i} = G(s_i) \oint_{\gamma} \frac{j\rho e^{j\theta}\, d\theta}{\rho e^{j\theta}} = jG(s_i) \int_{0}^{2\pi} d\theta = j2\pi G(s_i) \qquad \text{(2-6.11)}$$

It now remains to evaluate the first term of Eq. (2-6.10). Substituting $s - s_i = \rho e^{j\theta}$ and $ds = j\rho e^{j\theta}\, d\theta$

$$\oint_{\gamma} \frac{G(s) - G(s_i)}{s - s_i}\, ds = j \oint_{\gamma} [G(s) - G(s_i)]\, d\theta \qquad \text{(2-6.12)}$$

Since ρ is an arbitrarily small number (the value of Eq. 2-6.9 is independent of ρ, provided that γ encloses s_i), and the quantity $G(s) - G(s_i)$ approaches zero as $s - s_i$ diminishes to zero, the value of the integral in Eq. (2-6.12) is zero, and Eq. (2-6.10) becomes

$$\oint_{C} \frac{G(s)}{s - s_i}\, ds = j2\pi G(s_i) \qquad \text{(2-6.13)}$$

Rearranging

$$G(s_i) = \frac{1}{j2\pi} \oint_C \frac{G(s)}{s - s_i}\, ds \qquad (2\text{-}6.14)$$

This equation, known as Cauchy's integral formula, allows the calculation of $G(s_i)$, at any interior point within a closed region C, from specified boundary conditions. It can also be shown that an analytic function contains derivatives of all orders within the region of analyticity. In particular, the formula for the nth derivative of the analytic function $G(s_i)$ at any interior point s_i of R, in terms of the values of $G(s)$ on C, is

$$G^{(n)}(s_i) = \frac{n!}{j2\pi} \oint_C \frac{G(s)}{(s - s_i)^{n+1}}\, ds \qquad (2\text{-}6.15)$$

2-7 INFINITE SERIES

In this section we will examine the properties associated with power-series representations of analytic functions. Any real function $F(x)$ can be expanded in a power series about the point $x = x_i$, provided that x has derivatives of all orders at this point. This series may or may not converge to the correct value $F(x)$. Since every complex function $G(s)$ that is analytic at a point $s = s_i$ contains infinite-order derivatives, any analytic function can be expanded about this point in a corresponding power series. Thus

$$G(s) = \sum_{n=0}^{\infty} \frac{G^{(n)}(s_i)}{n!} (s - s_i)^n \qquad (2\text{-}7.1)$$

represents the power-series expansion for $G(s)$ about the point $s = s_i$. Furthermore, the analytic function can always be represented in terms of a power series, i.e., the series invariably converges to the value $G(s)$, provided that s lies within a circle of convergence of radius $|s - s_i|$ centered at s_i. Hence

$$G(s) = G(s_i) + G'(s_i)(s - s_i) + \frac{G''(s_i)}{2!}(s - s_i)^2 + \cdots$$

$$+ \frac{G^{(n)}(s_i)}{n!}(s - s_i)^n + \cdots \qquad (2\text{-}7.2)$$

where $G^{(n)}(s_i)$ represents the nth derivative of $G(s)$ with respect to s, evaluated at $s = s_i$. Equation (2-7.2) is the Taylor series of $G(s)$ expanded about the point $s = s_i$. This series can be used to evaluate $G(s)$ in the interior of the circular region centered at s_i and of radius equal to the distance from s_i to the nearest singular point of $G(s)$.

It can be proved that a function $G(s)$, which is analytic between and upon the boundaries of a circular ring, defined as $|s - s_i| = R_1$ and $|s - s_i| = R_2$, where $R_2 < R_1$, can be represented at every interior point in terms of the Laurent series

$$G(s) = \sum_{n=0}^{\infty} a_n(s - s_i)^n + \sum_{n=0}^{\infty} \frac{a_{-n}}{(s - s_i)^n} \qquad (2\text{-}7.3)$$

where

$$a_n = \frac{1}{j2\pi} \oint_{C_1} \frac{G(s)}{(s - s_i)^{n+1}} \, ds \qquad n = 0, 1, 2, \ldots \qquad (2\text{-}7.4)$$

and

$$a_{-n} = \frac{1}{j2\pi} \oint_{C_2} \frac{G(s)}{(s - s_i)^{n-1}} \, ds \qquad n = 0, 1, 2, \ldots \qquad (2\text{-}7.5)$$

It is often possible to avoid the analytical evaluation of Eqs. (2-7.4) and (2-7.5). Thus, for $G(s) = e^s/s^2$

$$e^s = 1 + s + \frac{s^2}{2!} + \frac{s^3}{3!} + \cdots + \frac{s^n}{n!} + \cdots \qquad (2\text{-}7.6)$$

and

$$G(s) = \frac{e^s}{s^2} = \frac{1}{s^2} + \frac{1}{s} + \frac{1}{2!} + \cdots + \frac{s^{n-2}}{n!} + \cdots \qquad (2\text{-}7.7)$$

Since Eq. (2-7.7) is a Laurent expansion about the origin, it is the unique Laurent expansion.

2-8 RESIDUE THEOREM: POLES AND ZEROS

An important group of complex functions are those that are analytic throughout the s-plane, with the exceptions of specified isolated locations. For example, consider the function

$$G(s) = \frac{(s + 1)(s + 3)}{s^3(s + 2)(s + j4)(s - j4)} \qquad (2\text{-}8.1)$$

which has four singular points located at $s = 0$, $s = -2$, and $s = \pm j4$. By definition, any value of s that causes $G(s)$ to become infinite is termed a *pole* of $G(s)$. Similarly, any value of s that causes $G(s)$ to vanish is defined as a *zero* of $G(s)$. Thus, Eq. (2-8.1) has poles located at $s = 0$, -2, and $\pm j4$, and zeros at $s = -1$ and -3. The poles at -2 and $\pm j4$ are simple poles, since an exponent of unity is associated with each of them. The pole at the origin, $s = 0$, is a multiple-order pole, however, of multiplicity 3. Thus, $s = 0$ depicts the location of a third-order pole. The poles and zeros of $G(s)$ are plotted (with poles denoted by the symbol X and zeros by the null symbol 0, and the third-order pole indicated by an X^3) upon the s-plane, as illustrated in Fig. 2-8.1.

As mentioned in the previous section, $G(s)$ can be represented by the Laurent series in the neighborhood of each of the poles $(s = p)$ of $G(s)$. Hence

$$G(s) = \sum_{n=0}^{\infty} a_n(s - p)^n + \sum_{n=0}^{\infty} \frac{a_{-n}}{(s - p)^n} \qquad (2\text{-}8.2)$$

For the type of function in Eq. (2-8.1), the expansion of Eq. (2-8.2) contains a finite number of coefficients with negative powers of $s - p$ such that

$$G(s) = \sum_{n=0}^{\infty} a_n(s - p)^n + \frac{a_{-1}}{s - p} + \frac{a_{-2}}{(s - p)^2} + \cdots + \frac{a_{-m}}{(s - p)^m} \qquad (2\text{-}8.3)$$

From Eq. (2-8.3), for a mth order pole, one can define a new function $F(s) = (s - p)^m G(s)$ so that $F(p) = a_m$. The function $F(s)$ is analytic at $s = p$, but the functions $(s - p)^{m-1}G(s)$, $(s - p)^{m-2}G(s)$, etc., are not analytic.

The coefficient a_{-1} in the Laurent series of Eq. (2-8.2) is an important quantity in the evaluation of integrals of analytic functions, and it is defined as the *residue* of $G(s)$ at $s = p$. When the singularity at $s = p$ is a pole of order m, the residue at p is calculated by multiplying Eq. (2-8.3) by $(s - p)^m$. Hence

$$F(s) = (s - p)^m G(s)$$
$$= a_{-m} + a_{-m+1}(s - p) + \cdots$$
$$+ a_{-1}(s - p)^{m-1} + \cdots \qquad (2\text{-}8.4)$$

Since this is a power-series represen-tation of $F(s)$ and is exactly equivalent to the Taylor series of Eq. (2-7.2) expanded about the point $s = p$, then the coefficient a_{-1} is the coefficient of the $(s - p)^{m-1}$ term of Eq. (2-7.2).

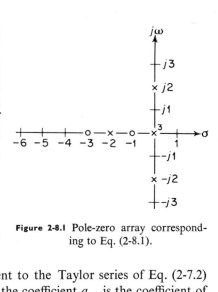

Figure 2-8.I Pole-zero array correspond-ing to Eq. (2-8.1).

$$a_{-1} = \frac{1}{(m - 1)!} \frac{d^{m-1}[(s - p)^m G(s)]}{ds^{m-1}} \bigg|_{s=p} \qquad (2\text{-}8.5)$$

If the point $s = p$ represents a simple (first-order) pole, then

$$a_{-1} = \lim_{s \to p} G(s)(s - p) \qquad (2\text{-}8.6)$$

As an example, let us calculate the residues of the poles of $G(s)$, where

$$G(s) = \frac{1}{s(s+1)^2} \qquad (2\text{-}8.7)$$

As shown, $G(s)$ has a simple pole at the origin and a second-order pole at $s = -1$. To compute the residue at $s = 0$, the application of Eq. (2-8.6) yields

$$a_{-1} = \frac{1}{s(s+1)^2} \, s \bigg|_{s=0} = 1$$

The pole at $s = -1$ is of second order. Thus, applying Eq. (2-8.5)

$$a_{-1} = \frac{1}{1!} \frac{d}{ds}\left(\frac{1}{s}\right)\bigg|_{s=-1} = -\frac{1}{s^2}\bigg|_{s=-1} = -1$$

As a final consideration, let $G(s)$ be analytic in a region R bounded by a closed contour C, except at isolated singular points $s = p_1$, $s = p_2$, . . . , $s = p_m$. From the deformation-of-contour principle, the exterior contour C can be deformed into m small circles γ_i, each of which enclose a singular point. Then

$$\oint_C G(s)\,ds = \oint_{\gamma_1} G(s)\,ds + \oint_{\gamma_2} G(s)\,ds + \cdots + \oint_{\gamma_m} G(s)\,ds \qquad (2\text{-}8.8)$$

But, from Eq. (2-7.5), for $n = 1$

$$a_{-1} = \frac{1}{j2\pi} \oint_\gamma G(s)\,ds \qquad (2\text{-}8.9)$$

Hence, Eq. (2-8.9) is combined with Eq. (2-8.8) to yield

$$\oint_C G(s)\,ds = j2\pi \sum_{i=1}^{m} (a_{-1})_i \qquad (2\text{-}8.10)$$

Equation (2-8.10) is a mathematical statement of the Residue Theorem: The integral of $G(s)$ over a contour C enclosing isolated singular points of $G(s)$ is evaluated as $j2\pi$ times the sum of the residues at these points. From a control systems point of view, Eq. (2-8.10) represents perhaps the most important relationship of complex-variable theory. Many useful results will be derived directly or indirectly from this theorem.

PROBLEMS

2.1 For each of the following complex numbers, draw the appropriate s-plane diagram to describe the number geometrically, and express in equivalent exponential polar coordinates.
  (a) $1 + j2$
  (b) $2.7 + j3.1$
  (c) $-6.4 + j6.4$
  (d) $3.1 - j8.4$
  (e) $-17.7 + j42.3$
  (f) $-3.0 - j0$
  (g) $5.0 - j5.0$

2.2 Transform each of the following into rectangular coordinates.
  (a) $18e^{j25°}$
  (b) $32e^{j270°}$
  (c) $8e^{j180°}$
  (d) $144e^{j350°}$
  (e) $9.7e^{j123°}$

2.3 For each of the complex number pairs listed below, form the quantities $s_1 s_2$ and s_1/s_2. Draw the required s-plane vector diagrams.
  (a) $s_1 = 2 + j3,\ s_2 = -4 + j8$
  (b) $s_1 = 0.5 + j7.1,\ s_2 = 14e^{j45°}$
  (c) $s_1 = 126e^{j67°},\ s_2 = 11e^{j345°}$
  (d) $s_1 = 18 + j0,\ s_2 = 0 + j3$
  (e) $s_1 = 4 - j5,\ s_2 = -2 - j7$

2.4 Compute the three cube roots of $+2$. Describe the results graphically.

2.5 Determine the five distinct fifth roots of the following numbers.
  (a) 1
  (b) -32
  (c) $j1$
  (d) $-1 - j1$
  (e) $14 + j11$
  (f) $6e^{j40°}$

2.6 Employing Eq. [2-4.13], evaluate the following.
  (a) j^j
  (b) $j^{(1+j1)}$
  (c) $(4 - j5)^{(1+j2)}$
  (d) j^2

2.7 Apply the Cauchy–Riemann equations to the following functions, and determine which (if any) are analytic.

(a) $G(s) = s + 2$

(b) $G(s) = s^2 + 5s + 6$

(c) $G(s) = \dfrac{1}{s}$

(d) $G(s) = \dfrac{3}{s^2 + 2s + 3}$

(e) $G(s) = \sin s$

(f) $G(s) = \dfrac{2(s + 1)}{s + 2}$

(g) $G(s) = \dfrac{s^2 + 3s + 17}{s(s + 6)}$

2.8 Evaluate the following line integrals.

(a) $G(s) = 2s$; along a straight line from the origin to the point $s = 2 + j1$

(b) $G(s) = \dfrac{1}{s}$; along a straight line from the origin to the point $s = 1 + j3$

2.9 For each of the following analytic functions, plot the pole-zero arrays and compute the residues at each system pole.

(a) $G(s) = \dfrac{1}{s(s + 3)}$

(b) $G(s) = \dfrac{10(s + 2)}{s^2(s + 1)(s + 10)}$

(c) $G(s) = \dfrac{100}{s^3(s + 30)}$

(d) $G(s) = \dfrac{1}{s^2(s + 3)^2(s + 5)^3}$

(e) $G(s) = \dfrac{s + 2}{[(s + 3)^2 + 2^2]}$

(f) $G(s) = \dfrac{10(s + 2)}{s^2(s + 1)[(s + 3)^2 + 2^2]}$

(g) $G(s) = \dfrac{10}{s(s + 1)(s + 2)(s + 3)}$

2.10 Evaluate the following contour integrals.

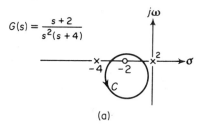

$$G(s) = \frac{s+2}{s^2(s+4)}$$

(a)

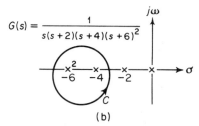

$$G(s) = \frac{1}{s(s+2)(s+4)(s+6)^2}$$

(b)

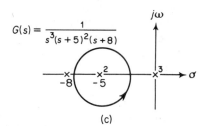

$$G(s) = \frac{1}{s^3(s+5)^2(s+8)}$$

(c)

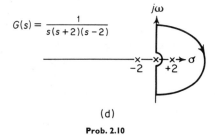

$$G(s) = \frac{1}{s(s+2)(s-2)}$$

(d)

Prob. 2.10

BIBLIOGRAPHY

1. Churchill, R. V., *Complex Variables and Applications.* New York: McGraw-Hill Book Company, 1960.

2. Franklin, P., *Functions of a Complex Variable.* Englewood Cliffs, N.J.: Prentice-Hall, Inc., 1958.

3. Salz, N. P., "Analytic Functions of a Complex Variable," *Electro-Technology*, November 1961.

PHYSICAL SYSTEMS: THE MATHEMATICAL MODEL

3

3-1 INTRODUCTION

The typical feedback control system can be visualized as a combination of independent operational components that are arranged within the system in such a way that a definite informational flow pattern (action and interaction) is established. The analysis of any practical control system is usually initiated by deriving a set of individual component mathematical models, i.e., mathematical relationships that exist between input (excitation) variables and output (response) variables associated with each element. The "building-block" models are then combined and processed to ultimately yield the over-all system model.

Because of its basic importance, the technique of translating physical system dynamical behavior into equivalent mathematical models will now be considered; in particular, representative electrical, mechanical, and electromechanical systems, in single and multiple degrees-of-freedom are investigated. It will be observed that the mathematical formulation invariably leads to a system of differential equations. Although differential equations are discussed in Sections 3.2, 3.3, and 3.4, the coverage is of a preliminary nature; the solutions of differential and integro-differential equations will be developed in Chapter 4 by using the Laplace transformation.

3-2 ORDINARY DIFFERENTIAL EQUATIONS

An equation of the form

$$f\left(y, t, \frac{dy}{dt}, \frac{d^2y}{dt^2}, \ldots, \frac{d^ny}{dt^n}\right) = 0 \qquad \text{(3-2.1)}$$

involving a function $y(t)$ and certain of its derivatives is referred to as a *differential* equation. The study of differential equations is essential to an understanding of dynamic phenomena, for it is precisely this type of equation that governs the vast majority of all physical systems. Differential equations are divided into two general classifications, based upon the number of independent variables that appear. If there is a single independent variable such that all derivatives of the variable are ordinary derivatives, the corresponding equation is designated as an *ordinary* differential equation. Conversely, if two or more independent variables are involved, resulting in the need for partial derivatives, a *partial* differential equation is formed. Partial differential equations describe the dynamics of engineering "field" problems in which space and time appear explicitly within the mathematical model (e.g., pressure surges in hydraulic circuits, transmission line problems, etc.). Since, in the automatic control system, components are normally assumed to consist of lumped parameters (independent of all space variables), the resulting mathematical model is formulated in terms of ordinary differential equations. Thus, the remainder of this text will deal exclusively with systems governed by ordinary differential equations.

3-3 SYSTEM LINEARITY IN TERMS OF DIFFERENTIAL EQUATIONS

Differential equations have thus far been categorized as either partial or ordinary. A second scheme of classification deals with the property of a differential equation known as *linearity*. Differential equations can be either linear with constant coefficients, linear with time-varying coefficients, or nonlinear. As an example of these concepts, consider the generalized ordinary differential equation of (3-3.1)

$$a_n\frac{d^ny}{dt^n} + a_{n-1}\frac{d^{n-1}y}{dt^{n-1}} + a_{n-2}\frac{d^{n-2}y}{dt^{n-2}} + \cdots + a_0y = f(t) \qquad \text{(3-3.1)}$$

Linearity can now be expressed in terms of the a_i coefficients as follows: (1) If *all* of the coefficients, i.e., a_n, a_{n-1}, a_{n-2}, $\ldots$, a_0, are constant, then Eq. (3-3.1) represents a linear differential equation with constant coefficients; (2)

If *any* of the coefficients is a function of the independent variable time, e.g., $\sin t$, $3t$, e^{-2t}, etc., then Eq. (3–3.1) is a linear differential equation with time-varying coefficients; and finally, (3) If *one or more* of the coefficients is a function of the dependent variable y, e.g., $3y$, $\sin y$, $\cos dy/dt$, y^2, etc., Eq. (3-3.1) is nonlinear.

All physical systems are basically nonlinear. An operational amplifier will saturate at some imput voltage level; mechanical systems exhibit back-lash, static friction and dead-space nonlinearity effects; hydraulic and pneu-matic systems are inherently nonlinear, etc. The difficulty encountered in dealing with nonlinear systems is that no comprehensive or universally applicable analysis techniques are available for solving the corresponding nonlinear mathematical models. Hence, whenever possible, the dynamic systems analyst uses linearizing assumptions, such as, "for small angles the sine of an angle is equal to the value of the angle expressed in radians." Another possible linearizing technique is that of constraining the system to operate only within the linear mode; thus, if an amplifier input signal is always considered to be less than the saturation voltage, then the amplifier may most certainly be considered as a linear element.

The Laplace transformation, being a linear operation, applies only to linear systems. Accordingly, Chapter 4 (and in fact this entire volume and Chapters 14–16 of *Advanced Control Systems Engineering*) will consider only linear system mathematical models. Chapters 17–23 of *Advanced*, however, illustrate a few of the common techniques applied to nonlinear controls systems.

3-4 SOLUTIONS OF DIFFERENTIAL EQUATIONS

In classical mathematics, the solution of differential equations represents an extension in complexity of one order of magnitude over the algebraic equation. The application of modern operational methods, however, reduces the complexity essentially to that of the algebraic expression. In this section, we will consider a simple differential equation and derive the corresponding solution by intuitive methods; Chapter 4 develops the topic of solutions of time domain differential equations by rigorous operational methods.

Consider the differential equation

$$\frac{dy}{dt} + y = 1 \tag{3-4.1}$$

As stated, Eq. (3-4.1) is a first-order differential equation. (The order of an equation is defined as the highest power of derivative involved.) An nth order differential equation requires the specification of n initial conditions to uniquely set the state of the system; this subject will receive more attention in later sections of the chapter. Since Eq. (3-4.1) is of first order, only one initial condition, i.e., the initial value of $y(t)$, is required. Assuming $y(0) = 0$, an obvious solution to Eq. (3-4.1) is

$$y(t) = 1 \qquad \qquad \textbf{(3-4.2)}$$

The solution of Eq. (3-4.2) is easily verified. Since the derivative of a constant is zero, then

$$\frac{d}{dt}(1) + 1 = 1$$

$$0 + 1 = 1 \qquad \qquad \textbf{(3-4.3)}$$

In addition, we know from integral calculus that

$$\frac{d}{dt}(e^{-t}) = -e^{-t}$$

hence, an alternate solution is evidently

$$y(t) = 1 - e^{-t} \qquad \qquad \textbf{(3-4.4)}$$

since, by substituting Eq. (3-4.4) into Eq. (3-4.1)

$$e^{-t} + 1 - e^{-t} = 1 \qquad \qquad \textbf{(3-4.5)}$$

an identity is generated. Equation (3-4.2) is termed the steady-state or static solution, whereas Eq. (3-4.4) is the complete solution, containing both

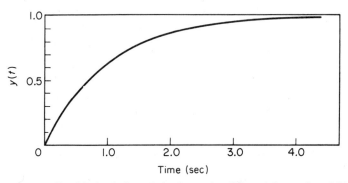

Figure 3-4.I Graphical solution of the first-order differential equation $dy/dt + y = 1$.

transient and steady-state contributions. Note that Eq. (3-4.4) satisfies the specified initial condition $y(0) = 0$. The graphical system solution obtained by evaluating Eq. (3-4.4) for various points in time is illustrated in Fig. 3-4.1.

3-5   ELECTRICAL NETWORK ELEMENTS[1,2,3,4]

Before any dynamic system can be analyzed, it is necessary that the analyst be familiar with both the internal system configuration and, in addition, the mathematical expressions that govern each individual component. To illustrate, the step-function response can be computed for an electrical "black

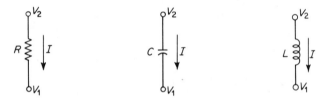

Figure 3-5.1 Resistive element.	**Figure 3-5.2** Capacitive element.	**Figure 3-5.3** Inductive element.

box" only when the number, size, and relative locations of all circuit elements are specified. Since electrical network problems comprise a large portion of all practical dynamic analysis problems, let us consider initially the mathematical relations that govern the three forms of passive electrical elements, i.e., resistors, capacitors, and inductors.

If a voltage difference $V_2 - V_1$ is applied across the terminals of a resistive element R as shown in Fig. 3-5.1, the resulting current is defined by Ohm's law

$$I = \frac{V_2 - V_1}{R} \tag{3-5.1}$$

where the current flow is in the direction of the voltage drop. Equation (3-5.1) is rearranged to form

$$V_2 - V_1 = IR \tag{3-5.2}$$

In a similar manner, the capacitive element of Fig. 3-5.2 is defined by the relationships

$$I = C\frac{d(V_2 - V_1)}{dt} \tag{3-5.3}$$

and

$$V_2 - V_1 = \frac{1}{C} \int I \, dt \qquad\qquad (3\text{-}5.4)$$

And finally, the inductor illustrated in Fig. 3-5.3 is governed by the expressions

$$V_2 - V_1 = L \frac{dI}{dt} \qquad\qquad (3\text{-}5.5)$$

and

$$I = \frac{1}{L} \int (V_2 - V_1) \, dt \qquad\qquad (3\text{-}5.6)$$

In Eqs. 3-5.3 through 3-5.6, the current flow is in the direction of decreasing potential.

3-6 KIRCHHOFF'S LAWS

Equations (3-5.1) through (3-5.6) describe the voltage drop and resulting current flow relations across the terminals of each of the normal passive network elements. We now combine these fundamental laws into usable form by stating Kirchhoff's loop and node laws.

KIRCHHOFF'S LOOP LAW: The algebraic sum of all voltage drops around any completely closed loop is zero.

KIRCHHOFF'S NODE LAW: The algebraic sum of all currents entering any electrical node is zero, i.e., a point in space cannot function as a current source or sink.

In the next four sections, Kirchhoff's laws will be successively applied to single-loop, single-node, multiple-loop, and multiple-node network configurations, and the corresponding system mathematical models will be derived.

3-7 SINGLE-LOOP *LRC* NETWORKS

Consider the single-loop network of Fig. 3-7.1, containing a resistor R, capacitor C, and inductor L. The circuit is excited, at time $t = 0$, by the application of an input voltage $V_{in}(t)$, as shown. If we assume a zero source impedance and infinite load impedance, the problem is one of defining the output voltage $V_{out}(t)$ for all times.

To initiate the analysis, we assign a loop current $I(t)$, flowing in a clockwise direction. From Kirchhoff's loop law, the sum of the voltage drops around the loop is zero. Thus

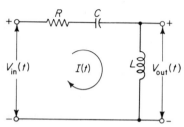

$$-V_{\text{in}}(t) + \Delta V_{\text{resistor}} + \Delta V_{\text{capacitor}}$$
$$+ \Delta V_{\text{inductor}} = 0 \qquad \text{(3-7.1)}$$

Figure 3-7.1 Typical single-loop LRC network.

In this equation, the input voltage is summed negatively, since, in the direction of assumed current flow, this represents an *increase* in voltage. The voltage drop across each circuit element is positive, however, due to the established fact that current flow is in the direction of decreasing voltage. Substituting the definitive expressions of Eq. (3-5.2), (3-5.4), and (3-5.5) into (3-7.1)

$$-V_{\text{in}}(t) + RI(t) + \frac{1}{C}\int I(t)\,dt + L\frac{dI(t)}{dt} = 0 \qquad \text{(3-7.2)}$$

Rearranging

$$L\frac{dI(t)}{dt} + RI(t) + \frac{1}{C}\int I(t)\,dt = V_{\text{in}}(t) \qquad \text{(3-7.3)}$$

Equation (3-7.3) is an integro-differential equation. Two initial conditions are required to specify the complete problem solution, namely, the initial capacitor voltage charge and the initial inductor current. Assuming that these quantities are given, and that Eq. (3-7.3) can be solved for $I(t)$, we can describe the output voltage as

$$V_{\text{out}}(t) = L\frac{dI(t)}{dt} \qquad \text{(3-7.4)}$$

3-8 SINGLE-NODE LRC NETWORK

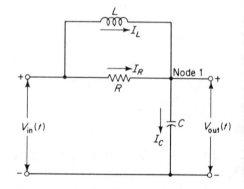

Figure 3-8.1 Typical single-node LRC network.

The single-node network of Fig. 3-8.1, consisting of a resistor R, inductor L, and capacitor C, is excited by an input voltage $V_{\text{in}}(t)$. Again assuming zero and infinite source and load impedances respectively, let us compute the output voltage $V_{\text{out}}(t)$.

If we arbitrarily assign current flow through each circuit element, Kirchhoff's node law applied at node 1 states

$$I_L + I_R - I_C = 0 \tag{3-8.1}$$

Substituting Eqs. (3-5.1), (3-5.3), and (3-5.6) into (3-8.1), and eliminating the function of time notation for brevity

$$\frac{1}{L}\int (V_{in} - V_{out})\, dt + \frac{1}{R}(V_{in} - V_{out}) - C\frac{dV_{out}}{dt} = 0 \tag{3-8.2}$$

Rearranging

$$\frac{1}{L}\int V_{out}\, dt + \frac{1}{R} V_{out} + C\frac{dV_{out}}{dt} = \frac{1}{L}\int V_{in}\, dt + \frac{1}{R} V_{in} \tag{3-8.3}$$

Equation (3-8.3) is again in the form of an integro-differential equation, and is subject to the specification of initial conditions. The expression can be solved directly for V_{out}.

3-9 MULTIPLE-LOOP NETWORKS

We now consider a combination of coupled electrical loops, illustrated in Fig. 3-9.1. Each independent loop is first assigned an arbitrary directional

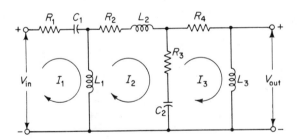

Figure 3-9.1 Typical multiple-loop network.

current flow as shown. Computing the voltage drops around loop 1, and in the assumed direction of I_1

$$-V_{in} + R_1 I_1 + \frac{1}{C_1}\int I_1\, dt + L_1\frac{d(I_1 - I_2)}{dt} = 0 \tag{3-9.1}$$

Summing the voltage drops in the direction of I_2

$$L_1 \frac{d(I_2 - I_1)}{dt} + R_2 I_2 + L_2 \frac{dI_2}{dt} + R_3(I_2 - I_3) + \frac{1}{C_2} \int (I_2 - I_3) \, dt = 0$$

$$\text{(3-9.2)}$$

and for loop 3

$$\frac{1}{C_2} \int (I_3 - I_2) \, dt + R_3(I_3 - I_2) + R_4 I_3 + L_3 \frac{dI_3}{dt} = 0 \qquad \text{(3-9.3)}$$

The output voltage V_{out} is determined from I_3 as

$$V_{\text{out}} = L_3 \frac{dI_3}{dt} \qquad \text{(3-9.4)}$$

Thus, if Eqs. (3-9.1), (3-9.2), and (3-9.3) can be solved simultaneously for I_3, then Eq. (3-9.4) is applied directly to define the output voltage V_{out}.

3-10 MULTIPLE-NODE NETWORKS

The electrical network of Fig. 3-10.1 contains seven independent loops but only three independent nodes. Thus, a considerable simplification is evidenced by applying the node law analysis. If we arbitrarily assign node

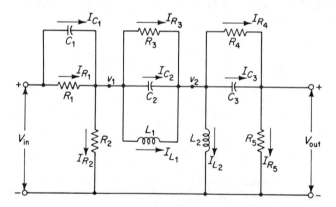

Figure 3-10.1 Typical multiple-node network.

voltages V_1 and V_2, and directional current flows through each of the circuit elements, the following Kirchhoff's node summation is obtained at node V_1

$$I_{C_1} + I_{R_1} = I_{R_2} + I_{R_3} + I_{C_2} + I_{L_1} \qquad \text{(3-10.1)}$$

at node V_2

$$I_{R_3} + I_{C_2} + I_{L_1} = I_{L_2} + I_{C_3} + I_{R_4} \qquad (3\text{-}10.2)$$

and at node V_{out}

$$I_{R_4} + I_{C_3} = I_{R_5} \qquad (3\text{-}10.3)$$

Rewriting the preceding in terms of node voltages

$$C_1 \frac{d(V_{in} - V_1)}{dt} + \frac{1}{R_1}(V_{in} - V_1) = \frac{1}{R_2} V_1 + \frac{1}{R_3}(V_1 - V_2)$$

$$+ C_2 \frac{d(V_1 - V_2)}{dt} + \frac{1}{L_1} \int (V_1 - V_2)\, dt = 0 \qquad (3\text{-}10.4)$$

$$\frac{1}{R_3}(V_1 - V_2) + C_2 \frac{d(V_1 - V_2)}{dt} + \frac{1}{L_1} \int (V_1 - V_2)\, dt$$

$$= \frac{1}{L_2} \int V_2\, dt + C_3 \frac{d(V_2 - V_{out})}{dt} + \frac{1}{R_4}(V_2 - V_{out}) = 0 \qquad (3\text{-}10.5)$$

and

$$\frac{1}{R_4}(V_2 - V_{out}) + C_3 \frac{d(V_2 - V_{out})}{dt} = \frac{1}{R_5} V_{out} \qquad (3\text{-}10.6)$$

Equations (3-10.4), (3-10.5), and (3-10.6) can now be solved simultaneously to yield the output voltage V_{out} in addition to the interior node voltages V_1 and V_2.

3-11 MAGNETIC COUPLING

Inductive elements are often placed in an electrical network in such a way that a changing current flow in the first inductor will induce a voltage drop across the second. This condition is referred to as *magnetic coupling*. For example, consider the network of Fig. 3-11.1, consisting of two loops with magnetically-coupled inductors L_1 and L_2. The coupling coefficient M defines the current change produced in L_2 due to a voltage drop across L_1. Since the elements are linear and bilateral, the converse is also true.

The system differential equations, based upon Kirchhoff's loop law are

$$-V_{in} + L_1 \frac{dI_1}{dt} + R(I_1 - I_2) \pm M \frac{dI_2}{dt} = 0 \qquad (3\text{-}11.1)$$

and

$$R_L I_2 + R(I_2 - I_1) + L_2 \frac{dI_2}{dt} \pm M \frac{dI_1}{dt} = 0 \qquad (3\text{-}11.2)$$

The polarity associated with M in the preceding equations is determined as follows. If a positive rate of change in current I_1 induces in inductor L_2 a voltage drop in the direction of I_2, then the polarity of M in Eq. (3-11.2) is positive. If a voltage increase is produced in L_2, then the sign is negative. The same reasoning is employed to define the polarity of M in Eq. (3-11.1).

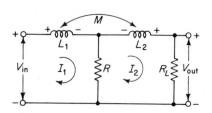

Figure 3-11.1 Dual-loop network with magnetic coupling.

A common method for indicating the induced voltage polarity is illustrated in Fig. 3-11.1. The plus and minus signs appearing at both L_1 and L_2 terminals indicate that, if a voltage drop is produced across L_1 (in a direction from $-$ to $+$) by a loop current I_1, then a corresponding voltage will be generated across L_2 with a polarity as given by the signs accompanying L_2.

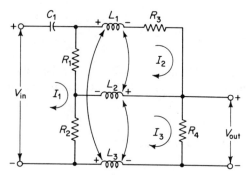

Figure 3-11.2 Another example of magnetic coupling.

Thus, in the example circuit, a changing current I_2 induces across L_2 a voltage decrease in the assumed direction of I_2, causing the potential at the minus terminal to be higher than the potential at the plus terminal. This same effect is transformed to L_1, i.e., the minus terminal of L_1 is higher in voltage than the positive terminal, due to a positive current in loop 2. In the direction of I_1, a voltage increase is produced; thus, the polarity of M in Eq. (3-11.1) is negative. Similarly, the sign of M in Eq. (3-11.2) is also negative.

To further demonstrate the concept of magnetic coupling, consider the three-loop network of Fig. 3-11.2. Inductive coupling coefficients are designated as M_{12}, M_{13}, and M_{23}, where the double subscripts describe the two inductors involved. The order of the subscripts signifies the direction of coupling action, i.e., M_{31} is the coefficient of voltage generated in L_1 due to a changing current in L_3. The system equations can now be written by inspection as

$$-V_{\text{in}} + \frac{1}{C}\int I_1\,dt + R_1(I_1 - I_2) + R_2(I_1 - I_3) = 0 \qquad (3\text{-}11.3)$$

$$R_1(I_2 - I_1) + L_1\frac{dI_2}{dt} + R_3I_2 + L_2\frac{d(I_2 - I_3)}{dt}$$

$$- M_{32}\frac{dI_3}{dt} - M_{31}\frac{dI_3}{dt} + M_{21}\frac{d(I_2 - I_3)}{dt} + M_{12}\frac{dI_2}{dt} = 0 \qquad (3\text{-}11.4)$$

$$R_2(I_3 - I_1) + L_2\frac{d(I_3 - I_2)}{dt} + R_4I_3 + L_3\frac{dI_3}{dt} - M_{12}\frac{dI_2}{dt}$$

$$+ M_{32}\frac{dI_3}{dt} - M_{13}\frac{dI_2}{dt} + M_{23}\frac{d(I_3 - I_2)}{dt} = 0 \qquad (3\text{-}11.5)$$

$$V_{\text{out}} = R_4I_3 \qquad (3\text{-}11.6)$$

3-12 CIRCUIT DUALS

It has been shown that series and parallel LRC circuits give rise to analogous integro-differential equations. In particular, the two equations that describe

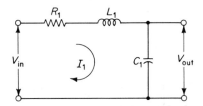

Figure 3-12.1   Series LRC network.

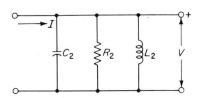

Figure 3.12.2   Parallel LRC network.

the behavior of the circuits shown in Figs. 3-12.1 and 3-12.2

$$V_{\text{in}} = L_1\frac{dI_1}{dt} + R_1I_1 + \frac{1}{C_1}\int I_1\,dt \qquad (3\text{-}12.1)$$

and

$$I = C_2\frac{dV}{dt} + \frac{1}{R_2}V + \frac{1}{L_2}\int V\,dt \qquad (3\text{-}12.2)$$

are numerically equivalent if $L_1 = C_2$, $L_2 = C_1$, and $R_1 = 1/R_2$. The corresponding networks are referred to as *circuit duals*. Thus, given a differential equation of the form indicated in Eqs. (3-12.1) and (3-12.2), one could construct two separate electrical circuits with equal validity. This duality of nature is also exhibited by mechanical engineering systems; the analog computer described in Chapter 6 is based upon the fact that every physical system possesses an equivalent (analogous) electrical network.

3-13 ELECTRON-TUBE CIRCUITS[5]

Thus far, we have considered only passive-element networks. In this and the following sections, the two familiar active network elements, vacuum tubes

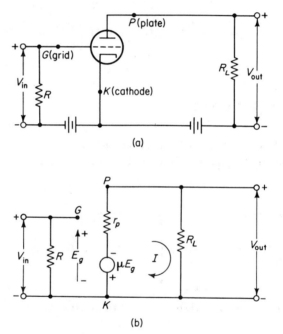

Figure 3-13.1 (a) Typical electron-tube amplifier, and (b) equivalent circuit.

and transistors, are introduced, and corresponding linearized mathematical models derived.

The common method of analyzing vacuum-tube circuts is that of assuming the governing tube parameters to be essentially constants over the applicable range of operation. This assumption represents an example of a linearizing constraint technique discussed in Section 3.3. Under these conditions, the simple electronic amplifier circuit of Fig. 3-13.1(a) can be replaced by the equivalent a-c voltage-source circuit of Fig. 3-13.1(b), in which E_g is the grid-to-cathode voltage differential, μ is the voltage amplification factor, and r_p represents the dynamic plate resistance. Since the amplifier draws no grid current under normal (idealized) operation, the grid-to-cathode potential E_g is identical to the input excitation voltage V_{in}. The over-all analysis is thus resolved into that of characterizing the simple single-loop network illustrated in Fig. 3-13.1(b).

Using Kirchhoff's loop law, and noting the polarity associated with the equivalent-circuit voltage generator

$$\mu E_g + I(r_p + R_L) = 0 \tag{3-13.1}$$

Substituting $E_g = V_{in}$ and solving for the loop current

$$I = - \frac{\mu V_{in}}{r_p + R_L} \tag{3-13.2}$$

The output voltage V_{out} is related to the loop current by the expression

$$V_{out} = R_L I = - \frac{\mu R_L V_{in}}{r_p + R_L} \tag{3-13.3}$$

Thus, the amplifier gain constant is

$$K = \frac{V_{out}}{V_{in}} = \frac{-\mu R_L}{r_p + R_L} \tag{3-13.4}$$

In addition to the voltage-source equivalent diagram of Fig. 3-13.1(b), a current-source equivalent diagram can be employed. To demonstrate the usefulness of this equivalent diagram, consider the feedback amplifier design of Fig. 3-13.2(a). The current-source equivalent circuit is illustrated in Fig. 3-13.2(b); g_m is the vacuum-tube transconductance parameter. The Kirchhoff current law is now applied to node G

$$\frac{V_{in} - E_g}{R_1} = \frac{E_g}{R_3} + C_2 \frac{dE_g}{dt} + \frac{E_g - V_{out}}{R_2} + C_1 \frac{d(E_g - V_{out})}{dt} \tag{3-13.5}$$

and to node P

$$\frac{E_g - V_{out}}{R_2} + C_1 \frac{d(E_g - V_{out})}{dt}$$
$$= g_m E_g + \frac{V_{out}}{r_p} + \frac{1}{L_3} \int V_{out}\, dt + \frac{V_{out}}{R_4} + C_3 \frac{dV_{out}}{dt} \tag{3-13.6}$$

Equations (3-13.5) and (3-13.6) can now be solved simultaneously for V_{out} in terms of V_{in}.

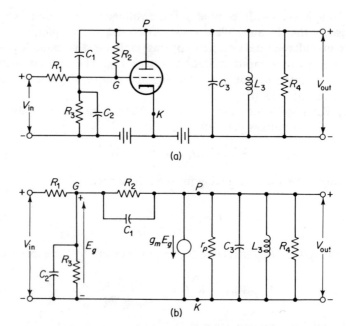

Figure 3-13.2   Analysis of the electron-tube circuit in (a) is simplified by the current-source equivalent diagram in (b).

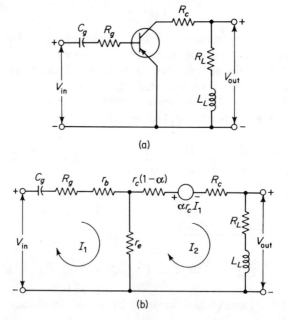

Figure 3-14.1   Transistor amplifier in (a) has a possible equivalent circuit, (b).

3-14 TRANSISTOR NETWORKS[6]

The grounded-emitter transistor amplifier configuration of Fig. 3-14.1(a) has a possible small-signal equivalent circuit as shown in Fig. 3-14.1(b). The transistor network parameters are

r_b = base resistance
r_e = emitter resistance
r_c = collector resistance
α = current amplification factor

Kirchhoff's loop law is now applied to loops 1 and 2 of Fig. 3-14.1(b).

$$\text{loop 1:} \quad V_{\text{in}} = \frac{1}{C_g} \int I_1 \, dt + (R_g + r_b + r_e)I_1 - r_e I_2 \qquad (3\text{-}14.1)$$

$$\text{loop 2:} \quad \alpha r_c I_1 + [r_c(1 - \alpha) + R_c + R_L + r_e]I_2 + L_L \frac{dI_2}{dt} - r_e I_1 \qquad (3\text{-}14.2)$$

Equations (3-14.1) and (3-14.2) can be solved for current I_2 in terms of the excitation voltage V_{in}. Once this has been accomplished, the output voltage is calculated as

$$V_{\text{out}} = R_L I_2 + L_L \frac{dI_2}{dt} \qquad (3\text{-}14.3)$$

3-15 NEWTON'S LAWS OF MOTION[1]

The translational and rotational dynamics of rigid-body mechanical engineering systems are governed by Newton's Laws of Motion.

TRANSLATING SYSTEMS: The algebraic sum of all the forces acting upon a rigid body is equal to the product of the mass and linear acceleration of the body. Newton's law of *linear motion* applies to motion of the center of gravity of the body, and it is expressed in the inertial coordinate system.

ROTARY SYSTEMS: The algebraic sum of all the moments acting upon a rigid body is equal to the product of the moment of inertia and rotational acceleration of the body. Newton's Law, as applied to rotary systems, defines the acceleration of the body about the center of gravity, and it is expressed in body coordinates.

3-16 MECHANICAL ELEMENTS

Two mechanical engineering components, in addition to component mass and inertia characterized in the previous section, appear in the majority of mechanical systems. The linear spring illustrated in Fig. 3-16.1 produces a reaction force that is proportional to the relative displacement of the two end terminals from their equilibrium positions. The constant of proportionality K is referred to as the spring constant.

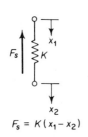

$$F_s = K(x_1 - x_2)$$

Figure 3-16.1 Idealized representation of the linear translatory spring.

The rotary spring of Fig. 3-16.2 produces a reaction moment proportional to the difference in angular displacement between the end terminals.

Mechanical damping is conventionally indicated by the dashpot arrangement of Fig. 3-16.3. The damping force produced by this element is proportional to the relative velocity difference between the end terminals. The rotational-system damping-element concept is analogous, i.e., a reaction torque is generated that is proportional to the difference in angular velocity across the terminals.

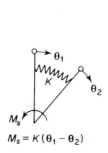

$$M_s = K(\theta_1 - \theta_2)$$

Figure 3-16.2 Rotary spring.

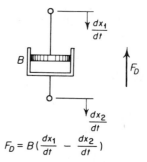

$$F_D = B\left(\frac{dx_1}{dt} - \frac{dx_2}{dt}\right)$$

Figure 3-16.3 Linear dashpot signifies system damping.

3-17 SINGLE DEGREE-OF-FREEDOM TRANSLATIONAL SYSTEM

Consider the single spring-mass-dashpot system of Fig. 3-17.1. The mass M is isolated from solid ground by a linear spring (with spring constant K) and viscous friction (with an equivalent dashpot damping coefficient B.) The system is initially in static equilibrium, i.e., no spring forces exist and the initial system velocity parameter is identically equal to zero. At $t = 0$, the system is excited by an input force F. It is now necessary to assign directional polarity to the resulting mass motion; in particular, let us define motion to be positive in the direction of the input force F. Then, applying Newton's law of translation

$$\sum F_x = M \frac{d^2x}{dt^2} \qquad \text{(3-17.1)}$$

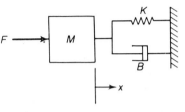

The sum of the forces acting upon the system are

$$\sum F_x = F \pm Kx \pm B \frac{dx}{dt} \qquad \text{(3-17.2)}$$

Figure 3-17.1   Single degree-of-freedom spring-mass-dashpot system.

To determine the polarity of K and B in Eq. (3-17.2), one can use an intuitive analysis. Hence, if the body deflects in the positive x direction, the linear spring is placed in compression; the spring reaction force then acts in opposition to F, or in the negative x direction. Similarly, a positive velocity dx/dt produces a pressure build-up within the dashpot that tends to react against the input forcing function. Thus, both the Kx and $B\,dx/dt$ components of Eq. (3-17.2) are of negative polarity such that, solving for F

$$F = M \frac{d^2x}{dt^2} + B \frac{dx}{dt} + Kx \qquad \text{(3-17.3)}$$

For a particular F, Eq. (3-17.3) can be solved for x to characterize the mechanical system transient response.

3-18   SINGLE DEGREE-OF-FREEDOM ROTATIONAL SYSTEM

The torsional system of Fig. 3-18.1, consisting of a body with moment of inertia J, torsional spring constant K, and rotational damping coefficient B, is excited by an input moment T. Assigning a positive rotational direction θ, and applying Newton's Law of Rotation

$$\sum T_\theta = J \frac{d^2\theta}{dt^2} \qquad \text{(3-18.1)}$$

where

$$\sum T_\theta = T \pm B \frac{d\theta}{dt} \pm K\theta \qquad \text{(3-18.2)}$$

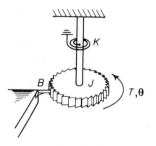

Figure 3-18.1 Rotary system in one degree-of-freedom.

The determination of the polarity associated with B and K is accomplished as follows: As θ increases in the positive direction, the coil spring winds up and generates a reaction moment that opposes the input moment. Similarly, a positive torsional velocity produces a negative reaction moment. Thus

$$T = J\frac{d^2\theta}{dt^2} + B\frac{d\theta}{dt} + K\theta \qquad (3\text{-}18.3)$$

One can again observe, from a comparison of Eq. (3-17.3) and (3-18.3), the duality exhibited by physical systems.

3-19 MULTIPLE DEGREE-OF-FREEDOM TRANSLATIONAL SYSTEM

The systems of Sections 3.17 and 3.18 were both of the single degree-of-freedom variety, i.e, the mathematical models were expressed in terms of a single dependent variable (x and θ respectively). The remainder of this

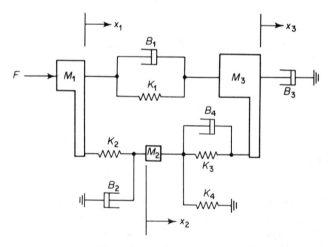

Figure 3-19.1 Three degree-of-freedom translatory system.

chapter deals with multiple degree-of-freedom mechanical and electro-mechanical configurations; in these systems, the knowledge of two or more dependent variables is necessary to specify completely the instantaneous system state. For example, consider the translational system of Fig. 3-19.1. The three masses are interconnected through dashpot and linear spring assemblies, and they are constrained to vibrate in the horizontal direction only.

If we arbitrarily assign positive directions x_1, x_2, and x_3 for the deflections of masses M_1, M_2, and M_3 respectively, the differential equations of motion are evidently, at mass M_1

$$F \pm B_1\left(\frac{dx_1}{dt} - \frac{dx_3}{dt}\right) \pm K_1(x_1 - x_3) \pm K_2(x_1 - x_2) = M_1\frac{d^2x_1}{dt^2} \qquad \text{(3-19.1)}$$

at mass M_2

$$\pm K_2(x_2 - x_1) \pm B_2\frac{dx_2}{dt} \pm B_4\left(\frac{dx_2}{dt} - \frac{dx_3}{dt}\right)$$

$$\pm K_3(x_2 - x_3) \pm K_4x_2 = M_2\frac{d^2x_2}{dt^2} \qquad \text{(3-19.2)}$$

and at mass M_3

$$\pm B_1\left(\frac{dx_3}{dt} - \frac{dx_1}{dt}\right) \pm K_1(x_3 - x_1) \pm B_4\left(\frac{dx_3}{dt} - \frac{dx_2}{dt}\right)$$

$$\pm K_3(x_3 - x_2) \pm B_3\frac{dx_3}{dt} = M_3\frac{d^2x_3}{dt^2} \qquad \text{(3-19.3)}$$

The polarity of each reaction force term in Eq. (3-19.1), (3-19.2), and (3-19.3) is determined by simple reasoning. Consider the first reaction term in Eq. (3-19.2); if the quantity $(x_2 - x_1)$ is positive, i.e., the deflection of mass M_2 from its equilibrium position is greater than that of mass M_1, then spring K_2 is placed in tension and exerts a force upon M_2 in a negative x_2 direction. Thus, this force tends to oppose the positive displacement of M_2 and represents a negative force acting upon M_2. The remaining terms are evaluated in an analogous manner, yielding

$$F - B_1\left(\frac{dx_1}{dt} - \frac{dx_3}{dt}\right) - K_1(x_1 - x_3) - K_2(x_1 - x_2) = M_1\frac{d^2x_1}{dt^2} \qquad \text{(3-19.4)}$$

$$-K_2(x_2 - x_1) - B_2\frac{dx_2}{dt} - B_4\left(\frac{dx_2}{dt} - \frac{dx_3}{dt}\right)$$

$$- K_3(x_2 - x_3) - K_4x_2 = M_2\frac{d^2x_2}{dt^2} \qquad \text{(3-19.5)}$$

$$-B_1\left(\frac{dx_3}{dt} - \frac{dx_1}{dt}\right) - K_1(x_3 - x_1) - B_4\left(\frac{dx_3}{dt} - \frac{dx_2}{dt}\right)$$

$$- K_3(x_3 - x_2) - B_3\frac{dx_3}{dt} = M_3\frac{d^2x_3}{dt^2} \qquad \text{(3-19.6)}$$

Equations (3-19.4), (3-19.5), and (3-19.6) can now be solved simultaneously for x_1, x_2, and x_3.

3-20 MULTIPLE DEGREE-OF-FREEDOM ROTATIONAL SYSTEM

The mathematical model describing the behavior of the multiple degree-of-freedom torsional system of Fig. 3-20.1 is generated in a manner exactly analogous to that employed for translational system of Section 3.19. The system differential equations of motion are, at J_1

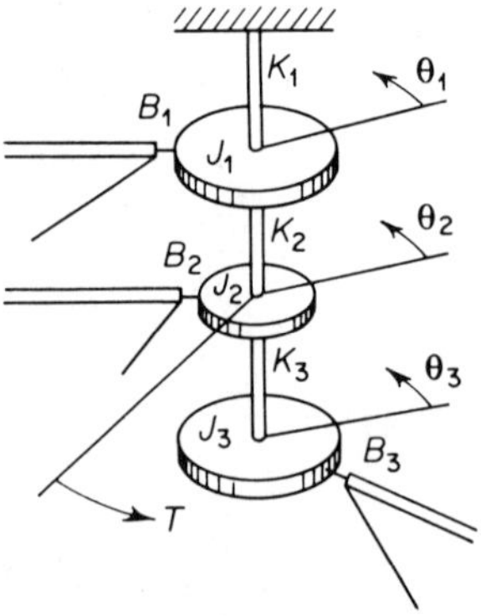

$$-K_1\theta_1 - K_2(\theta_1 - \theta_2) - B_1\frac{d\theta_1}{dt} = J_1\frac{d^2\theta_1}{dt^2}$$

$$(3\text{-}20.1)$$

at J_2

$$T - K_2(\theta_2 - \theta_1) - K_3(\theta_2 - \theta_3)$$
$$- B_2\frac{d\theta_2}{dt} = J_2\frac{d^2\theta_2}{dt^2} \quad (3\text{-}20.2)$$

and at J_3

$$-K_3(\theta_3 - \theta_2) - B_3\frac{d\theta_3}{dt} = J_3\frac{d^2\theta_3}{dt^2} \quad (3\text{-}20.3)$$

Figure 3-20.1 Three degree-of-freedom torsional system.

Equations (3-20.1), (3-20.2), and (3-20.3) form the torsional system mathematical model.

3-21 COMBINED TRANSLATION AND ROTATION

In the static (captive) test-firing of large solid-rocket motors, a test-stand arrangement similar to that shown in Fig. 3-21.1 is often employed.[7] Six force transducers (C_x, C_{y_1}, C_{y_2}, C_{y_3}, C_{z_1}, C_{z_2}) are oriented parallel to the xyz inertia coordinate axes; the load-cell outputs are processed to provide an approximation of the motor-force and moment-generation characteristics, i.e.,

$$F_x = C_x$$
$$F_y = C_{y_1} + C_{y_2} + C_{y_3}$$
$$F_z = C_{z_1} + C_{z_2}$$
$$M_x = C_{y_1}l_R - C_{y_2}l_R$$
$$M_y = C_{z_2}l_2 - C_{z_1}l_1$$
$$M_z = C_{y_3}l_2 - (C_{y_1} + C_{y_2})l_1 \quad (3\text{-}21.1)$$

When excited by transient input forces and moments, the combined test-stand motor assembly reacts by experiencing translation and rotation, thus generating reaction forces at each transducer location. The load cell functions as a linear spring, i.e., the output force is proportional to component deflection. In addition, structural (body) damping exists.

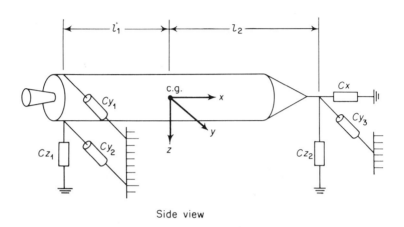

Side view

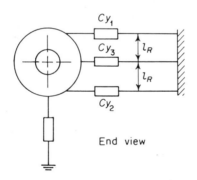

End view

Figure 3-21.1   Typical six-component test-stand assembly.

Let us assume that the system is excited by a transient force in the horizontal plane, as illustrated in the plan view of Fig. 3-21.2, and let us further use the gross assumption that no system interactions exist. Under these conditions, the six degree-of-freedom test stand is constrained to vibrate in two degrees-of-freedom. The linear spring constants $(K_{y_1}$ and $K_{y_2})$ and damping coefficients $(B_{y_1}$ and $B_{y_2})$, associated with force transducers C_{y_1} and C_{y_2}, are lumped into single equivalent units.

The input force F_y produces a system translation of the center of gravity

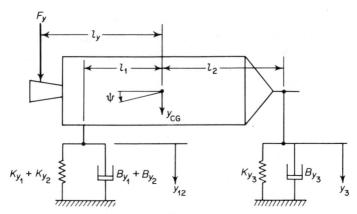

Figure 3-21.2   Plan view of test fixture.

y_{CG}, together with a yaw rotation ψ. If we assume positive deflections at each reaction position of y_3 and y_{12} as shown, the system differential equations become

$$F_y - (K_{y_1} + K_{y_2})y_{12} - (B_{y_1} + B_{y_2})\frac{dy_{12}}{dt}$$

$$- K_{y_3}y_3 - B_{y_3}\frac{dy_3}{dt} = M\frac{d^2y_{CG}}{dt^2} \qquad (3\text{-}21.2)$$

and

$$F_y l_y - (K_{y_1} + K_{y_2})l_1 y_{12} - (B_{y_1} + B_{y_2})l_1\frac{dy_{12}}{dt}$$

$$+ K_{y_3}l_2 y_3 + B_{y_3}l_2\frac{dy_3}{dt} = J\frac{d^2\psi}{dt^2} \qquad (3\text{-}21.3)$$

It now remains to define relationships between the four "unknowns" in the defining differential equations. Thus, from geometry

$$y_{12} = y_{CG} + l_1 \sin \psi \qquad (3\text{-}21.4)$$

$$y_3 = y_{CG} - l_2 \sin \psi \qquad (3\text{-}21.5)$$

Applying the linearizing small-angle approximation

$$\sin \psi = \psi \qquad (3\text{-}21.6)$$

Equations (3-19.4) and (3-19.5) are rewritten

$$y_{12} = y_{CG} + l_1\psi \qquad (3\text{-}21.7)$$

$$y_3 = y_{CG} - l_2\psi \qquad (3\text{-}21.8)$$

Equations (3-21.2), (3-21.3), (3-21.7), and (3-21.8) can now be solved simultaneously for y_{12} and y_3, or y_{CG} and ψ, depending upon the analytical requirements.

3-22 ELECTROMECHANICAL SYSTEMS

The six-component test-stand assembly of Fig. 3-21.1 is employed, as stated previously, to measure the solid-rocket motor reaction force components. For this purpose, the load cell is provided with strain gauges that generate a continuous voltage output, proportional to deflection (force). As such, the load cell can be considered as an ultra precise potentiometer.

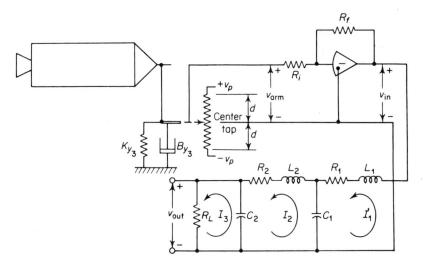

Figure 3-22.1   Electromechanical system.

The output voltage is next amplified, and can then be shaped through a passive-element filter network. The corresponding electromechanical system configuration is pictured in Fig. 3-22.1 for force transducer C_{y_3}.

If we assume that y_3, the deflection at C_{y_3}, can be computed from Eq. (3-21.2), (3-21.3), (3-21.7), and (3-21.8), then the remaining system equations are

$$V_{\text{arm}} = \frac{-y_3}{d} V_p \tag{3-22.1}$$

$$V_{\text{in}} = \frac{-R_f}{R_i} V_{\text{arm}} \tag{3-22.2}$$

$$-V_{\text{in}} + L_1 \frac{dI_1}{dt} + R_1 I_1 + \frac{1}{C_1} \int I_1 \, dt - \frac{1}{C_1} \int I_2 \, dt = 0 \tag{3-22.3}$$

$$L_2 \frac{dI_2}{dt} + R_2 I_2 + \frac{1}{C_2} \int I_2 \, dt + \frac{1}{C_1} \int I_2 \, dt - \frac{1}{C_2} \int I_3 \, dt - \frac{1}{C_1} \int I_1 \, dt = 0$$

(3-22.4)

$$R_L I_3 + \frac{1}{C_2} \int I_3 \, dt - \frac{1}{C_2} \int I_2 \, dt = 0 \qquad \text{(3-22.5)}$$

$$V_{\text{out}} = R_L I_3 \qquad \text{(3-22.6)}$$

Equations (3-22.1) through (3-22.6), together with the expressions of Section 3.21 that define y_3, form the complete electromechanical system mathematical model.

PROBLEMS

3.1   For the following *LRC* networks, compute the corresponding mathematical models.   Assume zero source and infinite load impedances.

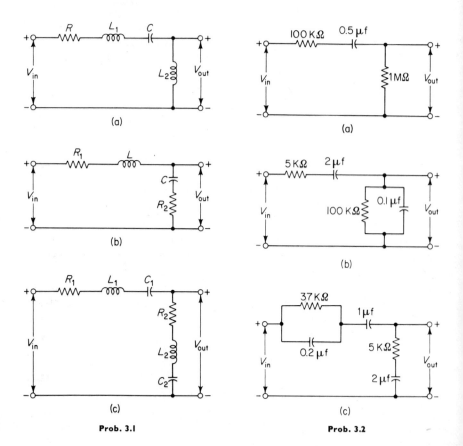

(a)

(b)

(c)

Prob. 3.1

(a)

(b)

(c)

Prob. 3.2

3.2 Deduce the mathematical model for each of the RC shaping networks illustrated. Assume zero source and infinite load impedances.

3.3 Determine the mathematical model for the following magnetically coupled networks.

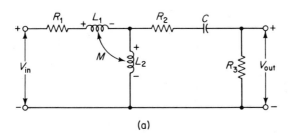

(a)

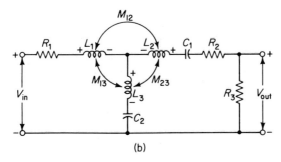

(b)

Prob. 3.3

3.4 What is the gain of the following amplifier?

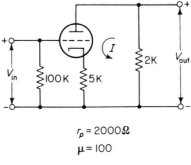

$r_p = 2000\,\Omega$

$\mu = 100$

Prob. 3.4

3.5 Compute mathematical models for the following multiple-node networks.

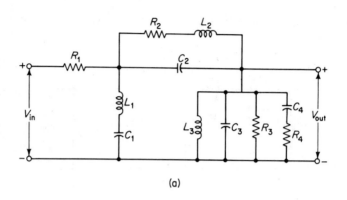

(a)

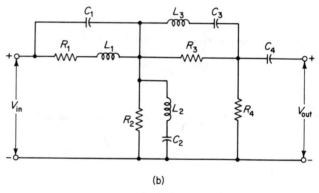

(b)

Prob. 3.5

3.6 Compute the equations of motion for the following translational systems.

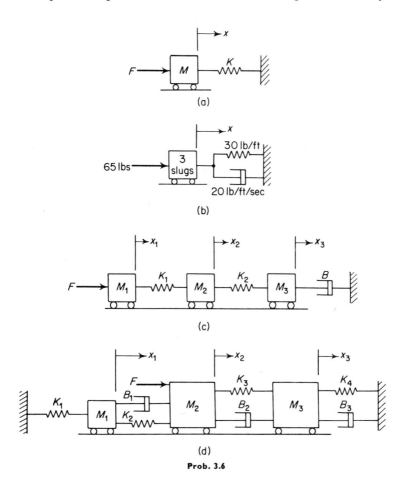

(a)

(b)

(c)

(d)

Prob. 3.6

3.7 Compute the mathematical model for the following torsional system.

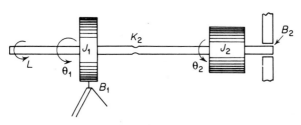

Prob. 3.7

3.8 Determine the equations of motion for the undamped system illustrated here. Assume that the equilibrium condition exists for no reaction in springs. At time $t = 0$, the system is released. $J = 57,000$ slug $-$ ft².

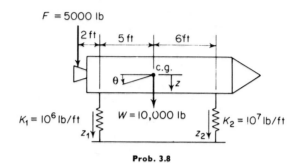

$F = 5000$ lb

$K_1 = 10^6$ lb/ft $W = 10,000$ lb $K_2 = 10^7$ lb/ft

Prob. 3.8

3.9 Derive the equations that govern the following electromechanical system.

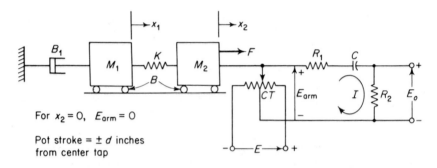

For $x_2 = 0$, $E_{arm} = 0$

Pot stroke = $\pm d$ inches
from center tap

Assume zero source and R_3 load impedances

Prob. 3.9

BIBLIOGRAPHY

1. Gardner, M. F. and J. L. Barnes, *Transients in Linear Systems*. New York: John Wiley & Sons, Inc., 1948.

2. Guillemin, E. A., *Introductory Circuit Theory*. New York: John Wiley & Sons, Inc., 1953.

3. Van Valkenburg, M. E., *Network Analysis* (2nd Ed.). Englewood Cliffs, N.J.: Prentice-Hall, Inc., 1964.

4. Wylie, C. R., Jr., *Advanced Engineering Mathematics*. New York: McGraw-Hill Book Company, 1960.

5. Seely, S., *Electron-tube Circuits*. New York: McGraw-Hill Book Company, 1950.

6. Coblenz, A. and H. L. Owens, *Transistors: Theory and Application*. New York: McGraw-Hill Book Company, 1955.

7. Langill, A. W., Jr., and G. N. Kapandritis, "Multi-Component Test Fixtures for Solid Rocket Motor Testing," *IEEE Trans. on Aerospace Support*, Vol. AS-1, n. 2, 1963.

TRANSIENT SYSTEMS ANALYSIS: THE LAPLACE TRANSFORMATION[1,2,3,4,5,6,7]

4

4-1 INTRODUCTION

In the last chapter, a number of linear mathematical models were developed from corresponding electrical and mechanical engineering systems. These analytical expressions took the form of linear differential equations with constant coefficients in one or more degrees-of-freedom. We will now consider the solution of the arbitrary mathematical model by means of Laplace transformation techniques.

4-2 DEFINITION OF THE LAPLACE TRANSFORMATION

The Laplace transformation of the time domain function $f(t)$ can be defined as

$$\mathscr{L}\{f(t)\} = \int_0^\infty f(t)e^{-st}\,dt = F(s) \qquad \textbf{(4-2.1)}$$

where s is a complex variable, i.e., $s = \sigma + j\omega$.

The process of transforming $f(t)$ into the s (complex frequency) domain is illustrated graphically in Fig. 4-2.1. $f(t)$ is first multiplied by the decaying exponential e^{-st}. The area under the resulting product curve is then summed for all positive times between the limits of zero and infinity. As shown, the integral is a function only

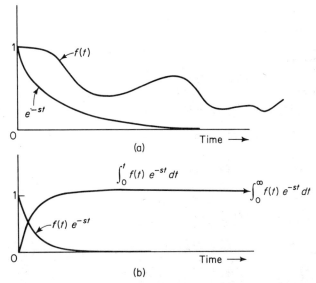

Figure 4-2.1   Graphical interpretation of Laplace transform integral; (a) arbitrary function and decaying exponential, (b) product of $f(t)\,e^{-st}$ and value of integral.

of s; if the value of s is large, the corresponding area under the curve is small; if s is small, then the resulting integral value is large. Thus, for a particular $f(t)$, the Laplace transform $F(s)$ is a function only of s, and it is completely independent of time. Although the integration required in Eq. (4-2.1) might appear, at first glance, a rather high price to pay for eliminating the function's time dependence, this property will prove the essential and basic key to a simple solution of ordinary linear differential equations.

4-3 ELEMENTARY FUNCTION TRANSFORMATIONS

In this section, the Laplace transformations of several time-domain forcing functions are generated through the direct computation of Eq. (4-3.1). As an initial example, consider the unit step function pictured in Fig. 4-3.1.

The mathematical definition of $U(t)$ is

$$U(t) = 1 \quad \text{for } t > 0$$

$$ = 0 \quad \text{for } t < 0 \quad \textbf{(4-3.1)}$$

Notice that a discontinuity exists at

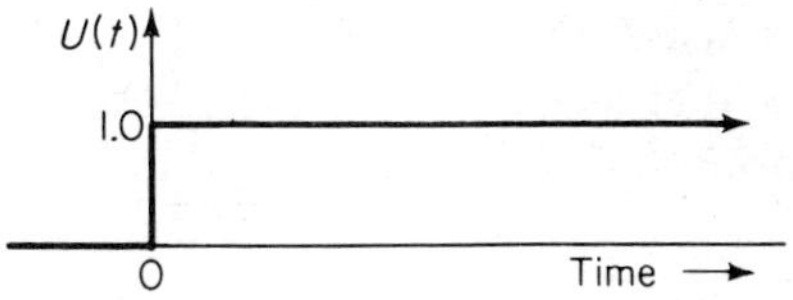

Figure 4-3.1   Unit step function excitation.

$t = 0$, such that $U(0)$ is undefined. This apparent dilemma is clarified, however, if one considers a more precise mathematical definition of the Laplace transformation

$$\mathscr{L}\{f(t)\} = \lim_{\substack{\epsilon \to 0 \\ T \to \infty}} \int_\epsilon^T f(t)e^{-st}\, dt \tag{4-3.2}$$

Thus, the lower limit of integration is not $t = 0$, but rather $t = 0^+$, i.e., a very small but finite positive time. Hence, within the limits of integration of Eq. (4-3.2), $U(t) = 1$. Substituting this value into Eq. (4-3.2)

$$\mathscr{L}\{U(t)\} = \int_{0^+}^\infty 1 \cdot e^{-st}\, dt \tag{4-3.3}$$

Equation (4-3.3) is now evaluated by standard integration

$$\mathscr{L}\{U(t)\} = -\frac{1}{s}\int_{0^+}^\infty e^{-st}\, d(-st) = -\frac{1}{s}e^{-st}\Big|_{t=0^+}^{t=\infty} \tag{4-3.4}$$

The upper limit of integration $t = \infty$, when substituted into Eq. (4-3.4), causes the expression to vanish. The lower limit of integration, however, yields a contribution of unity; hence

$$\mathscr{L}\{U(t)\} = -\frac{1}{s}(0 - 1) = \frac{1}{s} \tag{4-3.5}$$

It is a well-known fact that integration represents a linear mathematical process. Since the Laplace transform involves nothing more mysterious than a particular form of time-domain integration, it follows directly that the Laplace transformation is also a linear operation. Thus, if $\mathscr{L}\{U(t)\} = 1/s$, then $\mathscr{L}\{KU(t)\} = K/s$, where K is a constant independent of both time and s. In general, the property of superposition applies, i.e., if $\mathscr{L}\{f(t)\} = F(s)$ and $\mathscr{L}\{g(t)\} = G(s)$, then $\mathscr{L}\{Af(t) + Bg(t)\} = AF(s) + BG(s)$, where A and B are also constants.

Let us now derive the Laplace transformation of a unit sine function of arbitrary frequency, $f(t) = \sin \omega t$

$$\mathscr{L}\{\sin \omega t\} = \int_{0^+}^\infty \sin \omega t\, e^{-st}\, dt \tag{4-3.6}$$

To evaluate Eq. (4-3.6), one turns to the technique of integration by parts. It should be noted that this method applies only for those situations in which the function approaches a finite limit at the edges of the integration interval. If this criterion is realized, then in generalized form

$$\int_{0^+}^{\infty} u \, dv = uv \Big|_{0^+}^{\infty} - \int_{0^+}^{\infty} v \, du \tag{4-3.7}$$

We now arbitrarily assume

$$u = e^{-st}$$

$$dv = \sin \omega t \, dt \tag{4-3.8}$$

then

$$du = -se^{-st} \, dt$$

$$v = -\frac{1}{\omega} \cos \omega t \tag{4-3.9}$$

Substituting Eq. (4-3.8) and (4-3.9) into Eq. (4-3.7)

$$\int_{0^+}^{\infty} \sin \omega t \, e^{-st} \, dt = -\frac{1}{\omega} e^{-st} \cos \omega t \Big|_{0^+}^{\infty} - \int_{0^+}^{\infty} \frac{s}{\omega} e^{-st} \cos \omega t \, dt$$

$$= \frac{1}{\omega} - \frac{s}{\omega} \int_{0^+}^{\infty} e^{-st} \cos \omega t \, dt \tag{4-3.10}$$

Again applying integration by parts to Eq. (4-3.10), we let

$$u = e^{-st}$$

$$dv = \cos \omega t \, dt \tag{4-3.11}$$

so that

$$du = -se^{-st} \, dt$$

$$v = \frac{1}{\omega} \sin \omega t \tag{4-3.12}$$

and

$$\int_{0^+}^{\infty} \sin \omega t \, e^{-st} \, dt = \frac{1}{\omega} - \frac{s^2}{\omega^2} \int_{0}^{\infty} \sin \omega t \, e^{-st} \, dt \tag{4-3.13}$$

Rearranging the preceding equation

$$\int_{0^+}^{\infty} \sin \omega t \, e^{-st} \, dt = \mathscr{L} \{\sin \omega t\} = \frac{\omega}{s^2 + \omega^2} \qquad (4\text{-}3.14)$$

As a final example, we derive the Laplace transformation of the decaying exponential time function $f(t) = e^{-\alpha t}$

$$\mathscr{L} \{e^{-\alpha t}\} = \int_{0^+}^{\infty} e^{-\alpha t} e^{-st} \, dt = \int_{0^+}^{\infty} e^{-(s+\alpha)t} \, dt$$

$$= -\frac{1}{s + \alpha} \int_{0^+}^{\infty} e^{-(s+\alpha)t} \, d[-(s + \alpha)t]$$

$$\mathscr{L} \{e^{-\alpha t}\} = \frac{1}{s + \alpha} \qquad (4\text{-}3.15)$$

To demonstrate the application of Eq. (4-3.5), (4-3.14), and (4-3.15) a simple illustrative example will suffice. An excitation voltage $V(t)$ is developed across an electrical network input through a relay contact that is closed at $t = 0$. The input is comprised of a sinusoid, a decaying exponential, and a d-c bias

$$V(t) = 28 + 42 \sin 100t + 6e^{-16t} \qquad (4\text{-}3.16)$$

The problem is now one of computing the Laplace transform of Eq. (4-3.16). Transforming each component of the voltage signal in Eq. (4-3.16)

$$\mathscr{L} \{28\} = 28\mathscr{L} \{U(t)\} = \frac{28}{s} \qquad (4\text{-}3.17)$$

$$\mathscr{L} \{42 \sin 100t\} = 42\mathscr{L} \{\sin 100t\} = \frac{4200}{s^2 + 10{,}000} \qquad (4\text{-}3.18)$$

and

$$\mathscr{L} \{6e^{-16t}\} = 6\mathscr{L} \{e^{-16t}\} = \frac{6}{s + 16} \qquad (4\text{-}3.19)$$

Then, applying the property of superposition, we obtain the required transform

$$\mathscr{L} \{V(t)\} = \frac{28}{s} + \frac{4200}{s^2 + 10{,}000} + \frac{6}{s + 16} \qquad (4\text{-}3.20)$$

A short table of Laplace transformations can now be generated:

Time Domain Function	Laplace Transformed Function
K	$\dfrac{K}{s}$
$e^{-\alpha t}$	$\dfrac{1}{s + \alpha}$
$e^{+\beta t}$	$\dfrac{1}{s - \beta}$
$\sin \omega t$	$\dfrac{\omega}{s^2 + \omega^2}$
$\cos \omega t$	$\dfrac{s}{s^2 + \omega^2}$
$e^{-\alpha t} \sin \omega t$	$\dfrac{\omega}{(s + \alpha)^2 + \omega^2}$
$e^{-\alpha t} \cos \omega t$	$\dfrac{s + \alpha}{(s + \alpha)^2 + \omega^2}$
t^n	$\dfrac{n!}{s^{n+1}}$
$t^n e^{-\alpha t}$	$\dfrac{n!}{(s + \alpha)^{n+1}}$
$\sinh \omega t$	$\dfrac{\omega}{s^2 - \omega^2}$
$\cosh \omega t$	$\dfrac{s}{s^2 - \omega^2}$

4-4 TRANSFORMS OF DERIVATIVES

Before a complete differential equation can be transformed, an expression for the Laplace transform of the arbitrary time derivative must be derived. For the first-order derivative $df(t)/dt$, the basic transform relationship is

$$\mathscr{L}\left\{\frac{df(t)}{dt}\right\} = \int_{0^+}^{\infty} \frac{df(t)}{dt} e^{-st} \, dt \qquad \text{(4-4.1)}$$

Employing integration by parts, once more, for

$$u = e^{-st}$$

$$dv = \frac{df(t)}{dt} \, dt \qquad \text{(4-4.2)}$$

then

$$du = -se^{-st}\,dt$$

$$v = f(t) \tag{4-4.3}$$

Substituting into Eq. (4-3.7)

$$\mathcal{L}\left\{\frac{df(t)}{dt}\right\} = e^{-st}f(t)\Big|_{0^+}^{\infty} + \int_{0^+}^{\infty} se^{-st}f(t)\,dt \tag{4-4.4}$$

Assuming that $\mathcal{L}\{f(t)\} = F(s)$, i.e., that the function is Laplace transformable

$$\mathcal{L}\left\{\frac{df(t)}{dt}\right\} = sF(s) - f(0^+) \tag{4-4.5}$$

The term $f(0^+)$ in Eq. (4-4.5) is the value of $f(t)$ evaluated at $t = 0^+$; this component represents an initial system condition. Thus, the Laplace transform includes the effect of initial conditions directly within the mathematical formulation. Equation (4-4.5) can be generalized to the nth order derivative

$$\mathcal{L}\left\{\frac{d^n f(t)}{dt^n}\right\} = s^n F(s) - s^{n-1}f(0) - s^{n-2}\frac{df(0)}{dt} - s^{n-3}\frac{d^2 f(0)}{dt^2}$$

$$- \cdots - s\frac{d^{n-2}f(0)}{dt^{n-2}} - \frac{d^{n-1}f(0)}{dt^{n-1}} \tag{4-4.6}$$

The nth order differential equation must have specified n-distinct initial conditions to define completely the system state. This well-established fact is consistent with the generalized Laplace transformation of Eq. (4-4.6); all initial system conditions appear explicitly within the transform formula.

4-5 TRANSFORMS OF INTEGRALS

The transform of the first-order integral is computed in a manner similar to that employed in Section 4.4. Substituting the integral $\int f(t)\,dt$ into Eq. (4-2.1), we obtain the required integral expression

$$\mathcal{L}\left\{\int f(t)\,dt\right\} = \int_{0^+}^{\infty} [\int f(t)\,dt]e^{-st}\,dt \tag{4-5.1}$$

To compute Eq. (4-5.1), we use once again directly from Eq. (4-2.1), the familiar integration by parts,

$$u = e^{-st} \tag{4-5.2}$$

$$dv = f(t)\,dt$$

and

$$du = -se^{-st}\, dt$$
$$v = \int f(t)\, dt \tag{4-5.3}$$

such that

$$\int_{0^+}^{\infty} f(t)e^{-st}\, dt = e^{-st} \int f(t)\, dt \bigg|_{0^+}^{\infty} + s \int_{0^+}^{\infty} [\int f(t)\, dt]e^{-st}\, dt \tag{4-5.4}$$

Solving for the double-integral expression

$$\int_{0^+}^{\infty} [\int f(t)\, dt]e^{-st}\, dt = \frac{F(s)}{s} + \frac{f^{(-1)}(0^+)}{s} \tag{4-5.5}$$

we obtain

$$\mathscr{L}\{\int f(t)\, dt\} = \frac{F(s)}{s} + \frac{f^{(-1)}(0^+)}{s} \tag{4-5.6}$$

In Eq. (4-5.6), the term $f^{(-1)}(0^+)$ is equal to the initial condition impressed upon the integration at time $t = 0^+$.

4-6 S-DOMAIN SOLUTIONS OF NETWORK PROBLEMS

Let us now compute, in the complex-frequency domain, the solution of two typical electrical-network transient-response problems. As illustrated in Fig. 4-6.1, the single-loop LRC network is excited, at time $t = 0$, by a
decaying exponential voltage forcing
function

$$V_{in}(t) = e^{-2t} \tag{4-6.1}$$

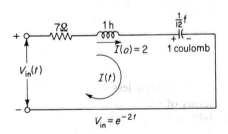

At $t = 0^+$, the capacitor contains
a charge of one coulomb, and an
initial current of two amperes exists
within the inductor. The problem is
now one of defining $I(t)$ for all posi-

Figure 4-6.1   Single-loop LRC network.

tive times. Since $I(t)$ and $I(0)$ are in the same direction, the initial system condition with respect to current is $I(0) = 2$ amps. Similarly, the first integral of current in amperes is charge in coulombs; thus, $I^{(-1)}(0^+) = 1$ coulomb.

Writing the system differential equation corresponding to Fig. 4-6.1

$$V_{in}(t) = L\frac{dI(t)}{dt} + RI(t) + \frac{1}{C}\int I(t)\, dt \tag{4-6.2}$$

Substituting the numerical values for L, C, and R into Eq. (4-6.2), and indicating the exponential nature of the input voltage

$$e^{-2t} = \frac{dI(t)}{dt} + 7I(t) + 12 \int I(t)\, dt \qquad (4\text{-}6.3)$$

with $I(0^+) = 2$, $I^{(-1)}(0^+) = 1$.

Each component of Eq. (4-6.3) is now Laplace transformed as

$$\mathscr{L}\{e^{-2t}\} = \frac{1}{s+2} \qquad (4\text{-}6.4)$$

$$\mathscr{L}\left\{\frac{dI(t)}{dt}\right\} = sI(s) - I(0) = sI(s) - 2 \qquad (4\text{-}6.5)$$

$$\mathscr{L}\{7I(t)\} = 7\mathscr{L}\{I(t)\} = 7I(s) \qquad (4\text{-}6.6)$$

$$\mathscr{L}\{12 \int I(t)\, dt\} = 12\mathscr{L}\{\int I(t)\, dt\} = 12\left[\frac{I(s)}{s} + \frac{I^{(-1)}(0^+)}{s}\right] = 12\left[\frac{I(s)}{s} + \frac{1}{s}\right]$$

$$(4\text{-}6.7)$$

Thus

$$\frac{1}{s+2} = sI(s) - 2 + 7I(s) + \frac{12I(s)}{s} + \frac{12}{s} \qquad (4\text{-}6.8)$$

Equation (4-6.8) is solved algebraically for $I(s)$ to yield the final s-domain expression

$$I(s) = \frac{2s^2 - 7s - 24}{(s+2)(s^2 + 7s + 12)} \qquad (4\text{-}6.9)$$

It is often less confusing to consider the initial condition $I^{(-1)}(0^+)$ in terms of an equivalent voltage source. This procedure is based upon definition of capacitance. Thus, if $I = C\, d(V_2 - V_1)/dt$ as shown in Eq. (3-5.3), then

$$Q = C(V_2 - V_1) \qquad (4\text{-}6.10)$$

In the present situation, $C = \frac{1}{12}$ farads and $Q = 1$ coulomb. Thus

$$V_2 - V_1 = \frac{Q}{C} = 12 \text{ volts} \qquad (4\text{-}6.11)$$

The effect of an initial capacitor charge has, in Eq. (4-6.11), been described by means of an equivalent initial voltage drop across the capacitor plates, and the differential equation that governs the network of Fig. 4-6.2 is modified to reflect this condition

$$-12 + e^{-2t} = \frac{dI(t)}{dt} + 7I(t) + 12\int_{0^+}^{t} I(t)\, dt$$

$$(4\text{-}6.12)$$

$$I(0^+) = 2 \qquad I^{(-1)}(0^+) = 0$$

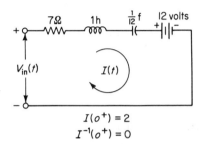

$$I(o^+) = 2$$
$$I^{-1}(o^+) = 0$$

Figure 4-6.2 Initial capacitor change replaced by equivalent voltage source.

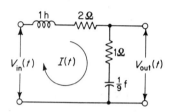

Figure 4-6.3 Second example consists of single-loop *LRC* network.

It is easily shown that the Laplace transformation of Eq. (4-6.12) gives rise to an equation identical to that of Eq. (4-6.9). These results are generalized as

$$\mathscr{L}\left\{\int f(t)\, dt\right\} = \frac{F(s)}{s} + \frac{f^{(-1)}(0^+)}{s}$$

while

$$\mathscr{L}\left\{\int_{0^+}^{t} f(t)\, dt\right\} = \frac{F(s)}{s}$$

The initial integrator condition that is missing in the above definite integral must now be expressed by an equivalent initial capacitor voltage.

As a second example, the single-loop network of Fig. 4-6.3 is excited by a unit step excitation voltage V_{in}; it is required to characterize the circuit output voltage V_{out}. If we assume that there are no initial conditions, the mathematical model corresponding to the physical system of Fig. 4-6.3 is derived by the application of Kirchhoff's loop law

$$V_{in}(t) = \frac{dI(t)}{dt} + 3I(t) + 9\int_{0}^{t} I(t)\, dt$$

$$(4\text{-}6.13)$$

$$V_{out}(t) = I(t) + 9\int_{0}^{t} I(t)\, dt$$

$$(4\text{-}6.14)$$

Taking the Laplace transformations of the preceding equations

$$\frac{1}{s} = sI(s) + 3I(s) + \frac{9}{s}I(s) \qquad (4\text{-}6.15)$$

$$V_{\text{out}}(s) = I(s) + \frac{9}{s}I(s) \qquad (4\text{-}6.16)$$

Solving Eqs. (4-6.15) and (4-6.16) for the transformed output voltage

$$V_{\text{out}}(s) = \frac{s+9}{s(s^2+3s+9)} \qquad (4\text{-}6.17)$$

4-7 THE INVERSE LAPLACE TRANSFORMATION

The relations of Eqs. (4-6.9) and (4-6.17) represent the desired transient-response solutions, but in a form not easily understood. Thus, it is now necessary for the complex-frequency domain solutions to be transformed back into the time domain so that meaningful information can be derived; this is accomplished by applying inverse Laplace transformation techniques.

In calculus, the inverse process of integration is considerably more difficult than the operation of differentiation. Similarly, the inverse Laplace transformation is a more complicated procedure than the straightforward direct transformation. However, just as extensive integral tables have been prepared, a great number of inverse Laplace transformations are available in tabular form. The inverse Laplace transformations associated with many possible s-domain configurations are presented in Appendix A.

The inverse Laplace transformation is defined implicitly as

$$\mathscr{L}^{-1}[\mathscr{L}\{f(t)\}] = f(t) \qquad (4\text{-}7.1)$$

Hence, since $\mathscr{L}\{e^{-4t}\} = 1/(s+4)$, then

$$\mathscr{L}^{-1}\left\{\frac{1}{s+4}\right\} = e^{-4t} \qquad (4\text{-}7.2)$$

In the next five sections we will develop techniques, based upon partial-fraction expansions, for decomposing an arbitrary complex-frequency domain solution into components, the inverse Laplace transforms of which are apparent.

4-8   PARTIAL-FRACTION EXPANSION TECHNIQUES: FIRST-ORDER REAL-AXIS POLES

In Chapter 2, the concepts of poles and zeros were developed in terms of an arbitrary function $G(s)$, consisting of a ratio of polynomials in the complex variable s. It was stated that the values of s that caused the polynomial numerator to vanish were identified as zeros of $G(s)$, whereas the values of s that caused the polynomial denominator to vanish were identified as poles of $G(s)$. These definitions obviously apply to the complex-frequency domain expressions of Eqs. (4-6.9) and (4-6.17).

The process of translating an arbitrary s-plane pole-zero array into the time domain by inverse Laplace transformation is initiated by using a set of partial-fraction expansions. The particular type of expansion employed is determined by the type of poles involved (first order, real axis; first order, complex; multiple order, real axis; and multiple order, complex). In this section, we consider the partial-fraction expansion of an s-plane array consisting of only first-order, real-axis poles

$$G(s) = \frac{s^n + \alpha s^{n-1} + \beta s^{n-2} + \cdots + 1}{(s + a)(s + b)(s + c)(s - d)(s - f) \cdots} \qquad \text{(4-8.1)}$$

where the order of the denominator is greater than that of the numerator.

The partial-fraction expansion of Eq. (4-8.1) is

$$G(s) = \frac{A}{s + a} + \frac{B}{s + b} + \frac{C}{s + c} + \frac{D}{s - d} + \frac{E}{s - f} + \cdots \qquad \text{(4-8.2)}$$

It can be shown that, if the coefficients A, B, C, ... are chosen correctly, then Eqs. (4-8.1) and (4-8.2) are identities. One can now write directly, in generalized form, the complete transient-response solution

$$g(t) = Ae^{-at} + Be^{-bt} + Ce^{-ct} + De^{dt} + Ee^{ft} + \cdots \qquad \text{(4-8.3)}$$

Thus, once A, B, C, ... are computed, the system transient-response solution is completed.

The problem of evaluating the partial-fraction coefficients can be attacked by two separate approaches. The first method, often used in elementary integral calculus, involves combining the sum of all partial-fraction components over a lowest common denominator. The coefficients are then evaluated by a direct comparison of the corresponding numerators. For example, consider the complex-frequency domain solution

$$I(s) = \frac{2s^2 - 7s - 24}{(s + 2)(s + 3)(s + 4)} \qquad \text{(4-8.4)}$$

The partial fraction expansion of Eq. (4-8.4) is

$$I(s) = \frac{A}{s+2} + \frac{B}{s+3} + \frac{C}{s+4} \tag{4-8.5}$$

Expressing over a lowest common denominator

$$I(s) = \frac{A(s+3)(s+4) + B(s+2)(s+4) + C(s+2)(s+3)}{(s+2)(s+3)(s+4)} \tag{4-8.6}$$

Since Eqs. (4-8.4) and (4-8.6) are identical, their respective numerators must be identical

$$2s^2 - 7s - 24 = (A + B + C)s^2 + (7A + 6B + 5C)s + 12A + 8B + 6C \tag{4-8.7}$$

Equating like coefficients of s

$$A + B + C = 2 \tag{4-8.8}$$

$$7A + 6B + 5 = -7 \tag{4-8.9}$$

$$12A + 8B + 6C = -24 \tag{4-8.10}$$

Equations (4-8.8), (4-8.9), and (4-8.10) are now solved simultaneously for A, B, and C to yield, $A = -1$, $B = -15$, and $C = 18$.

A simplified procedure for evaluating the coefficients becomes apparent, however, when one realizes that the coefficients A, B, and C represent the residues associated with the poles located at $s = -2$, $s = -3$, and $s = -4$, respectively. Thus, from Eq. (2-8.6) of Chapter 2

$$A = \lim_{s \to -2} (s+2)I(s) \tag{4-8.11}$$

$$B = \lim_{s \to -3} (s+3)I(s) \tag{4-8.12}$$

and

$$C = \lim_{s \to -4} (s+4)I(s) \tag{4-8.13}$$

Hence

$$A = \lim_{s \to -2} (s+2) \frac{(2s^2 - 7s - 24)}{(s+2)(s+3)(s+4)} = \lim_{s \to -2} \frac{2s^2 - 7s - 24}{(s+3)(s+4)}$$

$$= \frac{2(-2)^2 - (7)(-2) - 24}{(-2+3)(-2+4)} = \frac{8 + 14 - 24}{(1)(2)} = -1 \tag{4-8.14}$$

Similarly

$$B = \lim_{s \to -3} (s + 3) \frac{(2s^2 - 7s - 24)}{(s + 2)(s + 3)(s + 4)} = -15 \qquad \text{(4-8.15)}$$

$$C = \lim_{s \to -4} (s + 4) \frac{(2s^2 - 7s - 24)}{(s + 2)(s + 3)(s + 4)} = 18 \qquad \text{(4-8.16)}$$

Substituting the results of Eqs. (4-8.14), (4-8.15), and (4-8.16) into Eq. (4-8.5)

$$I(s) = -\frac{1}{s + 2} - \frac{15}{s + 3} + \frac{18}{s + 4} \qquad \text{(4-8.17)}$$

so that the desired transient response is

$$i(t) = -e^{-2t} - 15e^{-3t} + 18e^{-4t} \qquad \text{(4-8.18)}$$

4-9 MULTIPLE-ORDER REAL-AXIS POLES

The partial-fraction expansion for an s-domain system containing multiple-order real-axis poles is illustrated in generalized form

$$I(s) = \frac{s^m + \alpha s^{m-1} + \cdots + 1}{s(s + a)(s + b)^n} = \frac{H}{s} + \frac{A}{s + a} + \frac{B_n}{(s + b)^n}$$

$$+ \frac{B_{n-1}}{(s + b)^{n-1}} + \cdots + \frac{B_1}{s + b} \qquad \text{(4-9.1)}$$

Hence, for the particular expression

$$I(s) = \frac{s^2}{(s + 1)^3} \qquad \text{(4-9.2)}$$

the partial-fraction expansion becomes

$$I(s) = \frac{A}{(s + 1)^3} + \frac{B}{(s + 1)^2} + \frac{C}{s + 1} \qquad \text{(4-9.3)}$$

In Eq. (4-9.3), the coefficient C is the residue of the third-order pole located at $s = -1$, and it is evaluated by the direct computation of Eq. (2-8.5), Chapter 2.

$$C = \frac{1}{2!} \frac{d^2[(s + 1)^3 I(s)]}{ds^2}\bigg|_{s=-1} \qquad \text{(4-9.4)}$$

The coefficient B is evaluated by first multiplying Eq. (4-9.3) by the quantity $(s + 1)$

$$J(s) = \frac{s^2}{(s + 1)^2} = \frac{A}{(s + 1)^2} + \frac{B}{(s + 1)} + C \qquad \text{(4-9.5)}$$

In the preceding, the coefficient B represents the residue of a second-order pole located at $s = -1$, i.e.

$$B = \frac{d[(s + 1)^2 J(s)]}{ds}\bigg|_{s=-1} \qquad \text{(4-9.6)}$$

And finally, multiplying Eq. (4-9.5) by $(s + 1)$

$$L(s) = \frac{s^2}{s + 1} = \frac{A}{s + 1} + B + C(s + 1) \qquad \text{(4-9.7)}$$

such that A now corresponds to the residue of a first-order pole at $s = -1$

$$A = (s + 1)L(s)\bigg|_{s=-1} \qquad \text{(4-9.8)}$$

It is usually more convenient to reverse the process developed in Eqs. (4-9.4) through (4-9.8). Thus, we first multiply Eq. (4-9.3) by the term $(s + 1)^3$ to yield

$$s^2 = A + B(s + 1) + C(s + 1)^2 \qquad \text{(4-9.9)}$$

Evaluating Eq. (4-9.9) as s approaches -1

$$A = 1$$

Equation (4-9.9) is now differentiated with respect to s

$$2s = B + 2C(s + 1) \qquad \text{(4-9.10)}$$

Computing Eq. (4-9.10) as s approaches -1, $B = -2$. And finally, differentiating Eq. (4-9.10) with respect to s and allowing s to approach -1, $C = 1$. Thus

$$I(s) = \frac{1}{(s + 1)^3} - \frac{2}{(s + 1)^2} + \frac{1}{s + 1} \qquad \text{(4-9.11)}$$

Referring to the inverse Laplace transformations tabulated in Section 4.3

$$i(t) = \tfrac{1}{2}t^2 e^{-t} - 2te^{-t} + e^{-t} \qquad \text{(4-9.12)}$$

4-10 FIRST-ORDER IMAGINARY POLES

The partial-fraction expansion of an s-domain expression containing first-order imaginary poles is

$$I(s) = \frac{s^n + \alpha s^{n-1} + \cdots + 1}{(s^2 + \omega_1^2)(s^2 + \omega_2^2)(s^2 + \omega_3^2) \cdots} = \frac{A_1 s + B_1}{s^2 + \omega_1^2} + \frac{A_2 s + B_2}{s^2 + \omega_2^2} + \cdots$$

$$(4\text{-}10.1)$$

The computation of the coefficients $A_1, B_1, A_2, B_2, \ldots$ is illustrated by a numerical example. For the Laplace transformed current

$$I(s) = \frac{s + 2}{s(s^2 + 9)(s^2 + 1)} \qquad (4\text{-}10.2)$$

the pole-zero array corresponding to Eq. (4-10.2) is pictured in Fig. 4-10.1, and the required partial-fraction expansion is

$$I(s) = \frac{A}{s} + \frac{Bs + C}{s^2 + 9} + \frac{Ds + E}{s^2 + 1}$$

$$(4\text{-}10.3)$$

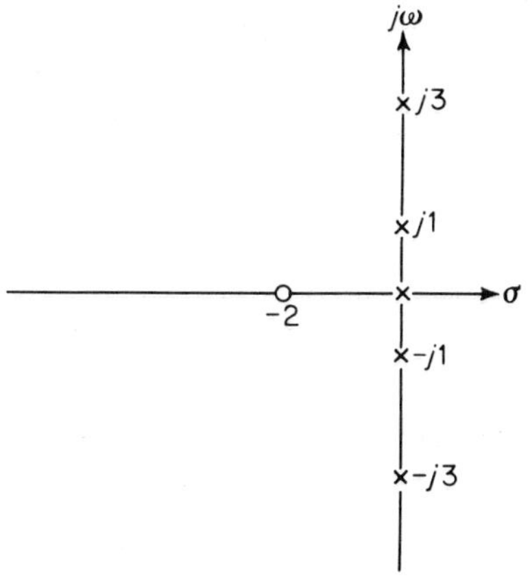

The computation of coefficient A is easily accomplished, as previously discussed, i.e.

$$A = \frac{s + 2}{(s^2 + 9)(s^2 + 1)}\bigg|_{s=0} = \frac{2}{9}$$

$$(4\text{-}10.4)$$

Figure 4-10.1 S-plane pole-zero array corresponding to Eq. (4-10.2).

To evaluate coefficients B and C, one first multiplies Eq. (4-10.3) by the denominator expression $s^2 + 9$.

$$\frac{s + 2}{s(s^2 + 1)} = \frac{A(s^2 + 9)}{s} + Bs + C + \frac{(Ds + E)(s^2 + 9)}{s^2 + 1} \qquad (4\text{-}10.5)$$

Equation (4-10.5) is now evaluated by substituting $s = j3$. Thus, the expressions $A(s^2 + 9)/s$ and $(Ds + E)(s^2 + 9)/(s^2 + 1)$ vanish, and

$$\left.\frac{s+2}{s(s^2+1)}\right|_{s=j3} = \left. Bs + C \right|_{s=j3} \tag{4-10.6}$$

which becomes

$$\frac{j3+2}{-j24} = j3B + C \tag{4-10.7}$$

The left-hand component of Eq. (4-10.7) is multiplied and divided by the complex conjugate of the denominator, thus forming a new denominator that is a real number.

$$\frac{j24(j3+2)}{(-j24)(j24)} = \frac{-3+j2}{24} = j3B + C \tag{4-10.8}$$

Equating real and imaginary parts

$$-\tfrac{3}{24} = C \qquad \tfrac{2}{24} = 3B \tag{4-10.9}$$

so that $B = \frac{1}{36}$ and $C = -\frac{1}{8}$.

Similarly, for the computation of D and E

$$\left.\frac{s+2}{s(s^2+9)}\right|_{s=j1} = \left.\frac{A(s^2+1)}{s}\right|_{s=j1} + \left.\frac{(Bs+C)(s^2+1)}{s^2+9}\right|_{s=j1} + \left. Ds + E \right|_{s=j1} \tag{4-10.10}$$

$$\frac{j+2}{j8} = \frac{j2-1}{-8} = jD + E \tag{4-10.11}$$

Solving Eq. (4-10.11), $D = -\frac{1}{4}, E = \frac{1}{8}$, and the final partial-fraction expansion is

$$I(s) = \frac{\frac{2}{9}}{s} + \frac{\frac{1}{36}s - \frac{1}{8}}{s^2+9} + \frac{-\frac{1}{4}s + \frac{1}{8}}{s^2+1} \tag{4-10.12}$$

Applying the inverse transformations tabulated in Section 4.3

$$i(t) = \tfrac{2}{9} + \tfrac{1}{36}\cos 3t - \tfrac{1}{24}\sin 3t - \tfrac{1}{4}\cos t + \tfrac{1}{8}\sin t \tag{4-10.13}$$

4-11 FIRST-ORDER COMPLEX POLES

The inverse Laplace transformations of systems containing first-order complex poles is identical, in theory, to that described in the previous section. For the particular pole-zero array

$$I(s) = \frac{s + 3}{s[(s + 1)^2 + 4]}$$
(4-11.1)

the required partial fraction expansion is

$$I(s) = \frac{A}{s} + \frac{Bs + C}{(s + 1)^2 + 4}$$
(4-11.2)

A is evaluated as before

$$A = \frac{s + 3}{(s + 1)^2 + 4}\bigg]_{s=0} = \frac{3}{5}$$
(4-11.3)

To compute B and C, one first multiplies by $(s + 1)^2 + 4$ to form

$$\frac{s + 3}{s} = \frac{A[(s + 1)^2 + 4]}{s} + Bs + C$$
(4-11.4)

As s approaches the value $-1 + j2$, the initial term to the right of the equality sign vanishes so that

$$\frac{s + 3}{s}\bigg]_{s=-1+j2} = Bs + C\bigg]_{s=-1+j2}$$
(4-11.5)

$$\frac{(-1 + j2) + 3}{-1 + j2} = (-1 + j2)B + C$$
(4-11.6)

Multiplying and dividing the initial term by the complex conjugate of the denominator

$$\frac{(2 + j2)(-1 - j2)}{(-1 + j2)(-1 - j2)} = \frac{2 - j6}{5} = C - B + j2B$$
(4-11.7)

Equating real and imaginary parts

$$2B = -\tfrac{6}{5} \qquad C - B = \tfrac{2}{5}$$
(4-11.8)

from which

$$B = -\tfrac{3}{5} \quad \text{and} \quad C = -\tfrac{1}{5}$$

Thus

$$I(s) = \frac{\tfrac{3}{5}}{s} + \frac{-\tfrac{3}{5}s - \tfrac{1}{5}}{(s + 1)^2 + 4}$$
(4-11.9)

Before the inverse transformation of Eq. (4-11.9) can be computed, it is necessary that the expression be arranged in a standard form compatible with the transform tables. Thus, adding and subtracting the quantity $\frac{3}{5}/[(s + 1)^2 + 4]$

$$I(s) = \frac{\frac{3}{5}}{s} - \frac{\frac{3}{5}(s + 1)}{(s + 1)^2 + 4} + \frac{\frac{2}{5}}{(s + 1)^2 + 4} \qquad \text{(4-11.10)}$$

and

$$i(t) = \frac{3}{5} - \frac{3}{5}e^{-t}\cos 2t + \frac{1}{5}e^{-t}\sin 2t \qquad \text{(4-11.11)}$$

4-12 MULTIPLE-ORDER IMAGINARY AND COMPLEX POLES

The inverse Laplace transformation of a generalized system containing multiple-order imaginary or complex poles is derived by an extension of the techniques already discussed. For a Laplace transformed current

$$I(s) = \frac{1}{[(s + a)^2 + \omega^2]^n(s + c)} \qquad \text{(4-12.1)}$$

the partial-fraction expansion is

$$I(s) = \frac{C}{s + c} + \frac{A_n s + B_n}{[(s + a)^2 + \omega^2]^n} + \frac{A_{n-1}s + B_{n-1}}{[(s + a)^2 + \omega^2]^{n-1}} + \cdots$$

$$+ \frac{A_1 s + B_1}{(s + a)^2 + \omega^2} \qquad \text{(4-12.2)}$$

To compute A_n and B_n, Eqs. (4-12.1) and (4-12.2) are equated and multiplied by the quantity $[(s + a)^2 + \omega^2]^n$

$$\frac{1}{s + c} = \frac{C[(s + a)^2 + \omega^2]^n}{s} + A_n s + B_n + (A_{n-1}s + B_{n-1})$$

$$\times [(s + a)^2 + \omega^2] + \cdots + (A_1 s + B_1)[(s + a)^2 + \omega^2]^{n-1} \qquad \text{(4-12.3)}$$

Evaluating Eq. (4-12.3) for $s = -a + j\omega$

$$\left. \frac{1}{s + c} \right|_{s=-a+j\omega} = \left. (A_1 s + B_1) \right|_{s=-a+j\omega}$$

The results of this calculation are now substituted into Eq. (4-12.3); the resulting expression is differentiated with respect to s, and, to solve for

A_{n-1} and B_{n-1}, the equation is evaluated again for $s = -a + j\omega$. This procedure is continued until all coefficients have been computed.

4-13 THE COMPLETE SOLUTIONS OF TYPICAL ENGINEERING PROBLEMS

In this section, we solve two typical problems drawn from the fields of electrical and mechanical engineering.

> EXAMPLE 1: *Combined Spring-Mass-Dashpot Translational System Step-Function Response*

Consider the single degree-of-freedom mechanical system illustrated in Fig. 4-13.1. The system is excited, at time $t = 0$, by the application of a step forcing function of 18 pounds. The system parameters and initial conditions are

$M = 1$ slug

$K_1 + K_2 = 2$ lb/ft

$B = 2$ lb/ft/sec

$x(0) = 2$ ft

$\dfrac{dx}{dt}(0) = 1$ ft/sec

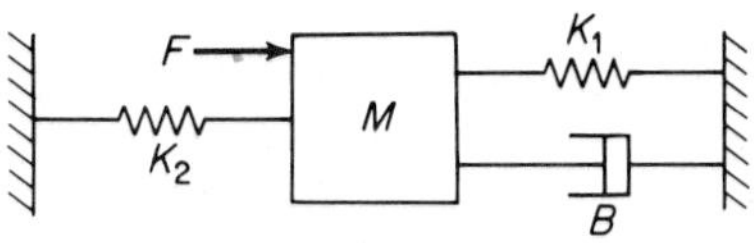

Figure 4-13.1

Defining $x(t)$ as the deflection from equilibrium, positive to the right, the differential equation of motion is

$$F(t) = M\frac{d^2x}{dt^2} + B\frac{dx}{dt} + (K_1 + K_2)x \qquad \text{(4-13.1)}$$

Transforming Eq. (4-13.1) for the arbitrary initial conditions $x(0)$ and $dx(0)/dt$

$$F(s) = M\left[s^2X(s) - sx(0) - \frac{dx}{dt}(0)\right] + B[sX(s) - x(0)] + (K_1 + K_2)X(s)$$

$$\text{(4-13.2)}$$

Equation (4-13.2) is solved for $X(s)$ to yield

$$X(s) = \frac{F(s) + sMx(0) + M\dfrac{dx}{dt}(0) + Bx(0)}{Ms^2 + Bs + (K_1 + K_2)} \qquad \text{(4-13.3)}$$

Since, as stated, $F(s) = 18/s$, Eq. (4-13.3) is evaluated numerically as

$$X(s) = \frac{2s^2 + 5s + 18}{s(s^2 + 2s + 2)} \qquad \text{(4-13.4)}$$

Before the final s-domain solution can be expanded by means of partial fractions, the quadratic term must be rearranged into the form $(s + a)^2 + b^2$ by completing the square. Thus, for an arbitrary constant α,

$$s^2 + 2s + 2 = (s + \alpha)^2 + 2 - \alpha^2$$
$$= (s^2 + 2\alpha s + \alpha^2) + 2 - \alpha^2 \qquad \text{(4-13.5)}$$

By inspection, $\alpha = 1$, and

$$s^2 + 2s + 2 = (s + 1)^2 + 1^2 \qquad \text{(4-13.6)}$$

Equation (4-13.4) is now expanded into partial fractions

$$\frac{2s^2 + 5s + 18}{s[(s + 1)^2 + 1^2]} = \frac{A}{s} + \frac{Bs + C}{(s + 1)^2 + 1^2} \qquad \text{(4-13.7)}$$

Solving for the arbitrary coefficient A by conventional means

$$A = \frac{2s^2 + 5s + 18}{(s + 1)^2 + 1^2}\bigg|_{s=0} = 9 \qquad \text{(4-13.8)}$$

To compute B and C, one multiplies Eq. (4-13.7) by the quadratic $(s + 1)^2 + 1^2$, then substitutes $s = -1 + j1$, i.e.

$$\frac{2(-1 + j1)^2 + 5(-1 + j1) + 18}{-1 + j1} = -6 - j7 = B(-1 + j1) + C \qquad \text{(4-13.9)}$$

Equating real and imaginary parts, $B = -7$ and $C = -13$. Thus

$$X(s) = \frac{9}{s} - \frac{(7s + 13)}{(s + 1)^2 + 1^2} = \frac{9}{s} - \frac{7(s + 1)}{(s + 1)^2 + 1^2} - \frac{6}{(s + 1)^2 + 1^2} \qquad \text{(4-13.10)}$$

and the standard inverse Laplace transformation is

$$x(t) = 9 - 7e^{-t} \cos t - 6e^{-t} \sin t \qquad \text{(4-13.11)}$$

It is always possible to verify that the final solution does indeed satisfy all initial conditions. For $t = 0$

$$x(0) = 9 - 7 - 0 = 2 \text{ ft}$$

Differentiating Eq. (4-13.11)

$$\frac{dx}{dt}(t) = -7(-e^{-t} \cos t - e^{-t} \sin t) - 6(-e^{-t} \sin t + e^{-t} \cos t) \qquad \text{(4-13.12)}$$

and, for $t = 0$

$$\frac{dx}{dt}(0) = 7 - 6 = 1 \text{ ft/sec}$$

Thus, the initial conditions are verified.

EXAMPLE 2:   *Single-Loop LRC Network Ramp-Function Response*

Consider the electrical network illustrated in Fig. 4-13.2, excited by a unit ramp input. The system mathematical model is

$$t = \frac{di(t)}{dt} + 3\,i(t) + 2\int i(t)\,dt \qquad (4\text{-}13.13)$$

$$V_{\text{out}}(t) = 3\,i(t) \qquad (4\text{-}13.14)$$

In the absence of initial conditions, the Laplace transformed mathematical model is

$$\frac{1}{s^2} = sI(s) + 3I(s) + \frac{2}{s}I(s) \qquad (4\text{-}13.15)$$

$$V_{\text{out}}(s) = 3I(s) \qquad (4\text{-}13.16)$$

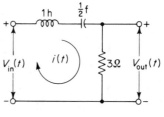

Figure 4-13.2

Combining Eq. (4-13.15) and (4-13.16)

$$V_{\text{out}}(s) = \frac{3}{s(s+1)(s+2)}$$

$$= \frac{A}{s} + \frac{B}{s+1} + \frac{C}{s+2}$$

$$(4\text{-}13.17)$$

The coefficients A, B, and C are computed as usual to yield $A = \frac{3}{2}$, $B = -3$, $C = \frac{3}{2}$. Thus

$$V_{\text{out}}(t) = \tfrac{3}{2} - 3e^{-t} + \tfrac{3}{2}e^{-2t} \qquad (4\text{-}13.18)$$

The final solution is again verified by the computation of initial conditions.

4-14   DELTA FUNCTION AND TIME DELAY

The delta function, or unit impulse, is defined explicitly by referring to the unit area pulse illustrated in Fig. 4-14.1

$$\delta(t) = \lim_{\Delta \to 0} \Delta\!\left(\frac{1}{\Delta}\right) \qquad (4\text{-}14.1)$$

In the limit, the pulse of Fig. 4-14.1 is compressed into an impulse of infinite amplitude and zero width; the area under the impulse, however, remains at unity.

Although the delta function is a mathematical fiction, i.e., all physical pulse excitations are of finite width and amplitude, the expression is invaluable as an analytical device for: (1) introducing the effects of initial conditions into control-system block-diagram mechanizations, (2) characterizing the sampling operation of sampled-data control-system theory, and

(3) approximating analytically a small-duration high-amplitude physical pulse.

To derive the Laplace transformation of the unit impulse, we return once again to the basic definition of Eq. (4-2.1); for $f(t) = \delta(t)$

$$\mathcal{L}\{\delta(t)\} = \int_0^\infty \delta(t)e^{-st}\,dt \qquad (4\text{-}14.2)$$

Before Eq. (4-14.2) can be computed, it is necessary to define the relationship between the lower limit of the integral and the limit of Eq. (4-14.1). Thus, since the delta function occurs at $t = 0$ and is zero throughout all further time, and the lower limit of the Laplace transformation integral is also zero, a possible discontinuity exists. However, since the delta function of Eq. (4-14.1) approaches the time-domain origin from the right (such that the unit area occurs during positive time), and since the Laplace transformation integral is intended to sum the values of the product $f(t)e^{-st}$ for *all* positive times, then the unit area must be between the limits of Eq. (4-14.2). Expanding into the sum of two integrals, and assuming that the unit impulse occurs within the interval $0^+ < t < 0^{++}$

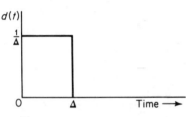

Figure 4-14.1   Pulse of duration Δ.

$$\mathcal{L}\{\delta(t)\} = \int_{0^+}^{0^{++}} \delta(t)e^{-st}\,dt + \int_{0^{++}}^\infty \delta(t)e^{-st}\,dt \qquad (4\text{-}14.3)$$

The second integral of Eq. (4-14.3) is zero, since the delta function's contribution is zero throughout the interval of integration. In the first integral, the function e^{-st} is evaluated as unity between the limits of integration. Thus

$$\mathcal{L}\{\delta(t)\} = \int_{0^+}^{0^{++}} \delta(t)\,dt \qquad (4\text{-}14.4)$$

But, since the area under the delta function is, by definition, unity

$$\mathcal{L}\{\delta(t)\} = 1 \qquad (4\text{-}14.5)$$

To indicate the method by which impulse functions are employed to introduce initial conditions, consider the first-order differential equation

$$\frac{dI}{dt}(t) + 2I(t) = 0 \qquad (4\text{-}14.6)$$

Transforming, for an initial system condition $I(0) = I_0$

$$sI(s) - I_0 + 2I(s) = 0 \qquad \text{(4-14.7)}$$

such that

$$I(s) = \frac{I_0}{s + 2} \qquad \text{(4-14.8)}$$

Now, let us transform Eq. (4-14.6) in the absence of initial conditions, but assuming an input impulse excitation of area I_0. Then

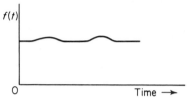

$$\frac{dI}{dt}(t) + 2I(t) = I_0\,\delta(t)$$

$$\text{(4-14.9)}$$

Transforming Eq. (4-14.9), and solving for $I(s)$

$$I(s) = \frac{I_0}{s + 2} \qquad \text{(4-14.10)}$$

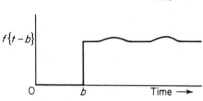

Since Eqs. (4-14.10) and (4-14.8) are identical, it is obvious that the delta function has indeed mechanized the effects of an initial condition.

Figure 4-14.2 Graphical description of time delay.

Let us now consider a linear operation that occurs in systems that exhibit pure time delay or transportation lags. Consider, as illustrated in Fig. 4-14.2, a function $f(t)$ that is delayed in time by b seconds. The delayed function is expressed as $f\{t - b\}$.

Note that the requirement that $f(t)$ is zero for $t < 0$ is transferred to the delayed function $f\{t - b\}$ such that $f\{t - b\} = 0$ for $t < b$.

If, by definition

$$\int_{0^+}^{\infty} f(t)e^{-st}\, dt = F(s) \qquad \text{(4-14.11)}$$

then, multiplying by e^{-bs}

$$\int_{0^+}^{\infty} f(t)e^{-(t+b)s}\, dt = e^{-bs}F(s) \qquad \text{(4-14.12)}$$

Defining the new time variable $\tau = t + b$, i.e.

$$t = \tau - b \qquad \text{(4-14.13)}$$

and substituting into Eq. (4-14.12)

$$\int_{0}^{\infty} f\{\tau - b\}e^{-s\tau}\, d\tau = e^{-bs}F(s) \qquad \text{(4-14.14)}$$

The variable τ is similar to t in that both are dummy variables of integration. From the fundamental theorem of integral calculus, we know that only the limits of the integration are of any physical significance; the variable of integration can be called t, τ, ϕ, φ, or any other convenient symbol. Thus

$$\mathscr{L}\{f\{t-b\}\} = e^{-bs}F(s) \qquad (4\text{-}14.15)$$

The time delay can be employed as a tool in computing the transient response associated with a system excited by a nonperiodic forcing function. Consider the first-order differential equation

$$\frac{di}{dt}(t) + 10i(t) = g(t)$$

$$i(0) = 0 \qquad (4\text{-}14.16)$$

in which the forcing function $g(t)$ is a unit pulse of six seconds duration. As described in the time plot of Fig. 4-14.3, the excitation $g(t)$ can be decomposed into a sum of two unit step functions; the first is positive-going and occurs at $t = 0$, the second is negative-going and occurs at $t = 6$ seconds. The sum of these step functions corresponds to the original time function.

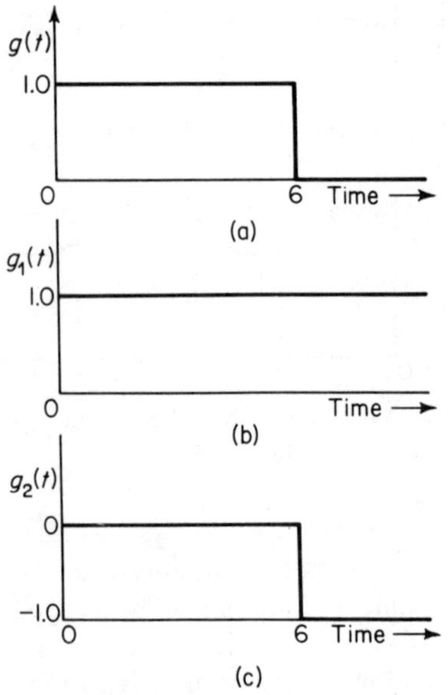

Thus

Figure 4-14.3 Decomposition of forcing function (a) into two step functions (b) and (c).

$$\mathscr{L}\{g(t)\} = \frac{1}{s} - \frac{1}{s}e^{-6s} = \frac{1-e^{-6s}}{s}$$

$$(4\text{-}14.17)$$

Transforming the left-hand portion of Eq. (4-14.16), equating to Eq. (4-14.17), and solving for the transformed current

$$I(s) = \frac{1}{s(s+10)} - \frac{e^{-6s}}{s(s+10)} \qquad (4\text{-}14.18)$$

The partial-fraction expansion of Eq. (4-14.18) is

$$I(s) = \frac{A}{s} + \frac{B}{s+10} - \frac{C}{s}e^{-6s} - \frac{D}{s+10}e^{-6s} \qquad (4\text{-}14.19)$$

Since $A = C = \frac{1}{10}$ and $B = D = -\frac{1}{10}$, the inverse transform is

$$i(t) = \tfrac{1}{10}[1 - e^{-10t} - U\{t - 6\} + e^{-10\{t-6\}}] \qquad \textbf{(4-14.20)}$$

In Eq. (4-14.20), the unit step function and decaying exponential, $U\{t - 6\}$ and $e^{-10\{t-6\}}$, are, by definition, equal to zero throughout the first six seconds of response time. The solution of Eq. (4-14.20) is plotted in Fig. 4-14.4.

4-15 INITIAL-VALUE THEOREM

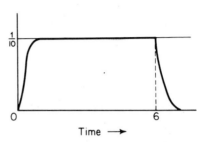

Time →

Figure 4-14.4 Graphical description of Eq. (4-14.20).

Given a Laplace transformed variable $I(s)$, it is possible to compute the initial value of the corresponding time-domain variable $i(t)$ by using the *initial-value theorem* that will now be developed. From Eq. (4-4.5)

$$\int_{0^+}^{\infty} \frac{di(t)}{dt} e^{-st}\, dt = sI(s) - i(0^+) \qquad \textbf{(4-15.1)}$$

As s approaches infinity

$$\lim_{s \to \infty} \int_{0^+}^{\infty} \frac{di(t)}{dt} e^{-st}\, dt = \lim_{s \to \infty} [sI(s) - i(0^+)] \qquad \textbf{(4-15.2)}$$

Since, in Eq. (4-15.2), the variable s is independent of the variable t, the order of integration and the limiting process can be reversed without altering the final result. But

$$\int_{0^+}^{\infty} \lim_{s \to \infty} \frac{di(t)}{dt} e^{-st}\, dt = \int_{0^+}^{\infty} \frac{di(t)}{dt} \cdot 0 \cdot dt = 0 \qquad \textbf{(4-15.3)}$$

so that

$$0 = \lim_{s \to \infty} [sI(s) - i(0^+)] \qquad \textbf{(4-15.4)}$$

Again, since $i(0^+)$ is independent of s

$$i(0^+) = \lim_{s \to \infty} sI(s) \qquad \textbf{(4-15.5)}$$

Equation (4-15.5) is arranged into final form

$$\lim_{t \to 0} i(t) = \lim_{s \to \infty} sI(s) \qquad (4\text{-}15.6)$$

which is a mathematical statement of the initial-value theorem.

4-16 FINAL-VALUE THEOREM

Given a Laplace transformed variable $X(s)$, we can compute the final or steady-state value of the corresponding time-domain solution by applying the *final-value theorem*. The derivation of this theorem is approached in a manner analogous to that employed in the previous section. Thus

$$\int_{0^+}^{\infty} \frac{dx(t)}{dt} e^{-st} \, dt = sX(s) - x(0^+) \qquad (4\text{-}16.1)$$

As s approaches zero

$$\lim_{s \to 0} \int_{0^+}^{\infty} \frac{dx(t)}{dt} e^{-st} \, dt = \lim_{s \to 0} [sX(s) - x(0^+)] \qquad (4\text{-}16.2)$$

$$\int_{0^+}^{\infty} \lim_{s \to 0} \frac{dx(t)}{dt} e^{-st} \, dt = \lim_{s \to 0} [sX(s) - x(0^+)] \qquad (4\text{-}16.3)$$

Since $\lim_{s \to 0} e^{-st} = 1$

$$\int_{0^+}^{\infty} \frac{dx(t)}{dt} \, dt = \lim_{s \to 0} [sX(s) - x(0^+)] \qquad (4\text{-}16.4)$$

Evaluating the integral of Eq. (4-16.4)

$$x(\infty) - x(0^+) = \lim_{s \to 0} sX(s) - x(0^+) \qquad (4\text{-}16.5)$$

$$x(\infty) = \lim_{s \to 0} sX(s) \qquad (4\text{-}16.6)$$

and finally

$$\lim_{t \to \infty} x(t) = \lim_{s \to 0} sX(s) \qquad (4\text{-}16.7)$$

Although implied in the derivation, it should be formally noted that the final-value theorem does not apply to those systems containing right-half plane or imaginary-axis poles.

To illustrate the application of the initial- and final-value theorems, assume the transformed loop current

$$I(s) = \frac{(s+1)^3}{s(s+2)(s+3)(s+4)} \qquad \text{(4-16.8)}$$

The initial value of $i(t)$ is, from Eq. (4-15.6)

$$\lim_{i \to 0} i(t) = \lim_{s \to \infty} s \left[\frac{(s+1)^3}{s(s+2)(s+3)(s+4)} \right] \qquad \text{(4-16.9)}$$

$$= \lim_{s \to \infty} \frac{s^4(1+1/s)^3}{s^4(1+2/s)(1+3/s)(1+4/s)} \qquad \text{(4-16.10)}$$

$$i(0) = \lim_{s \to \infty} \frac{(1+1/s)^3}{(1+2/s)(1+3/s)(1+4/s)} = 1 \qquad \text{(4-16.11)}$$

The final value of $i(t)$ is

$$\lim_{i \to \infty} i(t) = \lim_{s \to 0} s \left[\frac{(s+1)^3}{s(s+2)(s+3)(s+4)} \right] \qquad \text{(4-16.12)}$$

$$= \lim_{s \to 0} \frac{(s+1)^3}{(s+2)(s+3)(s+4)} = \frac{1}{24} \qquad \text{(4-16.13)}$$

It can be shown that the inverse Laplace transformation of $I(s)$ is

$$i(t) = \tfrac{1}{24} + \tfrac{1}{4}e^{-2t} - \tfrac{8}{3}e^{-3t} + \tfrac{27}{8}e^{-4t} \qquad \text{(4-16.14)}$$

To verify the results of Eq. (4-16.11) and (4-16.13)

$$i(0) = \tfrac{1}{24} + \tfrac{1}{4} - \tfrac{8}{3} + \tfrac{27}{8} = 1$$

$$i(\infty) = \tfrac{1}{24}$$

4-17 OTHER OPERATIONAL THEOREMS

In this section we will state, without proof, four interesting operational theorems, and demonstrate each by a representative example. The following theorems are based upon the implicit assumption that $\mathscr{L}\{f(t)\}$ does exist and is equal to $F(s)$.

SCALE-CHANGE THEOREM

If a is a positive constant, then

$$\mathscr{L}\left\{ f\left(\frac{t}{a}\right) \right\} = aF(as) \qquad \text{(4-17.1)}$$

To illustrate, since

$$\mathscr{L}\left\{e^{-\alpha t}\cos \omega t\right\} = \frac{s + \alpha}{(s + \alpha)^2 + \omega^2}$$

then

$$\mathscr{L}\left\{e^{-\alpha t/2}\cos \frac{\omega}{2}t\right\} = \frac{2(2s + \alpha)}{(2s + \alpha)^2 + \omega^2} = \frac{s + \alpha/2}{(s + \alpha/2)^2 + (\omega/2)^2}$$

COMPLEX-TRANSLATION THEOREM

If b is a complex number with a positive real part, then

$$\mathscr{L}\left\{e^{-bt}f(t)\right\} = F(s + b) \qquad (4\text{-}17.2)$$

The verification of Eq. (4-17.2) can be suggested by referring to the transform tables of Section 4.3. Since

$$\mathscr{L}\left\{\cos \omega t\right\} = \frac{s}{s^2 + \omega^2}$$

then according to Eq. (4-17.2)

$$\mathscr{L}\left\{e^{-bt}\cos \omega t\right\} = \frac{s + b}{(s + b)^2 + \omega^2}$$

The result is consistent with the standard transform table data of Section 4.3.

COMPLEX-DIFFERENTIATION THEOREM

Stated mathematically

$$\mathscr{L}\left\{tf(t)\right\} = -\frac{d}{ds}F(s) \qquad (4\text{-}17.3)$$

Thus, if $\mathscr{L}\left\{f(t)\right\}$ is known, $\mathscr{L}\left\{tf(t)\right\}$ can be simply derived, e.g.

$$\mathscr{L}\left\{e^{-\alpha t}\right\} = \frac{1}{s + \alpha}$$

then

$$\mathscr{L}\left\{te^{-\alpha t}\right\} = -\frac{d}{ds}\left(\frac{1}{s + \alpha}\right) = \frac{1}{(s + \alpha)^2}$$

Similarly

$$\mathscr{L}\left\{t^2 e^{-\alpha t}\right\} = -\frac{d}{ds}\left(\frac{1}{(s + \alpha)^2}\right) = \frac{2}{(s + \alpha)^3}$$

To generalize

$$\mathscr{L}\left\{t^n e^{-\alpha t}\right\} = \frac{n!}{(s + \alpha)^{n+1}} \qquad (4\text{-}17.4)$$

COMPLEX-INTEGRATION THEOREM

If $\displaystyle\int_s^\infty F(s)\,ds$ exists, then,

$$\mathscr{L}\left\{\frac{f(t)}{t}\right\} = \int_s^\infty F(s)\,ds \qquad (4\text{-}17.5)$$

The Laplace transformation of the unit ramp function is

$$\mathscr{L}\{t\} = \frac{1}{s^2}$$

Applying the complex-integration theorem

$$\mathscr{L}\left\{\frac{t}{t}\right\} = \mathscr{L}\{1\} = \int_s^\infty \frac{1}{s^2}\,ds$$

$$= -\frac{1}{s}\Big|_s^\infty = 0 - \left(-\frac{1}{s}\right) = \frac{1}{s}$$

which is obviously the Laplace transformation of the unit step.

4-18 THE INVERSION INTEGRAL[2]

To this point, the inverse Laplace transformation has been derived implicitly, i.e., by referring to the relation

$$\mathscr{L}^{-1}[\mathscr{L}\{x(t)\}] = x(t) \qquad (4\text{-}18.1)$$

It is often found necessary, however, to use an explicit inverse transform, based upon Cauchy's integral formula derived in Chapter 2.

$$G(s_i) = \frac{1}{j2\pi}\oint_c \frac{G(s)}{s - s_i}\,ds \qquad (4\text{-}18.2)$$

Thus, if s is a generalized point on the complex λ plane, the inverse Laplace transform of Eq. (4-18.2) is

$$g(t) = \mathscr{L}^{-1}\{G(s)\} = \frac{1}{j2\pi}\oint_c G(\lambda)\mathscr{L}^{-1}\left\{\frac{1}{s - \lambda}\right\}d\lambda$$

$$= \frac{1}{j2\pi}\oint_c G(\lambda)e^{+\lambda t}\,d\lambda \qquad (4\text{-}18.3)$$

where the contour integration c encompasses all poles of $G(\lambda)$.

Although Eq. (4-18.3) is a quantitative statement of the inversion integral, an alternative form is often developed. Specifically, we will now allude to the fact that the closed contour of integration c of Eq. (4-18.3) can be replaced by a straight line parallel to the imaginary axis.

In developing this relation, use is directed to the concept of the *order* of a function. A function is of order s^k as $s \to \infty$, described symbolically as

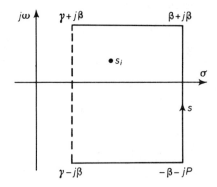

$$f(s) = 0(s^k)_{s \to \infty} \qquad \text{(4-18.4)}$$

if two positive numbers M and r_0 exist such that

$$|s^{-k}f(s)| < M \quad \text{when} \quad |s| > r_0$$
$$\text{(4-18.5)}$$

i.e.

$$|f(s)| < M\,|s|^k \qquad \text{(4-18.6)}$$

Figure 4-18.1 Closed s-plane contour consists of a rectangle.

for all sufficiently large values of $|s|$. Now consider a rectangular path of integration illustrated in Fig. 4-18.1, where the solid-line three-sided path P is directed counterclockwise, and a specific point s_i is situated within the rectangle. The rectangle is oriented so that all poles lie to the left of γ. Applying Cauchy's integral formula to the closed contour

$$G(s_i) = \frac{1}{j2\pi}\left[-\int_{\gamma-j\beta}^{\gamma+j\beta} \frac{G(s)\,ds}{s-s_i} + \int_P \frac{G(s)\,ds}{s-s_i}\right] \qquad \text{(4-18.7)}$$

In general, it is relatively easy to prove that over any path Q

$$\left|\int_Q \phi(s)\,ds\right| \leqslant \int_Q |\phi(s)\,ds| \qquad \text{(4-18.8)}$$

and, in addition

$$\int_Q |ds| = \text{length of path } Q$$

Now, due to the order condition on $G(s)$

$$\left|\frac{G(s)}{s-s_i}\right| < \frac{M}{|s^k|\,|s-s_i|} = \frac{M}{|s|^{k+1}\left|1-\dfrac{s_i}{s}\right|} \qquad \text{(4-18.9)}$$

The parameter β is now chosen sufficiently large to insure that $|s_i/s| < \frac{1}{2}$; hence, $|1 - s_i/s| > \frac{1}{2}$. Also, $|s| \geqslant \beta$ on the path P and hence

$$\left| \frac{G(s)}{s - s_i} \right| < \frac{2M}{\beta^{k+1}} \tag{4-18.10}$$

Thus, since the total path length $P = 4\beta - 2\gamma$

$$\left| \int_P \frac{G(s)\,ds}{s - s_i} \right| < \frac{2M}{\beta^{k+1}} \int_s |ds| = \frac{2M}{\beta^k}\left(4 - \frac{2\gamma}{\beta}\right) \tag{4-18.11}$$

However, since $k > 0$, the integral must vanish as $\beta \to \infty$ so from Eq. (4-18.7)

$$G(s_i) = -\frac{1}{j2\pi} \int_{\gamma-j\infty}^{\gamma+j\infty} \frac{G(s)}{s - s_i}\,ds \tag{4-18.12}$$

and again, if s is a generalized point on the complex λ plane

$$g(t) = \frac{1}{j2\pi} \int_{\gamma-j\infty}^{\gamma+j\infty} G(\lambda)e^{\lambda t}\,d\lambda \tag{4-18.13}$$

Although Eq. (4-18.13) is most commonly referred to as the *inversion formula*, Eq. (4-18.3) is conventionally employed in actually computing the inverse transform. The application of Eq. (4-18.3) is perhaps most suitably

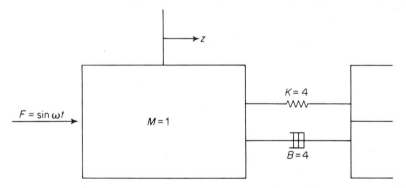

Figure 4-18.2 One degree-of-freedom mechanical system.

demonstrated by a simple example.[8] For the one degree-of-freedom mechanical system illustrated in Fig. 4-18.2, the differential equation that describes the system mass translation is

$$\frac{d^2z(t)}{dt^2} + \frac{4\,dz(t)}{dt} + 4z(t) = \sin \omega t \tag{4-18.14}$$

where ω is an arbitrary frequency. Initial conditions are

$$z(0) = z_0$$

$$\frac{dz}{dt}(0) = \dot{z}_0$$

The Laplace transform of Eq. (4-18.14), subject to the prescribed initial conditions, is

$$\frac{\omega}{s^2 + \omega^2} = (s^2 + 4s + 4)Z(s) - z_0 s - \dot{z}_0 - 4z_0 \qquad \text{(4-18.15)}$$

Solving for the Laplace transformed mass deflection

$$Z(s) = \frac{sz_0 + \dot{z}_0 + 4z_0}{(s+2)^2} + \frac{\omega}{(s^2 + \omega^2)(s+2)^2} \qquad \text{(4-18.16)}$$

The inverse Laplace transformation is now written directly by the substitution of Eq. (4-18.16) into Eq. (4-18.3), i.e.

$$z(t) = \frac{1}{j2\pi} \oint e^{\lambda t} \frac{(\lambda z_0 + \dot{z}_0 + 4z_0)}{(\lambda + 2)^2} d\lambda + \frac{\omega}{j2\pi} \oint \frac{e^{\lambda t} d\lambda}{(\lambda^2 + \omega^2)(\lambda + 2)^2} \qquad \text{(4-18.17)}$$

The contour integrals can most simply be evaluated by using the residue theorem of Chapter 2. Thus, for the first integral

$$j2\pi a_{-1_{(-2)}} = \left[\frac{d}{d\lambda} e^{\lambda t}(\lambda z_0 + \dot{z}_0 + 4z_0) \right]_{\lambda = -2}$$

$$= [z_0 + (\dot{z}_0 + 2z_0)t]e^{-2t} \qquad \text{(4-18.18)}$$

For the second integral, evaluating the residue associated with the pole at $\lambda = j\omega$

$$j2\pi a_{-1_{(j\omega)}} = \frac{-j(2 - j\omega)^2}{2(\omega^2 + 4)^2} e^{j\omega t} \qquad \text{(4-18.19)}$$

while, for the pole at $\lambda = -j\omega$

$$j2\pi a_{-1_{(-j\omega)}} = \frac{j(2 + j\omega)^2}{2(\omega^2 + 4)^2} e^{-j\omega t} \qquad \text{(4-18.20)}$$

Combining Eqs. (4-18.19) and (4-18.20)

$$j2\pi[a_{-1_{(j\omega)}} + a_{-1_{(-j\omega)}}] = \frac{(4 - \omega^2)\sin \omega t - 4\omega \cos \omega t}{(\omega^2 + 4)^2} \qquad \text{(4-18.21)}$$

And finally, computing the residue corresponding to the second-order real-axis pole in the second integral of Eq. (4-18.17)

$$j2\pi a_{-1_{(-2)}} = \omega \left[\frac{d}{d\lambda} \left(\frac{e^{\lambda t}}{\lambda^2 + \omega^2} \right) \right]_{\lambda=-2} = \frac{\omega e^{-2t}}{\omega^2 + 4} \left(t + \frac{4}{\omega^2 + 4} \right) \qquad \textbf{(4-18.22)}$$

Thus, summing the individual components

$$z(t) = [z_0 + (\dot{z}_0 + 2z_0)t]e^{-2t}$$

$$+ \frac{(4 - \omega^2) \sin \omega t - 4\omega \cos \omega t}{(\omega^2 + 4)^2} + \frac{\omega e^{-2t}}{\omega^2 + 4} \left(t + \frac{4}{\omega^2 + 4} \right) \qquad \textbf{(4-18.23)}$$

Although it is normally more convenient to compute an inverse Laplace transform implicitly, the explicit calculation is often employed in specialized situations and will be considered in this context in later chapters.

4-19 THE CONVOLUTION INTEGRAL

As a final consideration, we will investigate the operational property concerning complex multiplication. In particular, the definitive mathematical expression

$$\mathscr{L}\{f(t)\}\mathscr{L}\{g(t)\} = \mathscr{L}\left\{ \int_0^t f(t - \tau)g(\tau)\, d\tau \right\} \qquad \textbf{(4-19.1)}$$

is derived and applied to an illustrative example.

To begin, the basic definition of the Laplace transformation is applied to Eq. (4-19.1), i.e.

$$\mathscr{L}\left\{ \int_0^t f(t - \tau)g(\tau)\, d\tau \right\} = \int_0^\infty \left[\int_0^t f(t - \tau)g(\tau)\, d\tau \right] e^{-st}\, dt \qquad \textbf{(4-19.2)}$$

In addition, the delayed unit step function is described mathematically as

$$u(t - \tau) = \begin{array}{ll} 1, & t > \tau \\ 0, & t < \tau \end{array} \qquad \textbf{(4-19.3)}$$

Similarly

$$f(t - \tau)g(\tau)u(t - \tau) = \begin{cases} f(t - \tau)g(\tau), & \tau < t \\ 0, & \tau > t \end{cases}$$

Hence

$$\mathscr{L}\left\{\int_0^t f(t-\tau)g(\tau)\,d\tau\right\} = \int_0^\infty\left[\int_0^\infty f(t-\tau)g(\tau)u(t-\tau)\,d\tau\right]e^{-st}\,dt \qquad \text{(4-19.4)}$$

Interchanging the order of integration of Eq. (4-19.4)

$$\mathscr{L}\left\{\int_0^t f(t-\tau)g(\tau)\,d\tau\right\} = \int_0^\infty\left[\int_0^\infty f(t-\tau)g(\tau)u(t-\tau)e^{-st}\,dt\right]d\tau$$

$$= \int_0^\infty g(\tau)\left[\int_0^\infty f(t-\tau)u(t-\tau)e^{-st}\,dt\right]d\tau \qquad \text{(4-19.5)}$$

Because of the delayed unit step function in the integrand of the interior integral, the contribution to the integral is zero for $\tau > t$. Thus

$$\mathscr{L}\left\{\int_0^t f(t-\tau)g(\tau)\,d\tau\right\} = \int_0^\infty g(\tau)\left[\int_0^\infty f(t-\tau)e^{-st}\,dt\right]d\tau \qquad \text{(4-19.6)}$$

Substituting

$$t - \tau = \zeta \qquad dt = d\zeta$$

into Eq. (4-19.6)

$$\mathscr{L}\left\{\int_0^t f(t-\tau)g(\tau)\,d\tau\right\} = \int_0^\infty g(\tau)\left[\int_0^\infty f(\zeta)e^{-s(\tau+\zeta)}\,d\zeta\right]d\tau$$

$$= \int_0^\infty g(\tau)e^{-s\tau}\left[\int_0^\infty f(\zeta)e^{-s\zeta}\,d\zeta\right]d\tau$$

$$= \left[\int_0^\infty f(\zeta)e^{-s\zeta}\,d\zeta\right]\left[\int_0^\infty g(\tau)e^{-s\tau}\,d\tau\right] \qquad \text{(4-19.7)}$$

Thus

$$\mathscr{L}\left\{\int_0^t f(t-\tau)g(\tau)\,d\tau\right\} = \mathscr{L}\{f(t)\}\mathscr{L}\{g(t)\} \qquad \text{(4-19.8)}$$

Equation (4-19.8) can be employed to evaluate the inverse Laplace transformation of many s-plane pole-zero arrays. For ratios of polynomials in s, however, partial-fraction expansion methods are less complicated and are recommended. As an example of the application of convolution integral techniques, consider the inverse Laplace transformation of the transformed current

$$I(s) = \frac{2}{(s+1)(s^2+4)} \qquad \text{(4-19.9)}$$

Since

$$\mathscr{L}\left\{\frac{1}{s+1}\right\} = e^{-t}$$

and

$$\mathscr{L}\left\{\frac{2}{s^2 + 4}\right\} = \sin 2t$$

the inverse Laplace transform of Eq. (4-19.9) is

$$i(t) = \int_0^t e^{-(t-\tau)} \sin 2\tau \, d\tau \qquad\qquad \textbf{(4-19.10)}$$

Since the variable t in Eq. (4-19.10) is considered as constant with respect to the dummy variable of integrator τ

$$i(t) = e^{-t} \int_0^t e^\tau \sin 2\tau \, d\tau$$

$$= e^{-t} \left[\frac{e^\tau}{5} (\sin 2\tau - 2 \cos 2\tau)\right]_0^t$$

$$= \frac{e^{-t}}{5} [e^t(\sin 2t - 2 \cos 2t) - (-2)]$$

$$i(t) = \frac{\sin 2t - 2 \cos 2t}{5} + \frac{2e^{-t}}{5} \qquad\qquad \textbf{(4-19.11)}$$

The final result can be easily verified by using partial-fraction expansion procedures.

4-20 THE STABILITY OF PHYSICAL SYSTEMS

The stability of any physical system, in an absolute sense, is completely specified by the position of the Laplace transformed system poles, as follows: If *all* system poles contain negative real parts, the system is *stable*, and any bounded input function will give rise to a bounded response over all time. Conversely, if *one or more* system poles contain positive real parts, the system is *unstable*, and any bounded input will produce an unbounded output. These rules are easily justified by referring to the abbreviated table of Laplace transformations given in Section 4.3, together with the complex-translation theorem of Section 4.17. From the tables, the inverse Laplace transform of a first-order pole with a positive real part is an exponentially increasing time function, i.e.

$$\mathscr{L}^{-1}\left\{\frac{1}{s - \beta}\right\} = e^{+\beta t} \qquad\qquad \textbf{(4-20.1)}$$

Since the time response of Eq. (4-20.1) approaches infinity as time becomes large, the corresponding physical system is most certainly unstable. Further, the instability is not influenced by the type of input forcing function applied. From the complex-translation theorem, a Laplace transformed time function is multiplied by $e^{+\beta t}$ when s is replaced by $(s - \beta)$ in the original transform. Thus, a positive, real-part pole invariably results in an unstable,

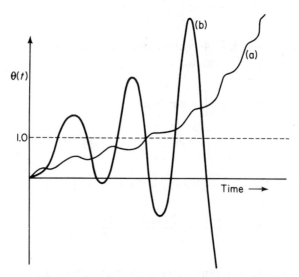

Figure 4-20.1   The step-function response characteristics of typical unstable systems; (a) Eq. (4-20.2), (b) Eq. (4-20.3)

exponentially increasing response. For the following generalized unstable systems

$$\theta_0(s) = \frac{A(s + \alpha)\theta_i(s)}{(s - a)(s + b)(s + c)[(s + d)^2 + e^2]} \qquad (4\text{-}20.2)$$

$$\theta(s) = \frac{A(s + \alpha)\theta_i(s)}{[(s - a)^2 + b^2](s + c)(s + d)} \qquad (4\text{-}20.3)$$

the typical step-function response characteristics are suggested in Fig. 4-20.1.

As a final comment, it should be noted that the zeros associated with any transformed-system response do not influence absolute stability, since the positions of loop-zeros influence only the values and polarities of the partial-fraction expansion coefficients. Thus, a loop may be perfectly stable with one or more positive real-part zeros.

PROBLEMS

4.1 By referring to the integral definition, compute the Laplace transformations of the following forcing functions:

(a) $f(t) = \sinh t$
(b) $f(t) = e^{4t}$
(c) $f(t) = te^{-2t}$

4.2 Determine the s-domain solution of the following differential equations:

(a) $\dfrac{d^2\theta}{dt^2} + 3\dfrac{d\theta}{dt} + 4\theta = 3 \sin 6t$, $\theta(0) = \dfrac{d\theta}{dt}(0) = 0$

(b) $\dfrac{dy}{dt} - 2 \int y\, dt = e^{-t}$, $y(0) = y^{(-1)}(0) = 0$

(c) $\dfrac{d^3y}{dt^3} + y = 0$, $\dfrac{d^2y(0)}{dt^2} = \dfrac{dy(0)}{dt} = 0$, $y(0) = 5$

(d) $\dfrac{d^2x}{dt^2} + 4\dfrac{dx}{dt} - 2x = 0$, $\dfrac{dx(0)}{dt} = 2$, $x(0) = -2$

(e) $\dfrac{d^4\theta}{dt^4} + \dfrac{d^3\theta}{dt^3} + 6\dfrac{d^2\theta}{dt^2} + 12\dfrac{d\theta}{dt} + \theta = 1 + \sin t$, no initial conditions

4.3 Expand each of the following s-domain pole-zero arrays into partial fractions:

(a) $G(s) = \dfrac{6(s + 1)}{s^2(s + 2)}$

(b) $G(s) = \dfrac{(s + 2)(s + 3)}{(s + 4)(s + 5)(s + 6)}$

(c) $G(s) = \dfrac{13(s + 2)}{s(s^2 + 9)}$

(d) $G(s) = \dfrac{10}{(s + 1)(s + 2)(s + 3)(s + 4)^2(s + 5)}$

(e) $G(s) = \dfrac{1}{(s^2 + 4)\,[(s + 1)^2 + 9]}$

(f) $G(s) = \dfrac{s^2 + 3s + 4}{s(s + 3)^2}$

(g) $G(s) = \dfrac{1}{[(s + 1)^2 + 1]^2\,(s + 2)}$

4.4 Find the complete time-domain solutions for the following differential equations (assume no initial conditions):

(a) $\dfrac{d^2x}{dt^2} + 3\dfrac{dx}{dt} + 2x = 1$

(b) $\dfrac{d^3x}{dt^3} + 6\dfrac{d^2x}{dt^2} = t$

(c) $\dfrac{d^2x}{dt^2} + 4\dfrac{dx}{dt} + 3x = 16$

(d) $\dfrac{dx}{dt} + 120x = 6e^{-120t}$

(e) $\dfrac{d^3x}{dt^3} + 3\dfrac{d^2x}{dt^2} + 3\dfrac{dx}{dt} + x = 1$

(f) $\dfrac{dx}{dt} - 12x = \sin 3t$

(g) $\dfrac{d^4x}{dt^4} = 1$

(h) $\dfrac{d^2x}{dt^2} + 2\dfrac{dx}{dt} + 6x = 4$

(i) $\dfrac{d^4x}{dt^4} + 2\dfrac{d^2x}{dt^2} + x = 1$

(j) $\dfrac{d^2x}{dt^2} + 6\dfrac{dx}{dt} + 25x = e^{-t}$

4.5 Compute the unit step-function of the following circuits. Assume no initial
conditions, zero source, and infinite load impedances.

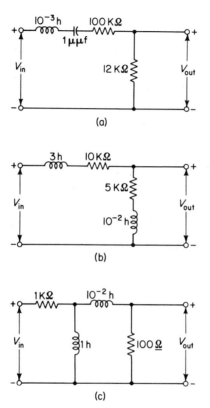

(a)

(b)

(c)

Prob. 4.5

4.6 Compute the position, as a function of time, for each of the following mechanical systems:

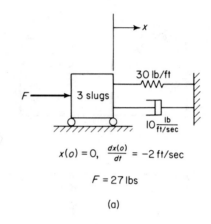

$$x(o) = 0, \quad \frac{dx(o)}{dt} = -2 \text{ ft/sec}$$

$$F = 27 \text{ lbs}$$

(a)

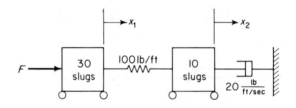

All initial conditions = 0

$$F = 200 e^{-2t}$$

(b)

Prob. 4.6

4.7 Solve the following system of differential equations for the variables $x(t)$ and $y(t)$ (assume no initial conditions):

(a) $\dfrac{dx}{dt} + 2y = 1$

$\dfrac{dy}{dt} + 2x = 0$

(b) $\dfrac{d^2x}{dt^2} + 2\dfrac{dy}{dt} + x = 0$

$\dfrac{dx}{dt} + y = 1$

(c) $\dfrac{d^2x}{dt^2} + 3\dfrac{dx}{dt} + 2x - 3y = 0$

$\dfrac{d^2y}{dt^2} + 6\dfrac{dy}{dt} + 5y - x = 1$

(d) $\dfrac{dy}{dt} + 3y - x = 0$

$\dfrac{d^2x}{dt^2} - y = 20e^{-t}$

4.8 Compute initial and final values of $x(t)$ for the s-domain pole-zero arrays listed below.

(a) $X(s) = \dfrac{100(s + 1)}{s(s + 2)}$

(b) $X(s) = \dfrac{10(s^2 + 4s + 27)}{s(s + 3)(s + 30)}$

(c) $X(s) = \dfrac{5(s + 2)}{s + 10}$

(d) $X(s) = \dfrac{106[(s + 1)^2 + 2](s + 305)}{s(s + 20)(s + 106)(s + 222)}$

(e) $X(s) = \dfrac{0.27(s + 0.8)(s + 1.0)(s + 8)}{s(s^2 + 0.1s + 0.9)(s + 1.1)}$

4.9 Compute the unit impulse response defined by the following differential equations, i.e., $F(s) = 1$. Assume no initial conditions.

(a) $\dfrac{d^2x}{dt^2} + 3\dfrac{dx}{dt} + 2x = F(t)$

(b) $\dfrac{d^3x}{dt^3} + 6\dfrac{d^2x}{dt^2} + 11\dfrac{dx}{dt} = F(t)$

(c) $\dfrac{d^2x}{dt^2} + \dfrac{dx}{dt} + 17x = F(t)$

(d) $\dfrac{dx}{dt} - 2x = F(t)$

(e) $x + 3 \int x \, dt = F(t)$

(f) $\dfrac{dx}{dt} + \dfrac{1}{5} \int x \, dt = F(t)$

4.10   Compute the Laplace transforms for the following graphical input excitations:

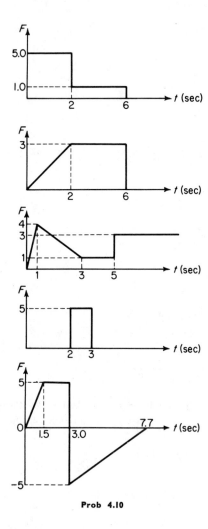

Prob 4.10

4.11   Apply the convolution integral to obtain $x(t)$ for the following s-domain expressions:

(a) $X(s) = \dfrac{1}{s} \cdot \dfrac{1}{s+1}$

(b) $X(s) = \dfrac{1}{s+2} \cdot \dfrac{1}{s+3}$

(c) $X(s) = \dfrac{1}{s} \cdot \dfrac{3}{s^2 + 9}$

(d) $X(s) = \dfrac{1}{s^2}$

4.12 Deduce the absolute stability (stable or unstable) characteristics of the following systems.

(a) $G(s) = \dfrac{s + 3}{s^2 + 4s + 5}$

(b) $G(s) = \dfrac{s - 3}{s^3 + 3s^2 + 2s + 4}$

(c) $G(s) = \dfrac{s^2 + 6s + 7}{s^2 + 3s - 7}$

(d) $G(s) = \dfrac{10(s + 1)}{s^4 + 3s^3 + 2s + 1}$

(e) $G(s) = \dfrac{s^4 + 6s^3 - 2s^2 - 4s + 1}{(s + 1)^2(s^3 + 2s^2 + 6s + 11)}$

BIBLIOGRAPHY

1. Aseltine, J. A., *Transform Method in Linear System Analysis.* New York: McGraw-Hill Book Company, 1958.

2. Churchill, R. V., *Operational Mathematics.* New York: McGraw-Hill Book Company, 1958.

3. Legros, R. and A. V. J. Martin, *Transform Calculus for Electrical Engineers.* Englewood Cliffs, N.J.: Prentice-Hall, Inc., 1961.

4. LePage, W. R., *Complex Variables and the Laplace Transform for Engineers.* New York: McGraw-Hill Book Company, 1961.

5. Pfeiffer, P. E., *Linear Systems Analysis.* New York: McGraw-Hill Book Company, 1961.

6. Savant, C. J., Jr., *Fundamentals of the Laplace Transform.* New York: McGraw-Hill Book Company, 1962.

7. Thompson, W. T., *Laplace Transformation.* Englewood Cliffs, N.J.: Prentice-Hall, Inc., 1960.

8. Carslaw, H. S. and J. C. Jaeger, *Operational Methods in Applied Mathematics.* London: Oxford University Press, 1953.

STEADY STATE SINUSOIDAL ANALYSIS[1,2,3]

5

5-I INTRODUCTION

The previous chapter has been devoted to a study of physical-system time-domain solutions, or transient-response calculations. It was shown that the solutions of ordinary linear differential equations with constant coefficients could be generated quite easily be using modern operational calculus techniques. In this chapter, we will apply Laplace transform theory to the problem of characterizing the linear-system frequency-domain response. Before proceeding, however, it will prove beneficial to pause, momentarily, and review the electrical system mathematical model in terms of a universal Ohm's law, based upon the concept of complex impedance.

5-2 COMPLEX IMPEDANCE

As developed in Chapter 3, the mathematical definitions of resistance, capacitance, and inductance are

$$V(t) = RI(t) \qquad (5\text{-}2.1\text{-}a)$$

$$V(t) = \frac{1}{C} \int I(t)\, dt \qquad (5\text{-}2.1\text{-}b)$$

$$V(t) = L\frac{dI(t)}{dt} \qquad (5\text{-}2.1\text{-}c)$$

where, in each case, $V(t)$ represents the voltage drop across the circuit element in the direction of assumed current flow. Equation (5-2.1-a) is, of course, the familiar Ohm's law expression. It is convenient to be able to express the mathematical definitions of Eqs. (5-2.1-b) and (5-2.1-c) in a form similar to that of Ohm's law, i.e., in terms of a linear algebraic relationship. This process is now accomplished by the application of transform techniques.

Transforming Eq. (5-2.1-a), (5-2.1-b), and (5-2.1-c), in the absence of initial conditions

$$V(s) = RI(s) \qquad \text{Resistance} \qquad\qquad \text{(5-2.2-a)}$$

$$V(s) = \frac{1}{Cs} I(s) \qquad \text{Capacitance} \qquad\qquad \text{(5-2.2-b)}$$

and

$$V(s) = LsI(s) \qquad \text{Inductance} \qquad\qquad \text{(5-2.2-c)}$$

The transformed expressions can now be solved for the transformed ratio $\frac{V}{I}$ (s), which is known as the network element's complex impedance.

$$Z_R(s) = \frac{V}{I}(s) = R \qquad \text{Resistance}$$
$$\text{(5-2.3-a)}$$

$$Z_C(s) = \frac{V}{I}(s) = \frac{1}{Cs} \qquad \text{Capacitance}$$
$$\text{(5-2.3-b)}$$

$$Z_L(s) = \frac{V}{I}(s) = Ls \qquad \text{Inductance}$$
$$\text{(5-2.3-c)}$$

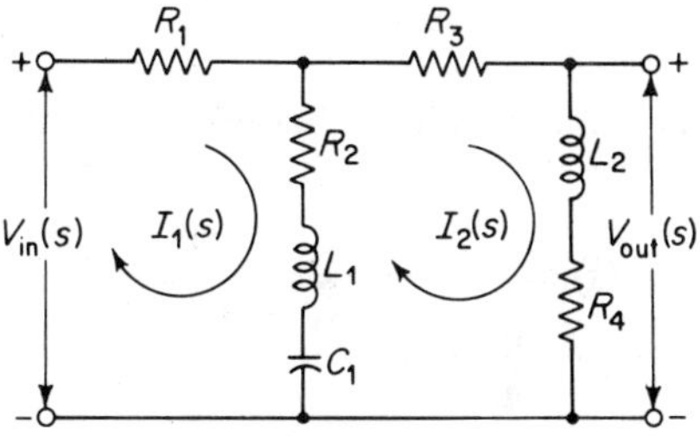

Figure 5-2.1 Circuit analysis is simplified through the use of complex impedance.

Equations (5-2.3-b) and (5-2.3-c) express linear algebraic relations between transformed voltage and current variables, and they are exactly analogous to the transformed Ohm's-law formula of Eq. (5-2.3-a). Thus, it is no longer necessary to write and then transform differential equations that govern the behavior of physical electrical circuits. These operations are compressed into a single process by the introduction of complex impedance. For example, consider the dual-loop network of Fig. 5-2.1. The mathematical model is now simply generated by using *Ohm's law of complex impedance*

$$V(s) = Z(s)I(s) \qquad\qquad \text{(5-2.4)}$$

$$V_{in}(s) = \left[L_1 s + (R_1 + R_2) + \frac{1}{C_1 s} \right] I_1(s) - \left[L_1 s + R_2 + \frac{1}{C_1 s} \right] I_2(s) \qquad \text{(5-2.5)}$$

$$0 = \left[(L_1 + L_2)s + (R_2 + R_3 + R_4) + \frac{1}{C_1 s}\right] I_2(s)$$

$$- \left[L_1 s + R_2 + \frac{1}{C_1 s}\right] I_1(s) \qquad \text{(5-2.6)}$$

$$V_{\text{out}}(s) = (sL_2 + R_4) I_2(s) \qquad \text{(5-2.7)}$$

Solving Eqs. (5-2.5) and (5-2.6) for $I_2(s)$

$$V_{\text{in}}(s) = \begin{aligned} &[L_1 s + (R_1 + R_2) + 1/C_1 s] \\ &\times \frac{[(L_1 + L_2)s + (R_2 + R_3 + R_4) + 1/C_1 s] I_2(s)}{[L_1 s + R_2 + 1/C_1 s]} \end{aligned}$$

$$- [L_1 s + R_2 + 1/C_1 s] I_2(s) \qquad \text{(5-2.8)}$$

Rearranging

$$I_2(s) = \frac{[L_1 s + R_2 + 1/C_1 s] V_{\text{in}}(s)}{[L_1 s + (R_1 + R_2) + 1/C_1 s][(L_1 + L_2)s + (R_2 + R_3 + R_4) + 1/C_1 s]}$$
$$- [L_1 s + R_2 + 1/C_1 s]^2$$
$$\text{(5-2.9)}$$

The final result is obtained by combining Eqs. (5-2.9) and (5-2.7)

$$V_{\text{out}}(s) = \frac{[L_1 s + R_2 + 1/C_1 s][sL_2 + R_4] V_{\text{in}}(s)}{[L_1 s + (R_1 + R_2) + 1/C_1 s][(L_1 + L_2)s + (R_2 + R_3 + R_4) + 1/C_1 s]}$$
$$- [L_1 s + R_2 + 1/C_1 s]^2$$
$$\text{(5-2.10)}$$

The usefulness of complex impedance is not restricted to electrical circuit problems; mechanical systems may also be analyzed directly by the use of this device. Since the concepts are analogous, however, this subject need not be developed in any elaborate manner. It is sufficient to note that the complex impedances associated with system mass, damping, and spring reaction are

$$F_m(s) = Ms^2 X(s) \qquad \text{Mass} \qquad \text{(5-2.11-a)}$$

$$F_d(s) = BsX(s) \qquad \text{Damping} \qquad \text{(5-2.11-b)}$$

and

$$F_s(s) = KX(s) \qquad \text{Spring} \qquad \text{(5-2.11-c)}$$

Thus, in the absence of initial system deflection and velocity, the Laplace transformed differential equations of motion can be written by inspection.

5-3 LINEAR SYSTEM SINUSOIDAL RESPONSE

One property of a linear system, based on the concept of superposition, is stated as follows: If a linear system is excited by a steady-state sinusoidal input excitation, and if sufficient time is allowed for the complete decay of all transient terms, then the system output variable will be a sinusoid with a frequency identical to that of the input, but with differing phase and amplitude characteristics. This familiar "Theorem of the Black Box" is illustrated in the following example.

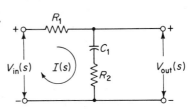

Figure 5-3.1   Simple electrical network.

Consider the simple RC circuit of Fig. 5-3.1, excited at time $t = 0$ by a sinusoidal signal of unity amplitude and an arbitrary frequency ω, radians/second. Applying the complex-impedance approach of Section 5.2

$$V_{in}(s) = \left[(R_1 + R_2) + \frac{1}{C_1 s}\right] I(s) \tag{5-3.1}$$

$$V_{out}(s) = \left[R_2 + \frac{1}{C_1 s}\right] I(s) \tag{5-3.2}$$

Solving for the transformed output voltage

$$V_{out}(s) = \frac{[R_2 + 1/C_1 s] V_{in}(s)}{[(R_1 + R_2) + 1/C_1 s]} \tag{5-3.3}$$

Rearranging

$$V_{out}(s) = \frac{R_2}{R_1 + R_2} \frac{(s + 1/R_2 C_1) V_{in}(s)}{[s + 1/(R_1 + R_2)C_1]} \tag{5-3.4}$$

For a unit cosine input function

$$V_{in}(s) = \frac{s}{s^2 + \omega^2} \tag{5-3.5}$$

so that

$$V_{out}(s) = \frac{R_2}{R_1 + R_2} \frac{s(s + 1/R_2 C_1)}{[s + 1/(R_1 + R_2)C_1][s^2 + \omega^2]} \tag{5-3.6}$$

Equation (5-3.6), when expanded in partial fractions, yields

$$V_{out}(s) = \frac{A}{s + 1/(R_1 + R_2)C_1} + \frac{Bs + C}{s^2 + \omega^2} \tag{5-3.7}$$

whereas the corresponding generalized time-domain solution is

$$V_{\text{out}}(t) = Ae^{-t/[(R_1+R_2)C]} + B\cos\omega t + \frac{C}{\omega}\sin\omega t \qquad (5\text{-}3.8)$$

If sufficient time is allowed for the decaying exponential transient $Ae^{-t/[(R_1+R_2)C]}$ to degenerate to zero, then the system response is a sinusoid with a frequency of ω, and it exhibits both amplitude attenuation and phase shift.

The frequency response of a system is its steady-state response to a unit sinusoidal excitation, expressed in either amplitude ratio and phase shift or, equivalently, in terms of real and imaginary parts, as the input frequency varies from zero to infinity.

5-4 FREQUENCY-RESPONSE CALCULATIONS

In this section, we will derive a general method for computing a linear-system frequency response, based again upon the Laplace transformation. No new concepts are involved, rather the technique represents only a reorientation and application of some fundamental theory derived in the previous chapters.

Consider a linear system governed by the transformed input-output expression

$$X_{\text{out}}(s) = G(s)X_{\text{in}}(s) \qquad (5\text{-}4.1)$$

The only assumption required of $G(s)$ is that the system is stable, i.e., all of the poles of $G(s)$ contain negative nonzero real parts. For $X_{\text{in}}(t) = \cos\omega t$,

$$X_{\text{in}}(s) = \frac{s}{s^2 + \omega^2} \quad \text{and} \quad X_{\text{out}}(s) = \frac{sG(s)}{s^2 + \omega^2} \qquad (5\text{-}4.2)$$

Expanding into partial fractions

$$\frac{sG(s)}{s^2 + \omega^2} = \frac{A}{s + p_1} + \frac{B}{s + p_2} + \cdots + \frac{\psi}{s + p_\psi} + \frac{\alpha s + \beta}{s^2 + \omega^2} \qquad (5\text{-}4.3)$$

where the finite number of coefficients A, B, C, ..., ψ correspond to a finite number of stable-system poles $-p_1$, $-p_2$, ..., $-p_\psi$. Since each pole of Eq. (5-4.3) is by definition stable, the resulting inverse Laplace transformation associated with the components of $G(s)$ rise to decaying exponential time-solution contributions $(Ae^{-p_1 t}, Be^{-p_2 t}, \ldots)$ which vanish as time becomes large. Only the term $(\alpha s + \beta)/(s^2 + \omega^2)$ yields a time-domain steady-state component. To compute the coefficients α and β of Eq. (5-4.3), we multiply each term by the quantity $s^2 + \omega^2$, and evaluate the resulting expression in the limit as s approaches $j\omega$. Thus

$$j\alpha\omega + \beta = j\omega G(j\omega) \tag{5-4.4}$$

Equating real and imaginary parts

$$\alpha = G(j\omega) \qquad \beta = 0$$

Thus, the cosine term appearing in the solution has associated with it the partial-fraction expansion coefficient $G(j\omega)$, while the sine term is zero. $G(j\omega)$ is, then, an analytical expression for the system frequency response. Since, from Chapter 2, the complex number s_i is defined in trigonometric and rectangular coordinates as

$$s_i = \text{Re} + j\,\text{Im} = A(\cos\theta + j\sin\theta) \tag{5-4.5}$$

it is evident that the input excitation $\cos\omega t$ is a real number, lying along the positive real axis. The corresponding output $G(j\omega)\cos\omega t$ is a complex number of amplitude $A = |G(j\omega)|$ and phase $\varphi = \tan^{-1}\text{Im }G(j\omega)/\text{Re }G(j\omega)$, multipled by $\cos\omega t$. The ratio of output to input is thus $G(j\omega)$.

To demonstrate a typical calculation, consider the transformed system equation

$$X_{\text{out}}(s) = \frac{s + 1}{s(s + 2)} X_{\text{in}}(s) \tag{5-4.6}$$

The frequency response of the Eq. (5-4.6) physical system is

$$\left.\frac{s + 1}{s(s + 2)}\right|_{s=j\omega} = \frac{j\omega + 1}{j\omega(j\omega + 2)} = \frac{\omega - j(\omega^2 + 2)}{\omega(\omega^2 + 4)} \tag{5-4.7}$$

Substituting an input frequency of one radian per second ($\omega = 1$) into Eq. (5-4.7)

$$\left.\frac{s + 1}{s(s + 2)}\right|_{s=j1} = \frac{1 - j(1 + 2)}{1(1 + 4)} = \frac{1}{5} - j\frac{3}{5} \tag{5-4.8}$$

Expressed in amplitude ratio and phase, Eq. (5-4.8) is

$$A = [(\tfrac{1}{5})^2 + (\tfrac{3}{5})^2]^{1/2} = \sqrt{\tfrac{2}{5}}$$

$$\varphi = \tan^{-1} - \frac{\tfrac{3}{5}}{\tfrac{1}{5}} = \tan^{-1} - 3$$

The point $G(j1)$ is illustrated graphically in Fig. 5-4.1.

5-5 RESONANT CIRCUITS

In the previous section, the Laplace transformed system function $G(s)$ was constrained to contain only stable poles. Let us now relieve this restriction to the extent that two marginally stable imaginary-axis poles are allowed, i.e., $s = j\omega_1$ and $s = -j\omega_1$. The new system function may then be expressed as

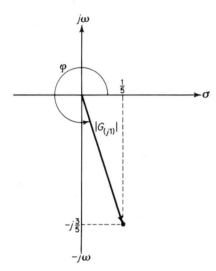

$$G_1(s) = \frac{F(s)}{s^2 + \omega_1^2} \qquad (5\text{-}5.1)$$

where $F(s)$ is again assumed to contain only stable poles. The frequency response associated with $G_1(s)$ is evidently

$$G_1(j\omega) = \frac{F(j\omega)}{\omega_1^2 - \omega^2} \qquad (5\text{-}5.2)$$

As the input-frequency variable ω approaches the value ω_1, the denominator of Eq. (5-5.2) approaches zero. Thus, the amplitude ratio becomes large. At $\omega = \omega_1$ the amplitude ratio is infinite, but, as ω increases beyond ω_1, the ratio is again finite. Note that, in addition, a 180° phase shift occurs at $\omega = \omega_1$; if $\omega < \omega_1$ the denominator of Eq. (5-5.2) is of positive polarity; when $\omega > \omega_1$, however, the denominator is negative. These frequency-response characteristics typify the resonant or marginally stable physical system. For example, consider the idealized tank circuit of Fig 5-5.1. The transformed mathematical model is

Figure 5-4.1   Plot of $G(j1)$ of Eq. (5-4.8).

$$V_{in}(s) = \left(sL + \frac{1}{Cs}\right)I(s) \qquad (5\text{-}5.3)$$

$$V_{out}(s) = \frac{1}{Cs}I(s) \qquad (5\text{-}5.4)$$

Solving for V_{out}

$$V_{out}(s) = \frac{(1/LC)V_{in}(s)}{s^2 + 1/LC} \qquad (5\text{-}5.5)$$

The system of Eq. (5-5.5) represents the simplest form of resonant circuit. The undamped natural frequency is $\sqrt{1/LC}$.

Antiresonant circuits are also of practical interest. If we assume that the system function contains imaginary-axis zeros at $\pm j\omega_2$, such that $G_2(s) = (s^2 + \omega_2{}^2)F(s)$, the frequency-response amplitude ratio degenerates to zero at the input frequency ω_2. Thus, in the steady state, a finite-valued sinusoidal excitation of frequency ω_2 radians per second will produce absolutely no response at the output terminals. The 180° phase shift exhibited at the resonant frequency of Eq. (5-5.2) also occurs at the antiresonant frequency ω_2 but is of opposite polarity, i.e., the resonant circuit produces a phase lag, whereas the antiresonant frequency results in a phase lead.

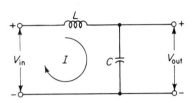

Figure 5-5.1   Idealized resonant circuit.

One final comment is appropriate at this time. If $G(s)$ contains one or more right half-plane poles, the entire concept of a frequency response is meaningless. Thus, for unstable systems, the transient components corresponding to all unstable singularities do not decay with time, but rather increase exponentially. Hence, the "steady-state" system condition, explicit within the frequency-response definition, does not exist.

PROBLEMS

5.1 Determine the mathematical models for the following electrical circuits by using complex-impedance methods.

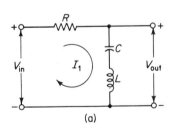 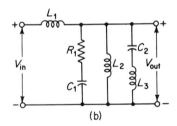

(a)   (b)

Prob. 5.1

5.2 Compute the unit step-function response for the following circuits.

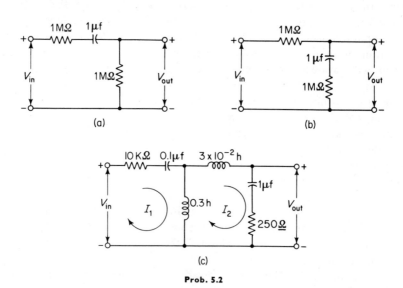

(a)

(b)

(c)

Prob. 5.2

5.3 For each of the circuits of Problem 5.2, assume V_{in} to be a unit sinusoid of frequency ω radian/second. Compute the arbitrary response expressions for each of the circuits, i.e.,

$$G(j\omega) = \operatorname{Re} G(j\omega) \pm j \operatorname{Im} G(j\omega)$$

Compute, for each network, the numerical values of $G(j1)$ and $G(j10)$.

BIBLIOGRAPHY

1. Ahrendt, W. R. and C. J. Savant, Jr., *Servomechanism Practice*. New York: McGraw-Hill Book Company, 1960.

2. Ahrendt, W. R. and J. F. Taplin, *Automatic Feedback Control*. New York: McGraw-Hill Book Company, 1951.

3. Brown, G. S. and D. P. Campbell, *Principles of Servomechanisms*. New York: John Wiley & Sons, Inc., 1948.

ANALOG SIMULATION OF LINEAR SYSTEMS[1,2,3,4,5]

6

6-1 INTRODUCTION

The Electronic Differential Analyzer (EDA), more commonly and incorrectly referred to as the *analog computer*, constitutes a relatively inexpensive and simple tool for the analysis of systems governed by ordinary differential equations. The expression "analog computer" actually encompasses a vast array of engineering devices, characterized by a continuity of the dependent variables of interest, in which an analogy is established between the computing device and the original physical system. Thus, the conventional slide rule, the aerodynamic scale model, the Link trainer, and literally hundreds of additional devices fall in this category. The wide acceptance of the Electronic Differential Analyzer, as witnessed by the fact that the device invariably comes to mind when one mentions analog computation, has been possible because of rapid advances in electronic and electrical componentry, coupled with an underlying demand on the part of industry for a general-purpose computer capable of simulating dynamic systems. Analog methods are particularly effective in the simulation of automatic control systems but can be applied to the analysis of any system governed by ordinary differential equations.

In addition to the obvious advantages inherent in automatic simulation, an appreciation of analog programming provides the control systems designer with an intuitive feeling for the physical system. For example, it is often simpler to visualize the step-function response phenomena of a complicated electrical filter network by analyzing the corresponding EDA mechanization than by a direct investigation of the original network. Similarly, many of the analytical methods developed later in the text are based heavily upon an initial EDA simulation of the physical configuration. Thus, the EDA programming methods developed in this chapter are important even though an actual computer may not be immediately available. From this point, we will adopt the incorrect but universal terminology and consider the terms analog computer and Electronic Differential Analyzer as identical quantities.

It is not the purpose of this chapter to describe in detail the electronic circuits and special methods of operation associated with the computer; these topics are considered in a great number of excellent texts devoted to analog simulation. Rather, we will concentrate our efforts in the area of understanding the basic principles of computer programming, and in applying these techniques to the simulation and solution of differential equations.

6-2 LINEAR ELEMENTS: AMPLIFIERS AND POTENTIOMETERS

Since this chapter is devoted exclusively to linear analog simulation techniques, only linear computing elements, i.e., operational amplifiers and linear potentiometers, need be investigated. The analog amplifier, shown schematically in Fig. 6-2.1, is a high-gain high input-impedance device exhibiting

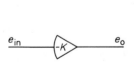

Figure 6-2.1 High-gain d-c amplifier.

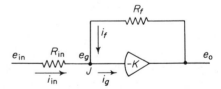

Figure 6-2.2 Operational amplifier with resistive input and feedback elements.

a flat frequency response from d-c through 200–2000 cycles per second. The conventional amplifier is drift stabilized through the application of chopper techniques, has a low output impedance, and is relatively free of noise disturbances. The mathematical model corresponding to the analog amplifier is

$$e_0 = -Ke_{\text{in}} \tag{6-2.1}$$

where e_0 and e_{in} are the output and input voltages respectively, while the gain parameter K is very large. Let us now introduce an input resistor R_{in} and a feedback resistor R_f, thus forming the operational amplifier illustrated in Fig. 6-2.2. The corresponding Kirchhoff's node-law summation at the summing junction J is

$$i_{\text{in}} + i_f = i_g \qquad (6\text{-}2.2)$$

However, the high input impedance exhibited by the analog amplifier implies that $i_g = 0$, so that

$$i_{\text{in}} + i_f = 0 \qquad (6\text{-}2.3)$$

Hence
$$\frac{e_{\text{in}} - e_g}{R_{\text{in}}} + \frac{e_0 - e_g}{R_f} = 0 \qquad (6\text{-}2.4)$$

Since the grid or summing junction voltage e_g of Eq. (6-2.4) is very small (for a finite output voltage and high open-loop amplifier gain, the grid voltage must be in the order of millivolts or less), Eq. (6-2.4) is rearranged to yield

$$e_0 = -\frac{R_f}{R_{\text{in}}} e_{\text{in}} \qquad (6\text{-}2.5)$$

Through a similar analysis, the input-output relationship of the operational amplifier with multiple input resistors shown in Fig. 6-2.3 is

$$e_0 = -\left(\frac{R_f}{R_{\text{in}_1}} e_{\text{in}_1} + \frac{R_f}{R_{\text{in}_2}} e_{\text{in}_2} + \frac{R_f}{R_{\text{in}_3}} e_{\text{in}_3} \right) \qquad (6\text{-}2.6)$$

Thus, this particular configuration permits the simultaneous amplification, summation, and phase inversion of a large number of independent input voltages, and is appropriately categorized as a summing amplifier. The large-scale analog computer facility contains many of these summing elements with input and feedback resistors permanently wired into the system. The feedback resistor is conventionally of one-megohm magnitude, while the input resistors can be of any reasonable values (1 megohm, 500 Kohm, 250 Kohm, 200 Kohm, 100 Kohm, 50 Kohm, 25 Kohm, etc.).

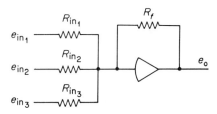

Figure 6-2.3 Analog summing amplifier.

External resistor connections, as well as a direct grid lead, are available at a central patchboard at which all component connections are made. The normal summing amplifier, as employed throughout the remainder of the text will be assumed to contain fixed input resistances of one megohm, 200

K ohm, and 100 K ohm, providing voltage gains of 1, 5, and 10 respectively. The symbol employed to denote the summing amplifier is a triangle, as illustrated in Fig. 6-2.4; the number associated with each input represents the corresponding voltage gain, and they are the reciprocals of the input resistor values expressed in megohms.

The feedback resistor of Fig. 6-2.2 is now replaced by a capacitor C, as shown in Fig. 6-2.5. If we use the complex-impedance techniques developed previously, the Kirchhoff's node summation applied at the summing junction is

$$\frac{e_{in}(s)}{R} + \frac{e_0(s)}{1/sC} = 0 \quad (6\text{-}2.7)$$

Accordingly

$$e_0(s) = \frac{-1}{R_{in}Cs} e_{in}(s) \quad (6\text{-}2.8)$$

and applying standard inverse Laplace transformation techniques

$$e_0(t) = -\frac{1}{R_{in}C} \int e_{in}(t) \, dt \quad (6\text{-}2.9)$$

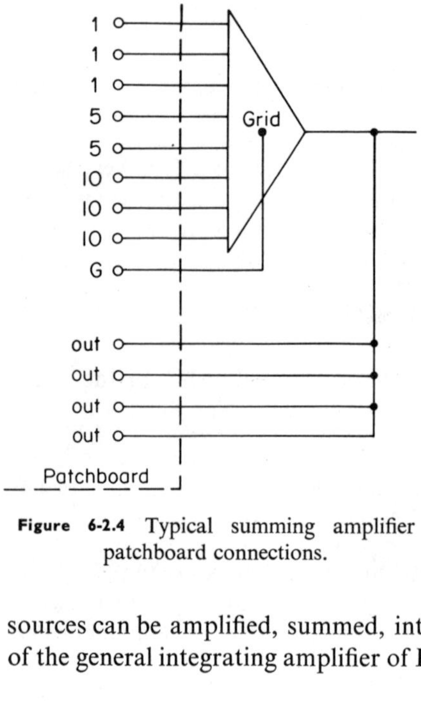

Thus, the system of Fig. 6-2.5 functions as a voltage integrator. Again, any number of independent voltage sources can be amplified, summed, integrated, and inverted through the use of the general integrating amplifier of Fig. 6-2.6, i.e.

$$e_0 = -\int \left(\frac{1}{R_{in_1}C} e_{in_1} + \frac{1}{R_{in_2}C} e_{in_2} + \frac{1}{R_{in_3}C} e_{in_3} \right) dt \quad (6\text{-}2.10)$$

Figure 6-2.4 Typical summing amplifier patchboard connections.

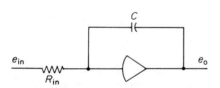

Figure 6-2.5 Integrating amplifier.

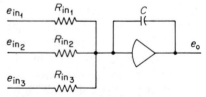

Figure 6-2.6 Integrators with multiple inputs.

Since integration implies the existence of an initial condition, it is not surprising that the analog computer is provided with relay switching such that an initial voltage can be impressed across the feedback capacitor. Hence, during the problem setup operation, a voltage source is supplied to an integrator "Initial Condition" terminal; the capacitor is thus charged to any desired initial voltage. Once the problem simulation is initiated, however, the charging voltage is removed, rendering the capacitor free to discharge the initial voltage. The conventional integrator is symbolized by the combined rectangle and triangle as pictured in Fig. 6-2.7; the initial condition (I.C.) terminal is shown as entering the rectangular portion of the integrator symbol.

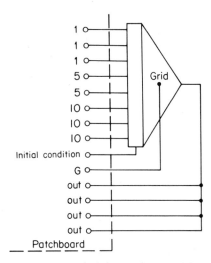

Figure 6-2.7 Typical integrating amplifier patchboard connections.

Grounded potentiometers are employed in the process of multiplying by a constant. The conventional potentiometer indicated in Fig. 6-2.8 is of high resolution and linearity, with a total resistance of from 5 to 100 K ohm. A constant attentuation is achieved for all input voltage levels by virtue of the voltage-divider action between the high or signal end and the low or grounded end. Thus, in the absence of loading effects, the arm senses a voltage

$$e_{\text{arm}} = \left(\frac{R_L}{R_L + R_H}\right) e_{\text{high}} \qquad (6\text{-}2.11)$$

The schematic representation of the grounded potentiometer is shown in Fig. 6-2.9. The problem of potentiometer loading is one that usually receives

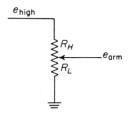

Figure 6-2.8 A potentiometer.

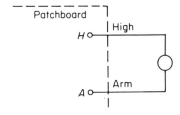

Figure 6-2.9 Potentiometer symbol employed in analog computer.

special attention in all standard analog computer texts. For example, assume that the potentiometer arm of Fig. 6-2.8 is connected, through a gain of 10, into a follow-up summing amplifier, as indicated in Fig. 6-2.10. Again, considering the amplifier grid to be at ground potential, the system equivalent network is given in Fig. 6-2.11. It can be easily proved that the potentiometer arm output voltage is

$$e_{\text{arm}} = \left[\frac{100R_L/(100 + R_L)}{R_H + 100R_L/(100 + R_L)} \right] e_{\text{high}} \qquad \textbf{(6-2.12)}$$

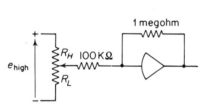

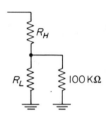

Figure 6-2.10 Example of potentiometer loading.

Figure 6-2.11 Equivalent circuit for Fig. 6-2.10.

Comparing Eqs. (6-2.11) and (6-2.12), it is observed that an error equal to

$$\left[\frac{R_L}{R_L + R_H} - \frac{100R_L/(100 + R_L)}{R_H + 100R_L/(100 + R_L)} \right] e_{\text{high}}$$

has been generated. Although loading errors may be of academic concern, the problem is easily obviated through use of a standard potentiometer setting technique. Potentiometers are adjusted to the correct values during a *balanced* mode of computer operation in which all amplifier grids are effectively grounded. In setting a particular potentiometer, we replace the input signal by an accurately regulated +100-v computer power-supply output, and the arm voltage is monitored on a direct-reading digital voltmeter. If the desired value happens to be 0.4567, the potentiometer is adjusted until +45.67 v appears on the voltmeter, thus automatically compensating for any loading, i.e., an electrical potentiometer setting is obtained which, under actual load condition, produces the desired signal attenuation.

6-3 THE SOLUTION OF DIFFERENTIAL EQUATIONS WITH CONSTANT COEFFICIENTS

It is interesting to note that the simulation of differential equations is accomplished by successive computer integration, rather than through the more obvious technique of computer differentiation. The process of differentiation is avoided by computer programmers whenever possible. Whereas integration is an averaging or smoothing operation, differentiation produces an amplification of any slight irregularities contained within the signal. Since noise is always present in varying degrees, pure computer differentiation invariably leads to difficulties. To ensure that only system integrations will be required, the differential equation is first solved for the highest-order derivative; this "unknown" is then expressed in terms of lower-order derivatives that are obtained through integration. The technique is now applied to the simulation of representative system mathematical models.

Consider the generalized second-order differential equation subject to a step forcing function ω_n^2

$$\frac{d^2\theta(t)}{dt^2} + 2\zeta\omega_n \frac{d\theta(t)}{dt} + \omega_n^2\theta(t) = \omega_n^2 \qquad (6\text{-}3.1)$$

We first solve Eq. (6-3.1) for the highest-order derivative $d^2\theta/dt^2$, i.e.

$$\frac{d^2\theta(t)}{dt^2} = \omega_n^2 - 2\zeta\omega_n \frac{d\theta(t)}{dt} - \omega_n^2\theta(t) \qquad (6\text{-}3.2)$$

Equation (6-3.2) states simply that, if the three quantities

$$\omega_n^2, \quad -2\zeta\omega_n\, d\theta(t)/dt, \quad \text{and} \quad -\omega_n^2\theta(t)$$

are available, the summation yields $d^2\theta(t)/dt^2$. Let us now assume that these required functions exist in terms of analogous voltages. As illustrated in Fig. 6-3.1, the summing amplifier can be employed to generate an output voltage analogous to the second derivative; note, however, that the 180° phase shift associated with a summer produces a similar polarity change in the second derivative such that $-d^2\theta(t)/dt^2$ is actually formed.

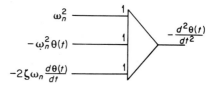

Figure 6-3.1 Simulation of Eq. (6-3.2).

In Fig. 6-3.1, it was arbitrarily assumed that the quantities $-\omega_n^2\theta(t)$ and $-2\zeta\omega_n\, d\theta(t)/dt$ were available (ω_n^2 is a constant and is thus analogous to a d-c voltage). It is now necessary to generate these variables. Since $\int d^2\theta(t)/dt^2\, dt = d\theta(t)/dt$, the first derivative is produced by a direct integration of the summing-amplifier output voltage, as shown in Fig. 6-3.2; a 180° phase shift is again exhibited by the integrating amplifier. Notice that the integrator output $+d\theta(t)/dt$ and one of the required summing-amplifier

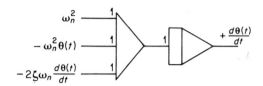

Figure 6-3.2   First derivative is formed through integration.

input components, $-2\zeta\omega_n \, d\theta(t)/dt$, differ by a factor of $-2\zeta\omega_n$. The negative polarity is obtained through the introduction of an inverting amplifier (i.e., a summing amplifier with a unity gain), while the factor $2\zeta\omega_n$ (assuming this quantity to be less than unity) is generated by means of a potentiometer. Thus, the mechanization of Fig. 6-3.2 is extended in Fig. 6-3.3 to develop one of the two required feedback terms. The final component $\omega_n^2\theta(t)$ is formed through the application of one additional integrating amplifier and potentiometer. Therefore, given an input voltage analogous to the step function ω_n^2, the complete simulation of Eq. (6-3.1) is represented by the final mechanization of Fig. 6-3.4.

If a step function of ω_n^2 volts is applied to the analog network of Fig. 6-3.4, the continuous output voltage is analogous to the system response variable $\theta(t)$, multiplied by -1. Similarly, the first and second derivatives of this function can also be monitored in terms of an analogous voltage.

The number of amplifiers required in Fig. 6-3.4 can be reduced to a total of three, if the second derivative $d^2\theta(t)/dt^2$ is not explicitly desired. To accomplish this reduction, Eq. (6-3.2) is first analytically integrated

$$\frac{d\theta(t)}{dt} = \int \left[\omega_n^2 - 2\zeta\omega_n \frac{d\theta(t)}{dt} - \omega_n^2\theta(t) \right] dt \qquad (6\text{-}3.3)$$

and Eq. (6-3.3) is mechanized so that the summing amplifier and integrator

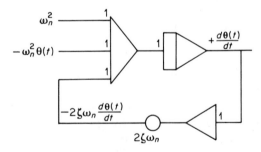

Figure 6-3.3   Closing the loop generates one of the assumed input quantities
$-2\zeta W_n[d\theta(t)/dt]$.

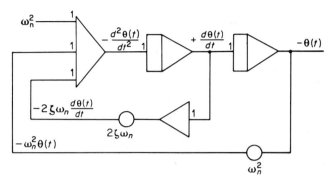

Figure 6-3.4   Complete simulation of Eq. (6-3.1).

of Fig. 6-3.2 are combined into the single integrator of Fig. 6-3.5. The remaining mechanization is accomplished by conventional methods to form the complete analog network of Fig. 6-3.6.

Let us now consider a more specific example, e.g., the third-order differential equation

$$\frac{d^3x(t)}{dt^3} + 3\frac{d^2x(t)}{dt^2} - 10\frac{dx(t)}{dt} + 7.41x(t) = 14 \qquad (6\text{-}3.4)$$

Solving for the highest-order derivative, and integrating the resulting expression

$$\frac{d^2x(t)}{dt^2} = \int\left[14 - 3\frac{d^2x(t)}{dt^2} + 10\frac{dx(t)}{dt} - 7.41x(t)\right] dt \qquad (6\text{-}3.5)$$

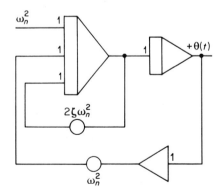

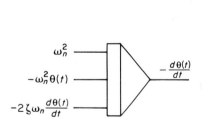

Figure 6-3.5   Simultaneous integration and summation is accomplished with a standard analog integrator.

Figure 6-3.6   Mechanization provides a saving of one amplifier over the circuit of Fig. 6-3.4.

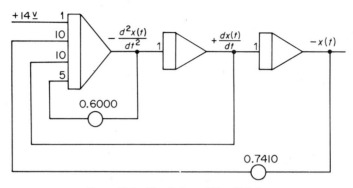

Figure 6-3.7 Simulation of Eq. (6-3.4).

The mechanization of Eq. (6-3.5) follows directly along the lines previously discussed. Note that the amplifier gains of Fig. 6-3.7 are computed such that, in conjunction with the potentiometer attenuation settings, the correct equation coefficients are established. In addition, observe that a positive feedback loop exists, i.e., an even number of amplifiers (two) are arranged in series within a single closed loop. Hence, the feedback associated with the term $10\ dx(t)/dt$ of Fig. 6-3.7 is regenerative, and the physical system governed by Eq. (6-3.4) is unstable.

As a final example, we will investigate the transient response characteristics of the coupled mechanical translational system of Fig. 6-3.8 for various values of the viscous friction coefficient B_3.

Writing the system differential equations in terms of the three dependent variables $x_1(t)$, $x_2(t)$, and $x_3(t)$ and the generalized system parameters, at M_1,

$$F - K_1(x_1 - x_2) - B_1\left(\frac{dx_1}{dt} - \frac{dx_2}{dt}\right) - K_{13}(x_1 - x_3) = M_1\frac{d^2x_1}{dt^2} \qquad (6\text{-}3.6)$$

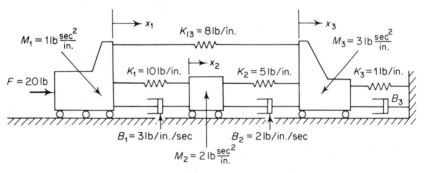

Figure 6-3.8 Coupled spring-mass-dashpot system.

at M_2

$$K_1(x_1 - x_2) + B_1\left(\frac{dx_1}{dt} - \frac{dx_2}{dt}\right) - K_2(x_2 - x_3) - B_2\left(\frac{dx_2}{dt} - \frac{dx_3}{dt}\right)$$

$$= M_2\frac{d^2x_2}{dt^2} \qquad (6\text{-}3.7)$$

and at M_3

$$K_2(x_2 - x_3) + B_2\left(\frac{dx_2}{dt} - \frac{dx_3}{dt}\right) - K_3x_3 - B_3\frac{dx_3}{dt} + K_{13}(x_1 - x_3) = M_3\frac{dx_3}{dt}$$

$$(6\text{-}3.8)$$

Substituting the numerical values illustrated in Fig. 6-3.8

$$20 - 10(x_1 - x_2) - 3\left(\frac{dx_1}{dt} - \frac{dx_2}{dt}\right) - 8(x_1 - x_3) = \frac{d^2x_1}{dt^2} \qquad (6\text{-}3.9)$$

$$10(x_1 - x_2) + 3\left(\frac{dx_1}{dt} - \frac{dx_2}{dt}\right) - 5(x_2 - x_3) - 2\left(\frac{dx_2}{dt} - \frac{dx_3}{dt}\right) = 2\frac{d^2x_2}{dt^2}$$

$$(6\text{-}3.10)$$

$$5(x_2 - x_3) + 2\left(\frac{dx_2}{dt} - \frac{dx_3}{dt}\right) - x_3 - B_3\frac{dx_3}{dt} + 8(x_1 - x_3) = 3\frac{d^2x_3}{dt^2}$$

$$(6\text{-}3.11)$$

Since Eqs. (6-3.9), (6-3.10), and (6-3.11) are already solved for the highest-order derivatives d^2x_1/dt^2, d^2x_2/dt^2, and d^2x_3/dt^2 respectively, we need now only arrange these governing expressions in more convenient form

$$\frac{d^2x_1}{dt^2} = 20 - 3\frac{dx_1}{dt} - 18x_1 + 3\frac{dx_2}{dt} + 10x_2 + 8x_3 \qquad (6\text{-}3.12)$$

$$\frac{d^2x_2}{dt^2} = -\frac{5}{2}\frac{dx_2}{dt} - \frac{15}{2}x_2 + \frac{3}{2}\frac{dx_1}{dt} + 5x_1 + \frac{dx_3}{dt} + \frac{5}{2}x_3 \qquad (6\text{-}3.13)$$

$$\frac{d^2x_3}{dt^2} = -\left(\frac{2 + B_3}{3}\right)\frac{dx_3}{dt} - \frac{14}{3}x_3 + \frac{2}{3}\frac{dx_2}{dt} + \frac{5}{3}x_2 + \frac{8}{3}x_1 \qquad (6\text{-}3.14)$$

If we assume that the system accelerations are of no special interest, Eqs. (6-3.12), (6-3.13), and (6-3.14) are integrated analytically

$$\frac{dx_1}{dt} = \int\left[20 - 3\frac{dx_1}{dt} - 18x_1 + 3\frac{dx_2}{dt} + 10x_2 + 8x_3\right]dt \qquad (6\text{-}3.15)$$

$$\frac{dx_2}{dt} = \int\left[-\frac{5}{2}\frac{dx_2}{dt} - \frac{15}{2}x_2 + \frac{3}{2}\frac{dx_1}{dt} + 5x_1 + \frac{dx_3}{dt} + \frac{5}{2}x_3\right]dt \qquad (6\text{-}3.16)$$

$$\frac{dx_3}{dt} = \int\left[-\left(\frac{2 + B_3}{3}\right)\frac{dx_3}{dt} - \frac{14}{3}x_3 + \frac{2}{3}\frac{dx_2}{dt} + \frac{5}{3}x_2 + \frac{8}{3}x_1\right]dt \qquad (6\text{-}3.17)$$

The integrations suggested in the final system equations are easily mechanized, as illustrated in Fig. 6-3.9. Note that the combinations of integrator gain and potentiometer settings again yield the desired equation coefficients. All input functions that, in Fig. 6-3.9, were explicitly assumed to exist are now generated in the final mechanization of Fig. 6-3.10. The coupling exhibited by the x_1, x_2, and x_3 amplifier loops is analogous to that of the original spring-mass dashpot system. It is now possible to vary the viscous damping factor B_3 between the limits of 0 and 28 lb/in./sec without requiring any modifications within the simulation, i.e., for $B_3 = 11$, the corresponding potentiometer is adjusted to an electrical attenuation of $(2 + 11)/30 = 0.4333$. Each of the three separate system variables x_1, x_2, and x_3 (and their respective derivatives) can be monitored at the appropriate amplifier output terminals, such that the transient response characteristics of the entire system are automatically generated. The response of mass M_1, in terms of deflection from an initial equilibrium position, for various values of B_3 is illustrated in Fig. 6-3.11.

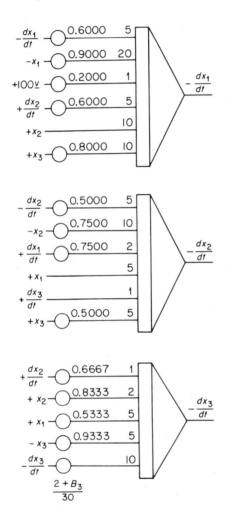

Figure 6-3.9 Three integrators mechanize relationships of Eqs. (6-3.15), (6-3.16), and (6-3.17).

6-4 FUNCTION GENERATION BY SUCCESSIVE DIFFERENTIATION

The analog computer, in addition to simulating systems governed by differential equations, can be employed to generate many of the familiar time-domain forcing functions normally encountered in dynamic systems analysis. Basically, we mechanize a differential equation that has, as its solution, the required forcing function. The analytical process of deriving the appropriate differential equation is

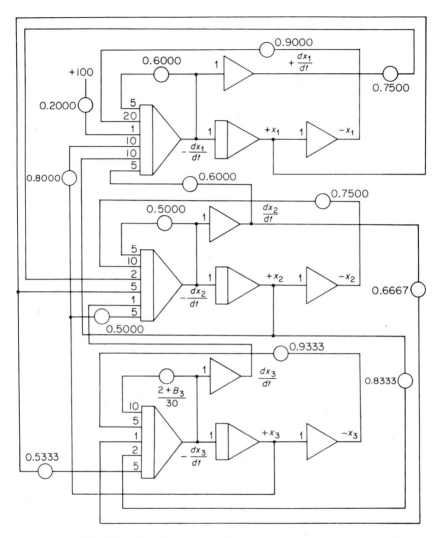

Figure 6-3.10 Complete simulation of coupled mechanical system of Fig. 6-3.8.

commonly referred to successive differentiation. The original function is differentiated until, at some point, a direct correspondence exists between the function and the derivative, i.e., the governing differential equation. For example, consider the sinusoidal forcing function

$$y = \sin \omega t \qquad\qquad (6\text{-}4.1)$$

Equation (6-4.1) is now successively differentiated to yield

$$\frac{dy}{dt} = \omega \cos \omega t \qquad (6\text{-}4.2)$$

$$\frac{d^2y}{dt^2} = -\omega^2 \sin \omega t \qquad (6\text{-}4.3)$$

Substituting Eq. (6-4.1) into Eq. (6-4.3), a differential equation

$$\frac{d^2y}{dt^2} = -\omega^2 y \qquad (6\text{-}4.4)$$

is produced which has the desired solution $y = \sin \omega t$. Equation (6-4.4) is

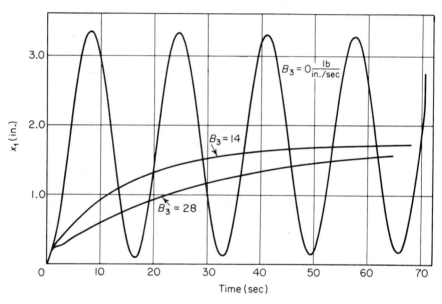

Figure 6-3.11 Response of mass M_1 of Fig. 6-3.8 for various values of B_3.

mechanized according to the techniques developed in the previous section; this results in the three-amplifier loop of Fig. 6-4.1. The series combination of an inverter (V–1) and two integrators (T–1 and T–2) forms an oscillator circuit. It should be noted that the output voltage at T–2 is analogous to the function $\cos \omega t$, since from Eq. (6-4.2)

$$\cos \omega t = \frac{1}{\omega} \frac{dy}{dt} \qquad (6\text{-}4.5)$$

Thus, an initial condition, cos (0), must be supplied as an integrator initial voltage (the actual voltage input is negative, however, because of the

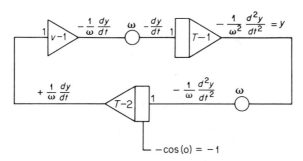

Figure 6-4.1   Sine-cosine generator.

180° amplifier phase shift). The analog oscillator generates sine and cosine waves simultaneously; this property will prove of prime importance in the later development of certain frequency-response techniques (Chapter 12).

A final example serves to illustrate the method of successive differentiation. The function

$$y = Ae^{-bt} \tag{6-4.6}$$

is differentiated to yield

$$\frac{dy}{dt} = -Abe^{-bt} \tag{6-4.7}$$

Combining the preceding

$$\frac{dy}{dt} = -by \tag{6-4.8}$$

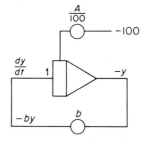

Figure 6-4.2   Exponential function generator.

Equation (6-4.8) is generated with the simple network of Fig. 6-4.2.

A multiplying constant A is introduced by means of the integrator initial condition. Thus, since $e^0 = 1$, the initial value of Ae^{-bt} is $+A$; again $-A$ volts must actually be applied because of the inherent 180° phase shift of the amplifier.

6-5   AMPLITUDE SCALE FACTORS

An adequate insight into amplitude-scaling procedures is essential to an understanding of basic analog computer programming. In any physical system, many different dependent variables can exist, e.g., temperature, pressure, velocity, force, etc. In the equivalent analog simulation, only one variable, voltage, is possible. Thus, conversion from the machine variable to the physical variable is necessary. The amplitude scale factor specifies the number of *machine units* (volts) that are analogous to one *physical system unit* (degree Fahrenheit, psi, inch per second, pound, etc.) at each position within the analog mechanization. After these amplitude factors have been specified, the voltage level existing at any point within the simulation can be related directly to the analogous physical system variable.

Before scale factors can be intelligently assigned, maximum variable values must be determined. The scale factors are then defined such that the corresponding machine variables are less than, or equal to, 100 v. Thus, if the particular system velocity will never exceed 5 ft/sec, a scale factor of 20 v/ft/sec could be employed since, at the maximum velocity, the corresponding voltage level is calculated as

$$\left(5\frac{dx}{dt}\text{ ft/sec}\right)(20\text{ v/ft/sec}) = 100\text{ v}$$

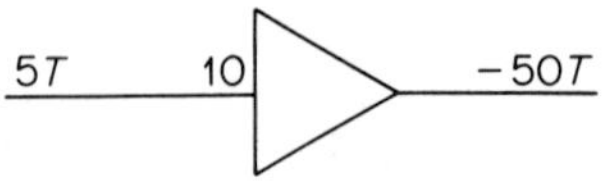

Figure 6-5.1   Amplitude scale factoring.

Note that this particular method of amplitude scaling is completely compatible with the concepts of voltage gain. In Fig. 6-5.1, an initial temperature variable, scaled at 5 v/deg, is amplified by a gain of 10. The amplifier output scaling is now observed to reflect the gain of 10 directly within the newly formed scale factor $-50T$, i.e., an amplifier output of -50 v is now analogous to $+1$ deg.

Potentiometers must also be scaled so that the actual settings are less than unity. To illustrate these concepts, consider the third-order differential equation

$$\frac{d^3x}{dt^3} + 42\frac{d^2x}{dt^2} + 165\frac{dx}{dt} + 3200x = 10 \qquad (6\text{-}5.1)$$

Assuming maximum variable values

$$\frac{d^2x}{dt^2}_{\text{max}} = 20\text{ ft/sec}^2$$

$$\frac{dx}{dt}_{\text{max}} = 2\text{ ft/sec}$$

$$x_{\text{max}} = 0.1\text{ ft}$$

the following amplitude scale factors are suggested

$$5\frac{d^2x}{dt^2}\text{ (v/ft/sec}^2)$$

$$50\frac{dx}{dt}\text{ (v/ft/sec)}$$

$$1000x\text{ (v/ft)}$$

Solving Eq. (6-5.1) for the highest-order derivative, and integrating the resulting expression

$$\frac{d^2x}{dt^2} = \int \left(10 - 42\frac{d^2x}{dt^2} - 165\frac{dx}{dt} - 3200x\right) dt \qquad \text{(6-5.2)}$$

If we assume that all terms of Eq. (6-5.2) are available, the simultaneous summation and integration processes are mechanized in Fig. 6-5.2 to form an output quantity $-d^2x/dt^2$. However, since it has been decided that 5 v

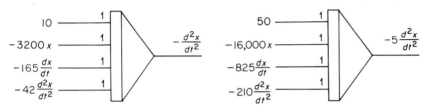

Figure 6-5.2 Simulation of Eq. (6-5.2).

Figure 6-5.3 Integrator of Fig. 6-5.2 adjusted for the desired output-variable scale factor.

would be analogous to an acceleration of 1 ft/sec², the integrator output variable must be scaled at $-5d^2x/dt^2$. Accordingly, both sides of Eq. (6-5.2) are multiplied by this factor

$$5\frac{d^2x}{dt^2} = 5\int \left(10 - 42\frac{d^2x}{dt^2} - 165\frac{dx}{dt} - 3200x\right) dt$$

$$= \int \left(50 - 210\frac{d^2x}{dt^2} - 825\frac{dx}{dt} - 16000x\right) dt \qquad \text{(6-5.3)}$$

resulting in the equivalent integrating amplifier mechanization of Fig. 6-5.3.

The additional forward loop network employed to generate the required velocity and position scaling (50 dx/dt and 1000x respectively) is illustrated in Fig. 6-5.4. It is now necessary to close the loop about each of the system integrators to produce the assumed input quantities. This operation is completed in Fig. 6-5.5. The large values of gain exhibited throughout the mechanization indicate that a time scale variation should be introduced.

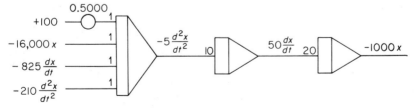

Figure 6-5.4 Forward loop mechanization of Eq. (6-5.1) with appropriate amplitude scale factors.

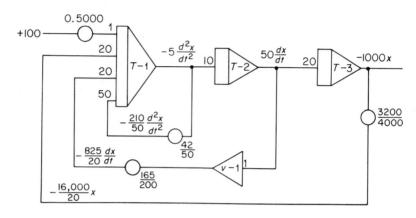

Figure 6-5.5 Complete simulation of Eq. (6-5.1).

6-6 TIME SCALING

Whereas amplitude scale factors represent a correspondence between machine and physical system dependent variables, the time scale expresses a particular relationship between the machine and system independent variable, time. A convenient and flexible method of time scaling is based upon the *fictitious integrator gain* technique, which can be derived intuitively as follows: Consider, in Fig. 6-6.1, three analog integrators T-1, T-2, and T-3. Assume that each integrator has associated with it a fictitious gain, as illustrated within each respective rectangle. Although each integrator has a real gain of unity (i.e., a 1-megohm input resistor and a 1-μf feedback capacitor), the total component gain is computed as the product of the real and fictitious gain parameters; thus, T-1 has an over-all gain of 10, T-2 has a gain of unity, while T-3 exhibits a gain of $\frac{1}{10}$. The amplitude scale factors appearing at the integrating-amplifier outputs reflect this combination of real and fictitious gain.

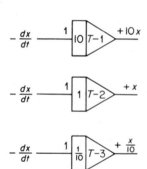

Figure 6-6.1 Fictitious integrator gain employed in amplitude scale factor.

If, now, a negative 1-v step excitation (equivalent to a constant positive 1 ft/sec velocity) is applied for a total of 10 seconds, the resulting integrator output would, in each case, be equal to $+10$ v. Because of the differing output scale factors, however, this 10-v level would be analogous to physical-system displacements of 1 ft, 10 ft, and 100 ft for integrators T-1, T-2, and T-3, respectively. Thus, with respect to T-1, a constant 1 ft/sec velocity integrated over 10 sec of "computer time" yields a displacement of 1 ft; the fictitious integrator gain of 10 has effectively introduced a 10-to-1 scale

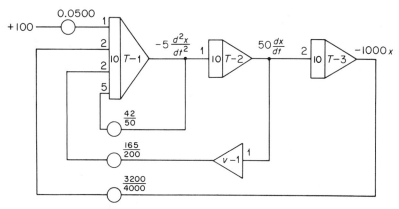

Figure 6-6.2 Simulation of Eq. (6-5.2) with 10 to 1 time scale.

factor such that 10 sec of computer operation is analogous to 1 sec of physical system operation. Integrator T-2 functions in real time, while T-3 yields a 1-to-10 time scale.

Since neither the attenuating potentiometer nor the summing amplifier is affected, operationally, by a changing time scale, only the integrating amplifier need be assigned a fictitious gain. Hence, to vary a simulation time scale from 1 to 5, it is only necessary to assign to *each* system integrator a fictitious gain of 5; the amplitude scale factors are then computed in accordance with the new over-all integrator gain parameters.

Returning to the mechanization of Fig. 6-5.5, one can see that a 10-to-1 time scale can be advantageously used. Each integrator is assigned a fictitious gain of 10; the products of real and fictitious gain of the subsequent mechanization (Fig. 6-6.2) are identical to the real gains employed in Fig. 6-5.5, so that potentiometer settings (with the exception of the input excitation potentiometer) remain fixed. Each second of computer operation now represents only 0.1 sec of physical system operation.

Although elaborate schemes are often presented for determining the appropriate time scale, a simple universal rule of thumb suffices. If the majority of true system gains are between 1 and 5, the correct time scale is in force. If gains are found to be predominantly above or below this range, a time-scale change is indicated. The fictitious integrator gain method of time scaling has distinct advantages over more classical procedures; the basic differential equations are never modified, and the mechanization can be completely re-time scaled with very little effort.

6-7 LINEAR SYSTEMS PROGRAMMING

Linear programming of the analog computer involves the arrangement of specific linear computer components and function generators, subject to amplitude-and time-scaling requirements, according to the particular system equations. As such, the mechanization of Fig. 6-6.2 represents a simple linear program.

The components and techniques discussed so far are now applied to the simulation of a coupled linear system specified by Eqs. (6-7.1) and (6-7.2).

$$\frac{d^2x}{dt^2} + 400\frac{dx}{dt} + 6000x - 576\frac{d^2y}{dt^2} - 750{,}000y = 100\sin 600t \qquad (6\text{-}7.1)$$

$$\frac{d^3y}{dt^3} + 86\frac{d^2y}{dt^2} + 10{,}000\frac{dy}{dt} - 7800x = 100e^{-840t} \qquad (6\text{-}7.2)$$

The system is subject to initial conditions, $\frac{dy}{dt}(0) = 0.001$ and $x(0) = 0.0018$, and has the following assumed maximum variable values

$$\frac{d^2x}{dt^2} = 100 \qquad \frac{d^2y}{dt^2} = 1$$

$$\frac{dx}{dt} = 1 \qquad \frac{dy}{dt} = 0.01$$

$$x = 0.01 \qquad y = 0.0001$$

$$\frac{d^3y}{dt^3} = 100$$

Based upon these data, the following amplitude scale factors are assumed

$$100\frac{dx}{dt} \qquad 10{,}000\frac{dy}{dt}$$

$$10{,}000x \qquad 1{,}000{,}000y$$

$$100\frac{d^2y}{dt^2}$$

Equations (6-7.1) and (6-7.2) are now solved for the highest-order derivatives, integrated, and multiplied by the respective scale factors

$$100\frac{dx}{dt} = 100\int\left[100\sin 600t - 400\frac{dx}{dt} - 6000x\right.$$
$$\left. + 576\frac{d^2y}{dt^2} + 750{,}000y\right]dt \qquad (6\text{-}7.3)$$

$$100\frac{d^2y}{dt^2} = 100\int\left[100e^{-840t} - 86\frac{d^2y}{dt^2} - 10{,}000\frac{dy}{dt} + 7800x\right]dt \qquad (6\text{-}7.4)$$

If we assume a scale factor of 100, the analog computer simulation of Eqs. (6-7.3) and (6-7.4) is generated in Fig. 6-7.1. Since the system gains are predominantly between 1 and 5, the time scale appears appropriate.

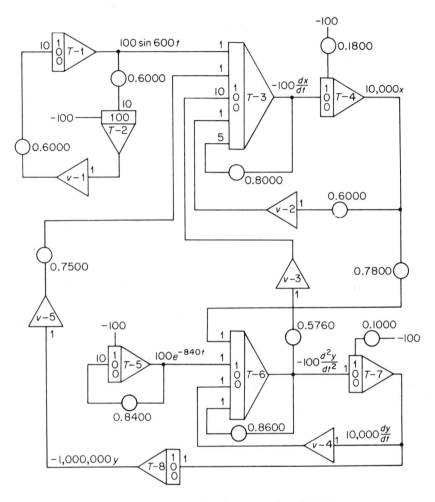

Figure 6-7.1 Simulation of Eqs. (6-7.3) and (6-7.4).

The process of linear analog computer programming is not as difficult as one might suspect, viewing the finalized schematic; but it consists of the repeated application of simple procedures and techniques. Once these methods have been formalized, they can be applied to the simulation of practically any continuous system described in terms of ordinary linear differential equations. The same comment also holds for nonlinear computer programming discussed in Chapter 18; although a wider variety of computer elements is introduced (e.g., diodes, servo multipliers, etc.) the basic rules of linear programming are applicable, whereas amplitude- and time-scaling techniques remain invariant.

PROBLEMS

6.1   Determine the mathematical relationships between $\theta(t)$, $x(t)$, $y(t)$, and $z(t)$ corresponding to each of the following:

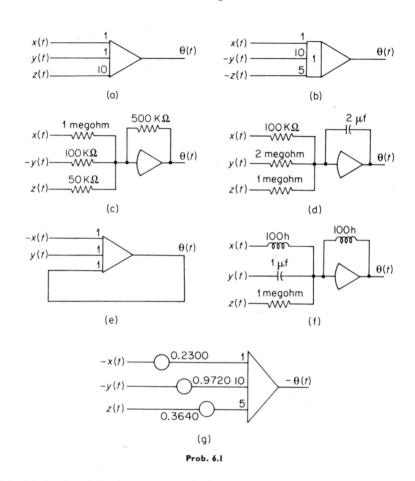

(a)   (b)   (c)   (d)   (e)   (f)   (g)

Prob. 6.1

6.2   Mechanize each of the following differential equations for analog computer simulation. Use a time scale of unity.

(a) $\dfrac{d^2\theta}{dt^2} + 3\dfrac{d\theta}{dt} + 15\theta = 10$ (No initial conditions)

(b) $\dfrac{d^3\theta}{dt^3} + 2\dfrac{d\theta}{dt} + 10\theta = 0$ (Initial conditions $\dfrac{d^2\theta}{dt^2}(0) = +10$)

(c) $\dfrac{d^3\theta}{dt^3} + 6\dfrac{d^2\theta}{dt^2} + 6\dfrac{d\theta}{dt} + 60\theta = 100 \sin t$ (No initial conditions)

(d) $\dfrac{d\theta}{dt} + 30 = 10 \sinh t + 60e^{-3t}$ (No initial conditions)

(e) $\dfrac{d^7\theta}{dt^7} + 2\dfrac{d^6\theta}{dt^6} + 5\dfrac{d^5\theta}{dt^5} + 10\dfrac{d^4\theta}{dt^4} + 50\dfrac{d^3\theta}{dt^3} + 100\dfrac{d^2\theta}{dt^2} + 500\dfrac{d\theta}{dt} + 1000t$

$= 100$ (No initial conditions)

(f) $\dfrac{d^4\theta}{dt^4} + 42\theta = 3t$ (Initial conditions $\dfrac{d^3\theta}{dt^3} = \dfrac{d^2\theta}{dt^2} = \dfrac{d\theta}{dt} = \theta = +100$)

6.3 For each of the following systems of equations, choose the appropriate time- and amplitude-scales and mechanize for computer simulation.

(a) $\dfrac{d^2x}{dt^2} + 35\dfrac{dx}{dt} + 600x - 45\dfrac{dy}{dt} = 10$ (No initial conditions)

$\dfrac{d^3y}{dt^3} + 7\dfrac{d^2y}{dt^2} + 72\dfrac{dy}{dt} + 450y - 60\dfrac{dx}{dt} - 500x = 0$ (No initial conditions)

Maximum Values

$\left(\dfrac{dx}{dt}\right)_{max} = 1$ $\left(\dfrac{dy}{dt}\right)_{max} = 1$

$x_{max} = 0.1$ $y_{max} = 0.1$

$\left(\dfrac{d^2y}{dt^2}\right)_{max} = 10$

(b) $\dfrac{d^2x}{dt^2} + 1400\dfrac{dx}{dt} + 20{,}000x - 62{,}000y = 0$

$\dfrac{d^2y}{dt^2} + 600\dfrac{dy}{dt} + 10{,}000y - 4000\dfrac{dz}{dt} - 35{,}000x = 100e^{-6t}$

$\dfrac{d^2z}{dt^2} + 800\dfrac{dz}{dt} + 36{,}000z - 1600\dfrac{dx}{dt} - 15{,}000y = 0$

(No initial conditions)

Maximum Values

$\left(\dfrac{dx}{dt}\right)_{max} = 0.1$ $y_{max} = 0.01$

$x_{max} = 0.01$ $\left(\dfrac{dz}{dt}\right)_{max} = 0.20$

$\left(\dfrac{dy}{dt}\right)_{max} = 0.10$ $z_{max} = 0.005$

6.4 For each of the following, compute the system mathematical models and mechanize for computer simulation.

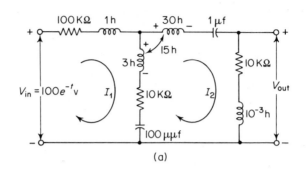

(a)

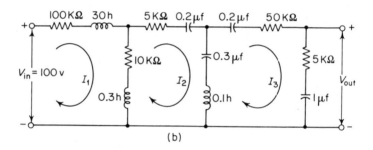

(b)

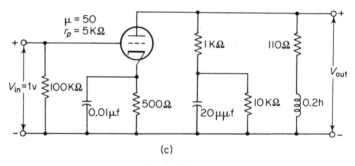

(c)

Prob. 6.4

6.5 For the following mechanical systems, derive the mathematical models and determine the corresponding analog simulations.

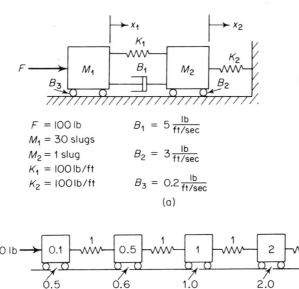

$F = 100$ lb $\qquad B_1 = 5\dfrac{\text{lb}}{\text{ft/sec}}$

$M_1 = 30$ slugs

$M_2 = 1$ slug $\qquad B_2 = 3\dfrac{\text{lb}}{\text{ft/sec}}$

$K_1 = 100$ lb/ft

$K_2 = 100$ lb/ft $\qquad B_3 = 0.2\dfrac{\text{lb}}{\text{ft/sec}}$

(a)

M in slugs
B in lb sec/ft

(b)

Prob. 6.5

6.6 For the following rocket-motor static thrust fixture parameters and for a step force input of 50,000 lbs, deduce the system mathematical model. Program for analog simulation to include explicit generation of the variables z, z_1, z_2, and θ.

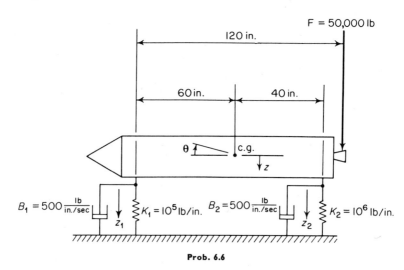

Prob. 6.6

BIBLIOGRAPHY

1. Jackson, A. S., *Analog Computer Techniques*. New York: McGraw-Hill Book Company, 1960.

2. Johnson, C. L., *Analog Computer Techniques*. New York: McGraw-Hill Book Company, 1956.

3. Karplus, W. J., *Analog Simulation*. New York: McGraw-Hill Book Company, 1958.

4. Karplus, W. J. and W. J. Soroka, *Analog Methods-Computation and Simulation*. New York: McGraw-Hill Book Company, 1959.

5. Korn, G. A. and T. M. Korn, *Electronic Analog Computers*. New York: McGraw-Hill Book Company, 1956.

TRANSFER FUNCTIONS AND BLOCK DIAGRAMS[1,2,3,4]

7

7-1 INTRODUCTION

Within the past two decades and in practically all fields of engineering, the theory of operational calculus has found tremendous practical application. In particular, the transfer-function representation of complex linear systems has markedly reduced the degree of mathematical ingenuity required of the design engineer by providing a simple yet formalistic method of analysis. The further introduction of block diagrams (based upon the transfer function) allows the flow of information associated with any linear system to be easily visualized and, of more direct importance, processed according to definite rules. Thus, the block diagram bridges the very real chasm between the mathematician's world of differential equations and the engineer's world of algebra and flow charts.

7-2 OPEN-LOOP TRANSFER FUNCTIONS

For any linear system, the system transfer function is defined as the ratio of the Laplace transformed output variable to the Laplace transformed input variable. Thus, for the Laplace transformed electrical network mathematical model

$$V_{out}(s) = \frac{(s + 2)(s + 5)V_{in}(s)}{s^2 + 3s + 10} \qquad (7\text{-}2.1)$$

the corresponding transfer function is

$$\frac{V_{\text{out}}}{V_{\text{in}}}(s) = \frac{(s+2)(s+5)}{s^2+3s+10} \tag{7-2.2}$$

As observed in Eq. (7-2.2), the transfer function is completely independent of the particular form of system forcing function. Although not stated explicitly, the implication is clear that the transfer function cannot be generated for a system containing initial conditions. For example, consider the second-order differential equation with an arbitrary forcing function $F(t)$

$$\frac{d^2x}{dt^2} + K_1\frac{dx}{dt} + K_2x = F(t) \tag{7-2.3}$$

Transforming under the assumption of initial conditions x_0 and dx_0/dt

$$s^2X(s) - sx_0 - \frac{dx_0}{dt} + K_1[sX(s) - x_0] + K_2X(s) = F(s) \tag{7-2.4}$$

$$X(s)[s^2 + K_1s + K_2] = F(s) + x_0s + \frac{dx_0}{dt} + K_1x_0 \tag{7-2.5}$$

Forming the ratio of transformed output variable $X(s)$ to transformed input variable $F(s)$

$$\frac{X}{F}(s) = \frac{1}{s^2 + K_1s + K_2} + \frac{x_0s + (dx_0/dt) + K_1x_0}{F(s)[s^2 + K_1s + K_2]} \tag{7-2.6}$$

Thus, unless $x_0 = dx_0/dt = 0$, the right-hand portion of Eq. (7-2.6) is not independent of the input function. Accordingly, transfer functions are formed by ignoring all initial system conditions. The effects of the initial values are then introduced through the application of impulse excitations placed at appropriate positions within the block diagram. This technique will be detailed in a subsequent section.

7-3 BLOCK DIAGRAM CONVENTIONS

The intrinsic usefulness of transfer functions becomes apparent only when considered in conjunction with the system block diagram. Let us assume two elements arranged in series as described in the functional diagram of Fig.

7-3.1. The system is governed by differential equations associated with each individual component, e.g.

$$x(t) = \frac{d^2y(t)}{dt} + A_1\frac{dy(t)}{dt} + A_2y(t) \tag{7-3.1}$$

$$y(t) = \frac{dz(t)}{dt} + B_1z(t) \tag{7-3.2}$$

Transforming the preceding under the assumption of no initial conditions

$$X(s) = (s^2 + A_1s + A_2)Y(s)$$
$$Y(s) = (s + B_1)Z(s) \tag{7-3.3}$$

and eliminating $Y(s)$ from the two equations, the over-all system transfer function is

$$\frac{Z}{X}(s) = \frac{1}{(s^2 + A_1s + A_2)(s + B_1)} \tag{7-3.4}$$

Instead of using this procedure, however, let us now replace the functional diagram of Fig. 7-3.1 by a less descriptive but more meaningful diagram, in

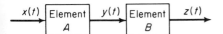

Figure 7-3.1   Functional block diagram.

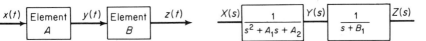

Figure 7-3.2   Block diagram corresponding to functional diagram in Fig. 7-3.1.

which the terms "Element A" and "Element B" are replaced by the individual component transfer functions $Y/X(s)$ and $Z/X(s)$ respectively. The resulting flow diagram of Fig. 7-3.2 is referred to as a block diagram. Note that the over-all system transfer function $Z/X(s)$ is obtained by a simple multiplication of the individual transfer functions. This general rule applies to any number of series-oriented elements, i.e., the system transfer function is obtained by multiplying the individual element transfer functions.

In addition to the basic block, one more element appears in the typical closed-loop diagram. The summing junction, illustrated in Fig. 7-3.3 functions as a symbolic adder. The algebraic sign associated with each informational path determines the polarity with which the variable is summed. For example, the equation corresponding to Fig. 7-3.3 is

$$E(s) = X(s) - Y(s) \tag{7-3.5}$$

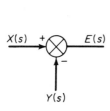

Figure 7-3.3 Symbolic adder or summing junction.

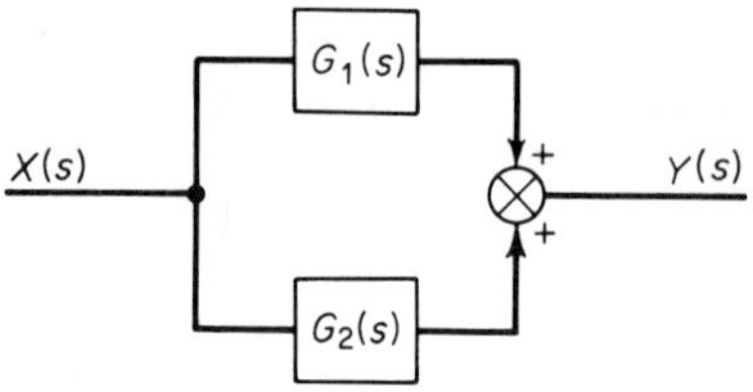

Figure 7-3.4 Blocks arranged in parallel.

It is now possible to combine blocks appearing in parallel into an equivalent single block. Thus, from Fig. 7-3.4

$$\frac{Y}{X}(s) = G_1(s) + G_2(s) \qquad (7\text{-}3.6)$$

To generalize, for a finite number of components arranged in parallel, the over-all system transfer function is obtained by a simple linear addition of the individual element transfer functions.

7-4 THE CLOSED-LOOP TRANSFER FUNCTION

Thus far we have considered only open-loop physical systems, i.e., configurations without the property of feedback in the normal sense. Since, as stated in Chapter 1, the main body of this text is devoted to a study of negative feedback systems, we shall now initiate an investigation of this topic by deriving the closed-loop transfer function. In Fig. 7-4.1, the simple single loop system is characterized by the following definitive terminology:

$R(s)$ is the Laplace transformed reference or excitation variable
$C(s)$ is the Laplace transformed controlled or output variable
$E(s)$ is the Laplace transformed system error signal
$G(s)$ is the forward path transfer function

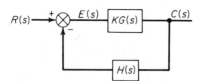

Figure 7-4.1 Closed-loop system block diagram.

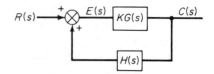

Figure 7-4.2 Closed-loop system with positive feedback.

$H(s)$ is the feedback path transfer function
K is the open-loop system gain parameter (which is assumed for the present to exist within the forward loop, i.e., the gain of the feedback element is considered unity).

To derive the closed-loop transfer function $C/R(s)$, Fig. 7-4.1 is analyzed by conventional methods

$$C(s) = KG(s)E(s) \qquad\qquad (7\text{-}4.1)$$

$$E(s) = R(s) - H(s)C(s) \qquad\qquad (7\text{-}4.2)$$

Solving Eq. (7-4.1) for $E(s)$ and substituting into Eq. (7-4.2), the governing expression of the closed-loop control system is

$$\frac{C}{R}(s) = \frac{KG(s)}{1 + KGH(s)} \qquad\qquad (7\text{-}4.3)$$

The closed-loop transfer function corresponding to the positive-feedback control system of Fig. 7-4.2, is generated in an analogous manner. Thus

$$C(s) = KG(s)E(s) \qquad\qquad (7\text{-}4.4)$$

$$E(s) = R(s) + H(s)C(s) \qquad\qquad (7\text{-}4.5)$$

and

$$\frac{C}{R}(s) = \frac{KG(s)}{1 - KGH(s)} \qquad\qquad (7\text{-}4.6)$$

Let us now apply Eq. (7-4.3) to the analysis of the simple unity-feedback (follower) control system illustrated in the functional diagram of Fig. 7-4.3. The purpose of the system is that of controlling a missile fin position $C(s)$

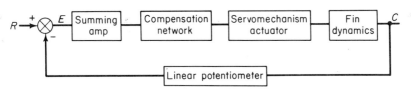

Figure 7-4.3 Functional diagram of missile steering system.

by means of an electrical input signal $R(s)$. The forward loop is comprised of a summing amplifier, a compensation network, an electrohydraulic actuator servomechanism, and the fin dynamics. The output fin position is sensed by a linear potentiometer.

For the open-loop transfer functions

$$G_A(s) = \frac{1000}{s + 600}$$

$$G_1(s) = \frac{10(s + 10)}{s + 100}$$

$$G_2(s) = \frac{50}{s(s + 50)}$$

$$G_3(s) = \frac{400}{s^2 + 28s + 400}$$

and

$$H(s) = 1$$

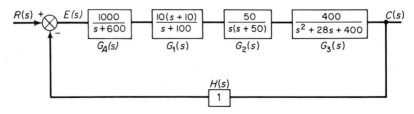

Figure 7-4.4   Block diagram corresponding to Fig. 7-4.3.

The equivalent block diagram of Fig. 7-4.4 is now compressed into a single closed-loop block by using Eq. (7-4.3), i.e.

$$
\frac{C}{R}(s) = \frac{\left[\dfrac{1000}{s + 600}\right]\left[\dfrac{10(s + 10)}{s + 100}\right]\left[\dfrac{50}{s(s + 50)}\right]\left[\dfrac{400}{s^2 + 28s + 400}\right]}{1 + \left[\dfrac{1000}{s + 600}\right]\left[\dfrac{10(s + 10)}{s + 100}\right]\left[\dfrac{50}{s(s + 50)}\right]\left[\dfrac{400}{s^2 + 28s + 400}\right]}
$$

$$
= \frac{2 \times 10^8(s + 10)}{s(s + 50)(s + 100)(s + 600)(s^2 + 28s + 400) + 2 \times 10^8(s + 10)}
$$

$$(7\text{-}4.7)$$

The transient-response characteristics of the closed-loop system can be ascertained only after the denominator polynomial is factored into poles. This is a laborious task at best when approached by classical mathematical procedures. In Chapter 10 we will consider this problem at length by the application of graphical root-locus techniques.

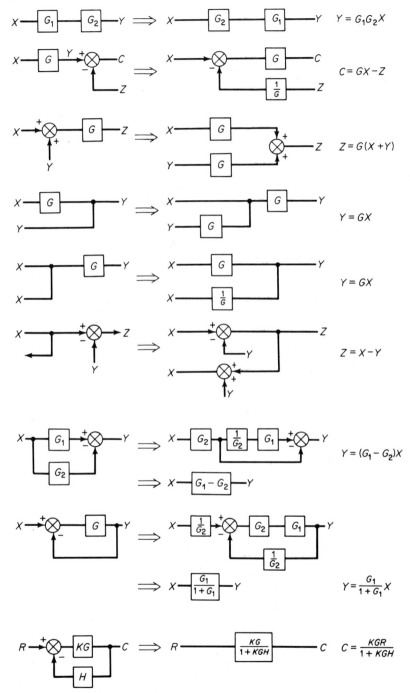

Figure 7-5.1 Block-diagram algebra.

7-5 BLOCK-DIAGRAM ALGEBRA

The results obtained to this point, together with additional block-diagram manipulations (loosely referred to as block-diagram algebra), are summarized in Fig. 7-5.1.

7-6 INITIAL CONDITIONS AND IMPULSE EXCITATIONS

Although the transfer function precludes, by definition, all nonzero initial conditions, one is often interested in computing the response of the physical system to an initial-condition excitation. Consider the system of Fig. 7-6.1, consisting of a summing amplifier, servomotor, and position transducer. It is required to compute the system response to an initial condition of 0.5 radians. As demonstrated in Chapter 4, the unit impulse excitation has a Laplace transform of unity. Thus, a unit impulse applied to a system integration will produce, at the integrator output, a unit step function. This process is illustrated in Fig. 7-6.2. Since

$$C(s) = \frac{\delta(s)}{s} \tag{7-6.1}$$

then, for a unit impulse excitation $\delta(s) = 1$

$$C(s) = \frac{1}{s} \tag{7-6.2}$$

Hence, to simulate an initial condition $C(0)$ in Fig. 7-6.1, the system integration is separated from the servomotor transfer function such that the integrator output function is $C(s)$. (Since the transfer function is linear, the particular order in which the system elements appear is unimportant.) The output integrator is now excited by an impulse function of magnitude 0.5 radians, producing an integrator initial condition $C(0) = 0.5$ radians. The system response to this impulse excitation, and the response to the desired initial condition, are thus identical. For the final block diagram described in Fig. 7-6.3, the closed-loop transfer function is

$$\frac{C(s)}{\delta(s)} = \frac{1/2(s + \omega_b)}{s^2 + \omega_b s + K_A K_p \omega_b} \tag{7-6.3}$$

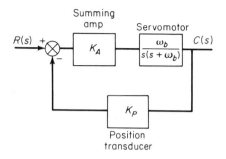

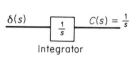

Figure 7-6.1　Simple closed-loop servo system.

Figure 7-6.2　Impulse into an integrator produces a step output.

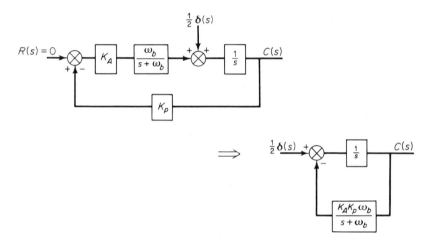

Figure 7-6.3　Block diagram reduction that allows the introduction of an initial condition into Fig. 7-6.1.

For $\delta(s) = 1$

$$C(s) = \frac{1/2(s + \omega_b)}{s^2 + \omega_b s + K_A K_p \omega_b} \qquad (7\text{-}6.4)$$

Equation (7-6.4) can now be solved to yield the required transient response.

7-7 ANALOG SIMULATION OF TRANSFER FUNCTIONS[5]

Two separate techniques are widely employed in the simulation of transfer functions; the passive-element approach requires an absolute minimum of fixed computer components, whereas the conventional programmed mechanization is both flexible and easily adjusted. The passive-network method is a direct consequence of the generalized operational amplifier input-output relationship, which is derived as follows. In Fig. 7-7.1, the input and feedback elements are assumed to consist of passive RC networks with short-circuit impedances of Z_{in} and Z_f respectively. The Kirchhoff's current summation applied at the summing junction J is

$$i_{sc_{in}} + i_{sc_f} = 0 \qquad (7\text{-}7.1)$$

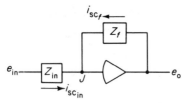

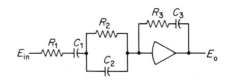

Figure 7-7.1 Generalized operational amplifier.

Figure 7-7.2 Single-amplifier simulation of the transfer function of Eq. (7-7.5).

where the subscript sc represents the fact that both input and feedback networks are effectively short circuited. Thus

$$\frac{e_{in}}{Z_{in}} = -\frac{e_o}{Z_f} \qquad (7\text{-}7.2)$$

and

$$e_o = -\frac{Z_f}{Z_{in}} e_{in} \qquad (7\text{-}7.3)$$

Given particular input and feedback RC networks such as illustrated in Fig. 7-7.2, the corresponding analog transfer function can be computed by substituting the respective short-circuit impedances directly into Eq. (7-7.3). Thus, in Fig. 7-7.2

$$Z_{in} = R_1 + \frac{1}{C_1 s} + \frac{1}{(1 + R_2 C_2 s)/R_2}$$

$$= \frac{1 + (R_1 C_1 + R_2 C_1 + R_2 C_2)s + R_1 R_2 C_1 C_2 s^2}{C_1 s (R_2 C_2 s + 1)} \qquad (7\text{-}7.4\text{-a})$$

and

$$Z_f = R_3 + \frac{1}{C_3 s} = \frac{R_3 C_3 s + 1}{C_3 s} \qquad (7\text{-}7.4\text{-b})$$

Hence, substituting Eqs. (7-7.4-a) and (7-7.4-b) into Eq. (7-7.3)

$$\frac{E_0}{E_{in}}(s) = -\frac{C_1(R_3C_3s + 1)(R_2C_2s + 1)}{C_3[1 + (R_1C_1 + R_2C_1 + R_2C_2)s + R_1R_2C_1C_2s^2]} \qquad (7\text{-}7.5)$$

The transfer function of Eq. (7-7.5) can thus be simulated directly by the simple operational amplifier configuration of Fig. 7-7.2. Unfortunately, the inverse process, i.e., that of determining an analog network to simulate a specific desired transfer function, involves a problem in network synthesis. In Appendix C of Volume II, *Advanced Control Systems Engineering*, however, a large number of typical *RC* networks are tabulated, together with the corresponding transfer functions and transfer admittances. In particular, the transfer admittance and short-circuit impedance are observed to be reciprocal quantities (the transfer admittance is defined as the ratio $I_{out}/E_{in}(s)$ with the output terminals short circuited). Hence

$$Y(s) = \frac{1}{Z_{sc}}(s) \qquad (7\text{-}7.6)$$

and, for the amplifier circuit of Fig. 7-7.1

$$e_0 = -\frac{Y_{in}}{Y_f}e_{in}(s) \qquad (7\text{-}7.7)$$

Thus, given a transfer function, appropriate input and feedback transfer admittances are assumed, and the corresponding *RC* networks are obtained from Appendix C of Volume II, *Advanced Control Systems Engineering*.

The passive-element procedure has two distinct disadvantages: (1) initial system conditions, simulated through initial capacitor charges, are quite difficult to apply, and (2) once resistance and capacitance values have been assigned, it is not possible to vary the corresponding transfer function. A second simulation technique, which overcomes these difficulties at the expense of additional equipment, is that of the standard programming procedure. As an example of this technique, consider the simple second-order system

$$\frac{C}{R}(s) = \frac{\omega_n^2}{s^2 + 2\zeta\omega_n s + \omega_n^2} \qquad (7\text{-}7.8)$$

Both numerator and denominator of Eq. (7-7.8) are now multiplied by an auxiliary variable $Z(s)$.

$$\frac{C}{R}(s) = \frac{\omega_n^2 Z(s)}{(s^2 + 2\zeta\omega_n s + \omega_n^2)Z(s)} \qquad (7\text{-}7.9)$$

Equating the numerators and denominators of Eq. (7-7.9), two parametric transformed expressions arise

$$C(s) = \omega_n^2 Z(s) \tag{7-7.10}$$

$$R(s) = (s^2 + 2\zeta\omega_n s + \omega_n^2)Z(s) \tag{7-7.11}$$

Performing the indicated inverse Laplace transformations

$$c(t) = \omega_n^2 z(t) \tag{7-7.12}$$

$$r(t) = \frac{d^2 z(t)}{dt^2} + 2\zeta\omega_n \frac{dz(t)}{dt} + \omega_n^2 z(t) \tag{7-7.13}$$

In general, the input function $r(t)$ is known so that Eq. (7-7.13) contains only one dependent variable, $z(t)$. Since $d^2z(t)/dt^2$ is not required in the parametric equation, Eq. (7-7.12), Eq. (7-7.13) is solved for the highest-order derivative and integrated to yield

$$\frac{dz(t)}{dt} = \int \left[r(t) - 2\zeta\omega_n \frac{dz(t)}{dt} - \omega_n^2 z(t) \right] dt \tag{7-7.14}$$

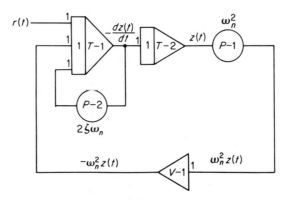

Figure 7-7.3   Mechanization of Eq. (7-7.14).

Equation (7-7.14) is easily mechanized in Fig. 7-7.3. Refer now to Eq. (7-7.12). The output $c(t)$ is described in terms of the auxiliary variable $z(t)$ which has been generated in Fig. 7-7.2. In particular, the output of potentiometer P–1 yields the required output, i.e., $c(t) = \omega_n^2 z(t)$.

To illustrate this technique as applied to a slightly more complicated transfer function, let us mechanize the expression of Eq. (7-7.15)

$$\frac{E_{\text{out}}}{E_{\text{in}}}(s) = \frac{-K[s^2 + (1/T_1 + 1/T_2)s + 1/T_1T_2]}{[s^2 + (1/T_3 + 1/T_4)s + 1/T_3T_4]} \qquad (7\text{-}7.15)$$

Multiplying the numerator and denominator of the transfer function in Eq. (7-7.15), by the auxiliary variable $Z(s)$

$$\frac{E_{\text{out}}}{E_{\text{in}}}(s) = \frac{-K[s^2 + (1/T_1 + 1/T_2)s + 1/T_1T_2]Z(s)}{[s^2 + (1/T_3 + 1/T_4)s + 1/T_3T_4]Z(s)} \qquad (7\text{-}7.16)$$

Equating numerators and denominators of Eq. (7-7.16) and using inverse Laplace transforms

$$E_{\text{out}}(t) = -K\left[\frac{d^2z(t)}{dt^2} + \left(\frac{1}{T_1} + \frac{1}{T_2}\right)\frac{dz(t)}{dt} + \frac{1}{T_1T_2}z(t)\right] \qquad (7\text{-}7.17)$$

$$E_{\text{in}}(t) = \frac{d^2z(t)}{dt^2} + \left(\frac{1}{T_3} + \frac{1}{T_4}\right)\frac{dz(t)}{dt} + \frac{1}{T_3T_4}z(t) \qquad (7\text{-}7.18)$$

Since, in this case, the parametric equations are of equal order, it is usually desirable to eliminate the highest-order derivatives in the equation containing the output variable $E_{\text{out}}(t)$. Multiplying Eq. (7-7.18) by K, adding to Eq. (7-7.17), and solving for $E_{\text{out}}(t)$

$$E_{\text{out}}(t) = -KE_{\text{in}}(t) + K\left(\frac{1}{T_3} + \frac{1}{T_4} - \frac{1}{T_1} - \frac{1}{T_2}\right)\frac{dz(t)}{dt} + K\left(\frac{1}{T_3T_4} - \frac{1}{T_1T_2}\right)z(t)$$

$$(7\text{-}7.19)$$

The parametric expression of Eq. (7-7.19) does not contain $d^2z(t)/dt^2$, therefore Eq. (7-7.18) can be solved for the highest-order derivative and integrated analytically

$$\frac{dz(t)}{dt} = \int\left[E_{\text{in}}(t) - \left(\frac{1}{T_3} + \frac{1}{T_4}\right)\frac{dz(t)}{dt} - \frac{1}{T_3T_4}z(t)\right]dt \qquad (7\text{-}7.20)$$

Equation (7-7.20) is mechanized in Fig. 7-7.4. The system output is now constructed according to the requirements of Eq. (7-7.19). Since $z(t)$ and $dz(t)/dt$ already appear explicitly in Fig. 7-7.4, three additional potentiometers and a single summing amplifier are sufficient to complete the simulation. The finalized circuit is presented in Fig. 7-7.5.

Although it has been necessary to employ a total of four amplifiers and five potentiometers, the programmed transfer-function simulation is found

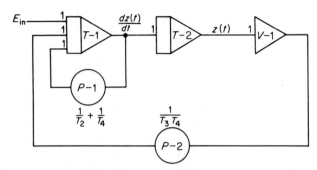

Figure 7-7.4   Simulation of the parametric relationship of Eq.(7-7.20).

to be extremely versatile. The over-all gain or any individual time-constant value may be varied by adjusting the appropriate potentiometers to the required settings. In addition, initial system conditions can be simulated by conventional methods.

In practice the passive-network approach is effectively applied to those transfer functions corresponding to "shelf-item" components. Thus, the dynamics of a particular gyroscope could be simulated using this technique since this transfer function would not be subject to variation. However, components that contain design parameters (e.g., linear equalization networks)

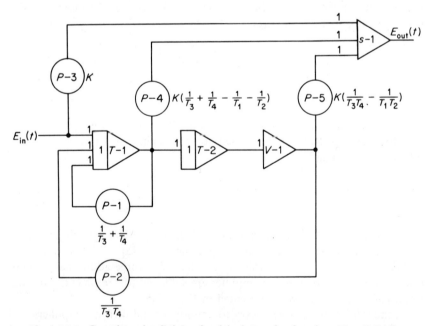

Figure 7-7.5   Complete simulation of original transfer function, Eq. (7-7.15).

are normally simulated through standard programming methods to permit maximum flexibility.

7-8 VERIFICATION OF THE ANALOG SIMULATION

One of the major problems associated with an analog simulation is to insure that the combination of amplifiers and potentiometers is indeed analogous to the original physical-system transfer function. Two methods are generally employed in this verification process; the second and ultimate check consists of analytically computing the transfer-function response to some known transient excitation. The corresponding analog computer network is then excited with the equivalent transient voltage and, after taking into account the appropriate system amplitude and time-scale factors, the analytical and computer responses are compared. If the two output-variable traces are nearly identical, the correct analog program has been generated.

Before this technique is applied, however, a simple reconstruction of the transfer function directly from the corresponding computer simulation is often desirable. For example, consider the linear mechanization of Fig. 7-8.1. As shown, a 10:1 time scale has been employed.

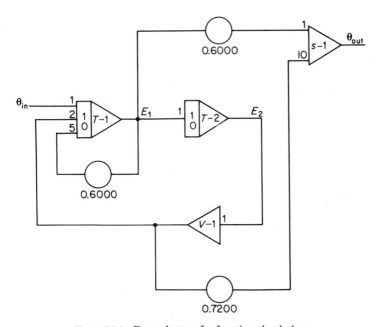

Figure 7-8.1   Example transfer-function simulation.

Arbitrary intermediate voltage points E_1 and E_2 are now assumed. The relationship expressed across integrator T-1 is evidently

$$E_1 = -\frac{10}{s}[\theta_{in} + (5)(0.6000)E_1 - 2E_2] \qquad (7\text{-}8.1)$$

The intermediate voltage point E_2 is now expressed in terms of E_1 as

$$E_2 = -\frac{10}{s}E_1 \qquad (7\text{-}8.2)$$

Substituting Eq. (7-8.2) into Eq. (7-8.1)

$$E_1 = -\frac{10}{s}\left[\theta_{in} + 3E_1 + \frac{20}{s}E_1\right] \qquad (7\text{-}8.3)$$

Equation (7-8.3) can now be solved directly for E_1

$$E_1 s + 30E_1 + \frac{200}{s}E_1 = -10\theta_{in}$$

$$E_1 = \frac{10\theta_{in}s}{(s^2 + 30s + 200)} \qquad (7\text{-}8.4)$$

Writing the governing expression across the output-variable summing amplifier

$$\theta_{out} = -(0.6E_1 - 7.2E_2)$$

$$= -\left(0.6 + \frac{72}{s}\right)E_1$$

$$\theta_{out} = \left(\frac{0.6s + 72}{s}\right)\left(\frac{10\theta_{in}s}{s^2 + 30s + 200}\right) \qquad (7\text{-}8.5)$$

Thus

$$\frac{\theta_{out}}{\theta_{in}}(s) = \frac{6(s + 120)}{s^2 + 30s + 200} \qquad (7\text{-}8.6)$$

Since Eq. (7-8.6) is indeed the original transfer function, the mechanization of Fig. 7-8.1 is analytically verified. The transient response of Fig. 7-8.1 when compared to the corresponding inverse Laplace transformation, will yield final proof that the array of amplifiers and potentiometers has been wired correctly. Although a step function is normally applied as the transient excitation, a unit ramp or acceleration input can be effectively employed;

in addition, a frequency-response simulation is also applicable. For this purpose, one employs the analog oscillator of Fig. 6-4.1 to generate all required input sinusoids.

PROBLEMS

7.1   Compute the open-loop transfer function $\dfrac{C}{E}$ (s) for each of the systems given here.

(a) $\dfrac{d^2x}{dt^2} + 3\dfrac{dx}{dt} + 2x = 4e$

$\dfrac{d^3y}{dt^3} + 6\dfrac{d^2y}{dt^2} + 4\dfrac{dy}{dt} + 6y$

$= 4\dfrac{dx}{dt} + 6x$

$\dfrac{d^2c}{dt^2} + 3\dfrac{dc}{dt} + 6c = 4y$

Prob. 7.1

(b) $\dfrac{d^5x}{dt^5} + 10\dfrac{d^4x}{dt^4} + 60\dfrac{d^3x}{dt^3} + 100\dfrac{d^2x}{dt^2} + \dfrac{dx}{dt} + x = \dfrac{d^2e}{dt^2} + 2\dfrac{de}{dt} + 16e$

$3\dfrac{d^2y}{dt^2} + 6\dfrac{dy}{dt} + 20y = \dfrac{dx}{dt} + 62x$

$\dfrac{dc}{dt} - 6c = 4\dfrac{d^3y}{dt^3} + 16\dfrac{d^2y}{dt^2} + 42\dfrac{dy}{dt} + 101y$

7.2 Reduce each of the following system block diagrams to a simple equivalent block.

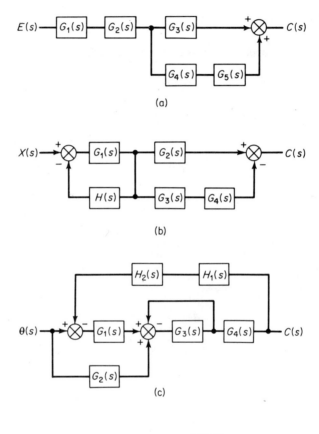

(a)

(b)

(c)

(d)

Prob. 7.2

7.3   Compute the closed-loop transfer functions for the following systems.

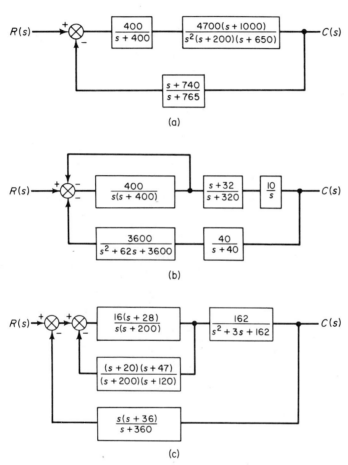

(a)

(b)

(c)

Prob. 7.3

7.4 Compute the transformed solution of the following systems (for initial conditions, and forcing functions, as indicated), i.e., what is $X(s)$.

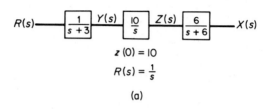

$$z(0) = 10$$
$$R(s) = \frac{1}{s}$$

(a)

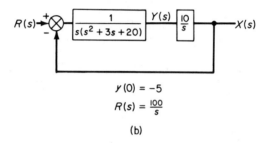

$$y(0) = -5$$
$$R(s) = \frac{100}{s}$$

(b)

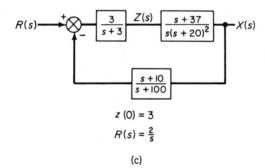

$$z(0) = 3$$
$$R(s) = \frac{2}{s}$$

(c)

Prob. 7.4

BIBLIOGRAPHY

1. Bower, J. L. and P. M. Schultheiss, *Introduction to the Design of Servomechanisms.* New York: John Wiley & Sons, Inc., 1958.

2. Chestnut, H. and R. W. Mayer, *Servomechanisms and Regularing Systems Design.* New York: John Wiley & Sons, Inc., 1951.

3. Raven, R. H., *Automatic Control Engineering.* New York: McGraw-Hill Book Company, 1961.

4. Thaler, G. J. and R. G. Brown, *Analysis and Design of Feedback Control Systems.* New York: McGraw-Hill Book Company, 1960.

5. Langill, A. W., Jr., "Analog Simulation of Transfer Functions," *Electronic Design,* June 21, 1962.

FIRST-
AND SECOND-
ORDER
SYSTEMS[1,2]

8

8-1 INTRODUCTION

In the previous chapters, the transient and frequency response characteristics associated with generalized physical systems have been considered. The techniques derived to this point will now be applied to the two most elementary forms of control loops, i.e., the first- and second-order systems. In addition, the chapter introduces the control motor as an active system element, while defining many of the transient- and frequency-response indicators normally encountered in design specifications.

8-2 THE FIRST-ORDER LAG

As discussed in the first chapter, the basic control system contains a minimum of three elements, i.e., a summer, a power converter and an output transducer. A common method of power conversion involves the use of a control motor or servomotor. In its simplest form, the control motor may be visualized as an element which, for a given input voltage level, yields a constant output shaft rotational rate. Thus, the relationship between input voltage and output shaft position is evidently,

$$\frac{d\theta}{dt} = ke_{\text{in}} \qquad (8\text{-}2.1)$$

Transforming Eq. (8-2.1), we find that the control

motor open-loop transfer function is

$$\frac{\theta}{E_{\text{in}}}(s) = \frac{k}{s} \tag{8-2.2}$$

The control motor can be employed as the power unit of a single-loop control system as illustrated in Fig. 8-2.1. An input signal $R(s)$ produces an equivalent output shaft position $\theta(s)$ that is sensed by an output potentiometer; the potentiometer arm voltage forms the system feedback signal as shown. The system closed-loop transfer function is

$$\frac{\theta}{R}(s) = \frac{k}{s+k} \tag{8-2.3}$$

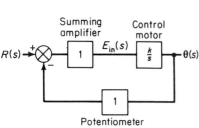

Figure 8-2.1   First-order control system.

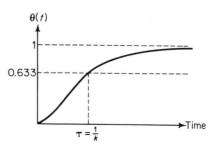

Figure 8-2.2   First-order system step-function response illustrating the system time constant.

For a unit step-function input excitation

$$\theta(s) = \frac{k}{s(s+k)} \tag{8-2.4}$$

Expanding Eq. (8-2.3) into partial fractions

$$\theta(s) = \frac{A}{s} + \frac{B}{s+k} \tag{8-2.5}$$

from which, $A = 1$, $B = -1$ and

$$\theta(t) = 1 - e^{-kt} \tag{8-2.6}$$

The control motor open-loop gain k represents a very significant property of the first-order system and, in fact, completely characterizes the loop. In particular, the reciprocal of this quantity is referred to as the system *time constant*, while k is described as the system *break frequency* or *corner frequency*. The term *time constant* arises from the fact that, for a step-function excitation, the system output attains (Fig. 8-2.2) a magnitude $1 - 1/e = 0.633$ of its steady-state value at this time. The first-order lag transfer function can be written directly in time-constant form

$$\frac{\theta}{R}(s) = \frac{1}{\tau s + 1} \tag{8-2.7}$$

where $\tau = 1/k$ of Eq. (8-2.3).

The frequency response associated with Eq. (8-2.3) illustrates the use of the terms *corner* or *break frequency*. If we substitute $s = j\omega$ into the system transfer function, the equivalent frequency response is

$$\frac{\theta}{R}(j\omega) = \frac{k}{j\omega + k} = \frac{k(-j\omega + k)}{(k^2 + \omega^2)} = \frac{k^2 - j\omega k}{k^2 + \omega^2} \tag{8-2.8}$$

Thus, in rectangular coordinates

$$\mathrm{Re}\,\frac{\theta}{R}(j\omega) = \frac{k^2}{k^2 + \omega^2} \tag{8-2.9}$$

$$\mathrm{Im}\,\frac{\theta}{R}(j\omega) = \frac{-\omega k}{k^2 + \omega^2} \tag{8-2.10}$$

Equivalently, in polar coordinates

$$\left|\frac{C}{R}(j\omega)\right| = \frac{k}{\sqrt{k^2 + \omega^2}} \tag{8-2.11}$$

$$\varphi = \tan^{-1} -\frac{\omega}{k} \tag{8-2.12}$$

For values of ω which are very small with respect to k, the frequency response of Eq. (8-2.11) and (8-2.12) yield practically no signal attenuation or phase shift. If ω is very large in comparison to k, the output approaches zero magnitude and a phase shift of $-90°$. To compute the "halfway point" i.e., the frequency at which $\varphi = -45°$, one substitutes into Eq. (8-2.12) the appropriate value to yield

$$\tan^{-1} -\frac{\omega}{k} = -45° \tag{8-2.13}$$

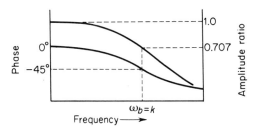

Figure 8-2.3 First-order system frequency-response characteristics.

so that $\omega = k$. Substituting into Eq. (8-2.11)

$$\left|\frac{\theta}{R}(j\omega)\right|_{\omega=k} = \frac{k}{\sqrt{k^2 + k^2}} = \frac{1}{\sqrt{2}} = 0.707 \qquad \text{(8-2.14)}$$

Thus, the corner frequency $\omega_b = k$ corresponds to that point of the frequency-response curve at which the low-frequency approximation ($\omega \to 0$) and the high frequency approximation ($\omega \to \infty$) are equally valid. The final consideration is illustrated in Fig. 8-2.3.

8-3 DESCRIPTION OF THE SECOND-ORDER SYSTEM

The simplified control-motor transfer function of Eq. (8-2.3) is based upon the implicit assumption that the output inertia is negligible. Often, however a purely inertial load is involved. To investigate this situation, the typical torque-speed characteristics of Fig. 8-3.1 are linearized as illustrated in Fig. 8-3.2.

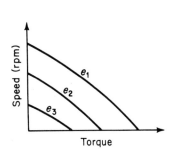

Figure 8-3.1 True control-motor operating characteristics.

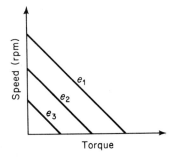

Figure 8-3.2 Linearized characteristics.

The output shaft speed is a function of both the input voltage and output torque, i.e.

$$\omega = f(e, L) \tag{8-3.1}$$

Differentiating

$$d\omega = \frac{\partial \omega}{\partial e}\, de + \frac{\partial \omega}{\partial L}\, dL \tag{8-3.2}$$

The torque-speed curves of Fig. 8-3.2 are linearized such that $\partial \omega / \partial e$ and $\partial \omega / \partial L$ are constants. Assuming $k_1 = \Delta \omega / \Delta L$ (the torque-speed curve slope) and $\Delta \omega / \Delta e = k_2$ (found from the intersection of the torque-speed curves with the $L = 0$ axis), and integrating Eq. (8-3.2)

$$\omega = k_1 L + k_2 e \tag{8-3.3}$$

Rearranging

$$L + m\omega = ke \tag{8-3.4}$$

Assuming that the motor drives a pure inertial load

$$L = J\frac{d^2\theta}{dt^2} \tag{8-3.5}$$

where θ is the instantaneous shaft position, and since

$$\omega = \frac{d\theta}{dt} \tag{8-3.6}$$

$$J\frac{d^2\theta}{dt^2} = ke - m\frac{d\theta}{dt} \tag{8-3.7}$$

Transforming Eq. (8-3.7) and rearranging

$$\frac{\theta}{E}(s) = \frac{k}{s(Js + m)} \tag{8-3.8}$$

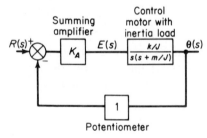

Figure 8-3.3   Second-order control system.

Let us now assume the simple servo system of Fig. 8-3.3, again consisting of a summing amplifier, control motor, and feedback potentiometer. The closed-loop transfer function is evidently

$$\frac{\theta}{R}(s) = \frac{K_A k/J}{s^2 + (m/J)s + K_A k/J} \tag{8-3.9}$$

As generated, Eq. (8-3.9) represents an example of a second-order system. It is now possible to generalize the above transfer function in terms of two quantities, the damping ratio ζ and undamped natural frequency ω_n

$$\frac{\theta}{R}(s) = \frac{\omega_n^2}{s^2 + 2\zeta\omega_n s + \omega_n^2} \qquad (8\text{-}3.10)$$

Thus, comparing Eqs. (8-3.9) and (8-3.10)

$$\omega_n = \sqrt{\frac{K_A k}{J}} \qquad (8\text{-}3.11)$$

$$\zeta = \frac{1}{2}\frac{m}{J}\sqrt{\frac{J}{K_A k}} = \frac{m}{2\sqrt{JK_A k}} \qquad (8\text{-}3.12)$$

Equation (8-3.10) represents a convenient format for the description of any second-order system. In particular, the undamped natural frequency is defined as that frequency at which the system will oscillate in the absence of any system damping. Thus, if $\zeta = 0$, the second-order system impulsive response is computed as

$$\frac{\theta}{R}(s) = \frac{\omega_n^2}{s^2 + \omega_n^2} \qquad (8\text{-}3.13)$$

For $R(s) = 1$

$$\theta(s) = \frac{\omega_n^2}{s^2 + \omega_n^2} \qquad (8\text{-}3.14)$$

so that

$$\theta(t) = \omega_n \sin \omega_n t \qquad (8\text{-}3.15)$$

Hence, the undamped second-order system is observed to oscillate with a constant (natural) frequency of ω_n radians/second. The system damping ratio ζ defines the degree of damping exhibited by the system. If $\zeta > 1$, the denominator of Eq. (8-3.10) factors into two real roots, i.e.

$$s = -\zeta\omega_n \pm \sqrt{\zeta^2 - 1}\,\omega_n \qquad (8\text{-}3.16)$$

Conversely, if $\zeta < 1$, the denominator factors into two complex roots

$$s = -\zeta\omega_n \pm j\sqrt{1 - \zeta^2}\,\omega_n \qquad (8\text{-}3.17)$$

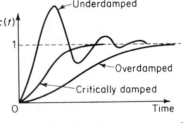

Figure 8-3.4 Step-function response of various second-order systems.

Finally, if $\zeta = 1$, a double real-axis root arises at $s = -\zeta\omega_n$. A system with $\zeta = 1$ is referred to as critically damped; for $\zeta < 1$ an underdamped response results; for $\zeta > 1$ the characteristic sluggish overdamped response is obtained. These final considerations are illustrated in Fig. 8-3.4.

8-4 CONTROL SYSTEM TIME-DOMAIN SPECIFICATIONS

The typical control system, as well as other engineering systems, are conventionally designed according to some set of governing specifications. In this section we will interpret some of the more common system design specification parameters which are expressed within the time domain. The step-function response associated with an underdamped second-order system can be characterized in terms of three quantities: the per cent overshoot, the rise time and the settling time.

OVERSHOOT: The system overshoot, expressed in a per cent of the final or steady-state step-function value, defines the maximum amount by which the output exceeds the steady-state value. As illustrated in Fig. 8-4.1, the system overshoot is $(A - 1)$ 100 per cent.

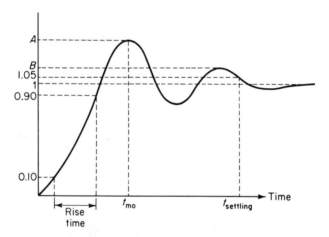

Figure 8-4.1 Time-domain specifications.

RISE TIME: The rise time is defined as the time required for the system step-function response variable to traverse the interval between 10 per cent and 90 per cent of the final value.

SETTLING TIME: The system settling time is described as the time at which the step-function response variable attains and, from that point, remains within a value of 5 per cent of the steady-state value.

The damping ratio associated with an underdamped second-order system step-function response can be deduced by observing the values of overshoot existing at two successive peaks of the oscillation. Thus, from Fig. 8-4.1

$$\zeta = \frac{\ln\left[(A-1)/(B-1)\right]/2\pi}{\sqrt{1+\ln\left[(A-1)/(B-1)\right]/2\pi}} \qquad \text{(8-4.1)}$$

8-5 SYSTEM TRANSIENT-RESPONSE CHARACTERISTICS

In this section, the underdamped second-order system step-function response is computed and, in particular, expressions which describe the time of maximum overshoot and the value of that maximum overshoot are developed. To determine the generalized second-order system step-function response, one substitutes $R(s) = 1/s$ into Eq. (8-3.10).

$$C(s) = \frac{\omega_n^2}{s(s^2 + 2\zeta\omega_n s + \omega_n^2)} \qquad \text{(8-5.1)}$$

Assuming an underdamped system response (i.e., $\zeta < 1$), and expanding by means of partial fractions

$$C(s) = \frac{A}{s} + \frac{Bs + C}{s^2 + 2\zeta\omega_n s + \omega_n^2} \qquad \text{(8-5.2)}$$

In Eq. (8-5.2), the coefficients A, B, and C are evaluated by normal methods. Thus

$$C(s) = \frac{1}{s} - \frac{s + \zeta\omega_n}{(s + \zeta\omega_n)^2 + (1 - \zeta^2)\omega_n^2} - \frac{\zeta\omega_n}{(s + \zeta\omega_n)^2 + (1 - \zeta^2)\omega_n^2} \qquad \text{(8-5.3)}$$

Taking the inverse Laplace transformation

$$c(t) = 1 - e^{-\zeta\omega_n t}\cos\sqrt{1 - \zeta^2}\,\omega_n t - \frac{\zeta}{\sqrt{1 - \zeta^2}}\,e^{-\zeta\omega_n t}\sin\sqrt{1 - \zeta^2}\,\omega_n t \qquad \text{(8-5.4)}$$

The quantity $\sqrt{1 - \zeta^2}\,\omega_n$ is the system damped natural frequency, i.e., the frequency at which the output response variable will oscillate when subjected to a transient excitation. Note that for $\zeta = 0$ (undamped system) the damped natural frequency and the undamped natural frequency are identical. The step-function response characteristics of various second-order systems are pictured in Fig. 8-5.1.

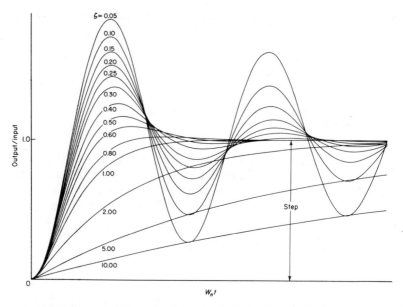

Figure 8-5.1   Second-order system step-function response.

The point of maximum overshoot corresponds to that particular value of time at which the response variable $c(t)$ attains an initial maximum, i.e., when $dc(t)/dt = 0$. Thus, differentiating Eq. (8-5.4)

$$\frac{dc(t)}{dt} = e^{-\zeta\omega_n t}[\sqrt{1 - \zeta^2}\,\omega_n \sin \sqrt{1 - \zeta^2}\,\omega_n t + \zeta\omega_n \cos \sqrt{1 - \zeta^2}\,\omega_n t]$$

$$- \frac{\zeta}{\sqrt{1 - \zeta^2}}\, e^{-\zeta\omega_n t}[\sqrt{1 - \zeta^2}\,\omega_n \cos \sqrt{1 - \zeta^2}\,\omega_n t - \zeta\omega_n \sin \sqrt{1 - \zeta^2}\,\omega_n t]$$

$$(8\text{-}5.5)$$

Equating Eq. (8-5.5-a) to zero and dividing by the quantity

$$e^{-\zeta\omega_n t} \cos \sqrt{1 - \zeta^2}\,\omega_n t$$

$$0 = \sqrt{1 - \zeta^2}\,\omega_n \tan \sqrt{1 - \zeta^2}\,\omega_n t + \zeta\omega_n - \zeta\omega_n$$

$$+ \frac{\zeta^2\omega_n}{\sqrt{1 - \zeta^2}} \tan \sqrt{1 - \zeta^2}\,\omega_n t \qquad (8\text{-}5.6)$$

Thus,

$$\tan \sqrt{1 - \zeta^2}\,\omega_n t \left[\sqrt{1 - \zeta^2}\,\omega_n + \frac{\zeta^2\omega_n}{\sqrt{1 - \zeta^2}}\right] = 0 \qquad (8\text{-}5.7)$$

or,

$$\tan \sqrt{1 - \zeta^2}\, \omega_n t = 0 \qquad (8\text{-}5.7\text{-}a)$$

The first value of time (other than $t = 0$, which represents a minimum) that satisfies Eq. (8-5.7-a) is evidently

$$t_{\text{max overshoot}} = \frac{\pi}{\sqrt{1 - \zeta^2}\, \omega_n} \qquad (8\text{-}5.8)$$

Substituting this quantity into Equation (8-5.4) and solving for the maximum system overshoot, it can be easily shown that

$$\text{per cent overshoot} = 100 e^{-\zeta \pi / \sqrt{1 - \zeta^2}} \qquad (8\text{-}5.9)$$

Hence, given an arbitrary output step-function response, an equivalent second-order system can be deduced by means of Eqs. (8-5.8) and (8-5.9); see Problem 8.3 at the end of this chapter.

Before leaving the general area of transient-response calculations, let us consider, once again, the effects of initial system conditions. In particular, we will assume that the system transfer function has been specified in the absence of initial conditions

$$\frac{\theta_{\text{out}}}{\theta_{\text{in}}} = \frac{\omega_n^2}{s^2 + 2\zeta\omega_n s + \omega_n^2} \qquad (8\text{-}5.10)$$

and it is now desired to compute the transient response for a combination of initial conditions, $\theta_{\text{out}}(0) = B$ and $d\theta_{\text{out}}(0)/dt = A$. The technique that is now developed will appear again in Chapter 19 of Volume II and will form an integral portion of the piecewise linear analysis of nonlinear control systems. Basically we have determined previously (Chapter 7) that an integrator output-variable initial condition is simulated by the application of a delta-function excitation applied to the integrator. Similarly, in mechanizing the second-order system transfer function for analog simulation, it was observed that two integrators were required (page 148).

It is now possible to combine these concepts as follows: The second-order system analog computer program of Fig. 8-5.2 is translated into an equivalent system block diagram consisting of only integration and gain parameters. The resulting diagram of Fig. 8-5.3 is then excited by the required impulse excitations A and B as shown in Fig. 8-5.4. And finally, the system output $c(t)$ is computed as a superposition of the two impulsive response profiles. (The problem of deriving transfer functions for multiple-loop systems is considered in detail in Chapter 15 of Volume II.) If $A = 0$, the block diagram of Fig. 8-5.5 is analyzed by conventional means; the inner loop is first replaced

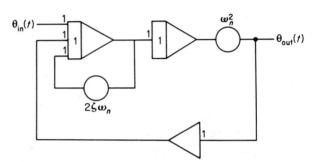

Figure 8-5.2   Analog simulation of Eq. (8-5.10).

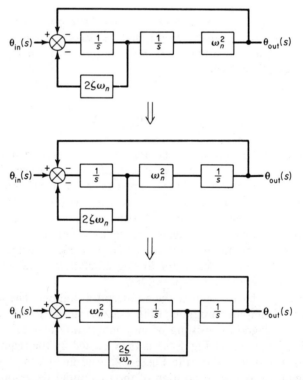

Figure 8-5.3   The process of translating the analog mechanization of Fig. 8-5.2 into a usable block diagram.

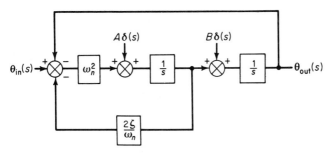

Figure 8-5.4 Introduction of initial conditions A and B by equivalent impulse excitations.

by the single closed-loop block of Fig. 8-5.5(b), and the system transfer function then written directly as

$$\frac{\theta_{\text{out}}}{B}(s) = \frac{1/s}{1 + \omega_n^2/(s^2 + 2\zeta\omega_n s)}$$

$$= \frac{s + 2\zeta\omega_n}{s^2 + 2\zeta\omega_n s + \omega_n^2} \qquad (8\text{-}5.11)$$

$$\theta_{\text{out}}(s) = \frac{B(s + 2\zeta\omega_n)}{s^2 + 2\zeta\omega_n s + \omega_n^2} \qquad (8\text{-}5.12)$$

Similarly, for $B = 0$, the block diagram reduction of Fig. 8-5.6 yields

$$\frac{\theta_{\text{out}}}{A}(s) = \frac{1}{s^2 + 2\zeta\omega_n s + \omega_n^2} \qquad (8\text{-}5.13)$$

$$\theta_{\text{out}}(s) = \frac{A}{s^2 + 2\zeta\omega_n s + \omega_n^2} \qquad (8\text{-}5.14)$$

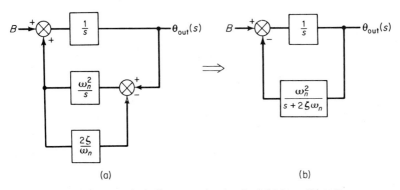

(a)   (b)

Figure 8-5.5 Block-diagram reduction for initial condition B.

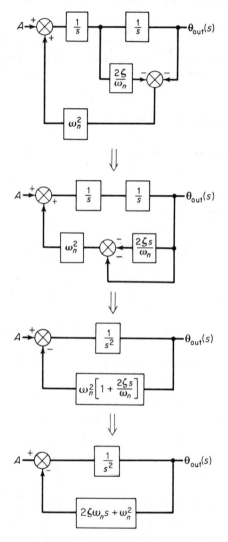

Figure 8-5.6   Block-diagram reduction for initial condition A.

Equations (8-5.12) and (8-5.14) are now combined to form the final Laplace-transformed system response to the specified initial conditions

$$\theta_{out}(s) = \frac{B(s + 2\zeta\omega_n) + A}{s^2 + 2\zeta\omega_n s + \omega_n^2} \qquad (8-5.15)$$

This method of introducing initial conditions, based upon an initial

analog simulation followed by a block diagram reconstruction can be applied
to any order system. The technique is especially useful, since only those areas
of the over-all system diagram under consideration are affected; the remainder of the loop diagram can be maintained in original form. Thus, all
the advantages inherent in the transfer-function and block-diagram presentation and processing of dynamic systems are preserved, while the major
disadvantage associated with the trans-
fer function (i.e., the requirement for
an absence of initial conditions) is
eliminated.

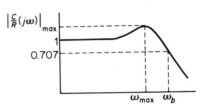

8-6 FREQUENCY RESPONSE

The second-order system can be characterized by a number of possible frequency-domain specifications, which
are illustrated in Fig. 8-6.1 and are described as follows:

Figure 8-6.1 Frequency-domain specifications.

BANDWIDTH: The system bandwidth is that frequency (ω_b) at which the
amplitude ratio has diminished to a ratio of 0.707 of the zero frequency
value.

MAXIMUM AMPLITUDE: The maximum amplitude $\left| \dfrac{C}{R}(j\omega) \right|_{max}$ is the
highest value that the amplitude ratio attains as frequency varies from zero
to infinity.

ω_{max}: The particular frequency that corresponds to the point of maximum amplitude.

The second-order system frequency response is obtained by substituting
$j\omega$ for s in Eq. (8-3.10)

$$\frac{C}{R}(j\omega) = \frac{\omega_n^2}{(\omega_n^2 - \omega^2) + j2\zeta\omega_n\omega} \tag{8-6.1}$$

The zero frequency or d-c value of Eq. (8-6.1) is evidently

$$\frac{C}{R}(j0) = \frac{\omega_n^2}{(\omega_n^2 - 0) + j0} = 1 \tag{8-6.2}$$

which verifies the steady-state step-function response of Eq. (8-5.4).

To compute the amplitude ratio associated with Eq. (8-6.1), one uses conventional RSS techniques to yield

$$\left| \frac{C}{R}(j\omega) \right| = \frac{\omega_n^2}{[(\omega^2 - \omega_n^2)^2 + 4\zeta^2\omega_n^2\omega^2]^{1/2}} \qquad (8\text{-}6.3)$$

The maximum amplitude is that value of Eq. (8-6.3) which is a maximum; this occurs for $\omega = \omega_{max}$. Hence, ω_{max} is computed by differentiating Eq. (8-6.3) and equating the resulting expression to zero, thus defining the point of zero slope. Equivalently, the denominator of Eq. (8-6.3) is evaluated for a minimum. Differentiating with respect to ω and equating to zero

$$2\omega[2(\omega_{max}^2 - \omega_n^2) + 4\zeta^2\omega_n^2] = 0 \qquad (8\text{-}6.4)$$

Solving for ω_{max}

$$\omega_{max}^2 - \omega_n^2 + 2\zeta^2\omega_n^2 = 0 \qquad (8\text{-}6.5)$$

and

$$\omega_{max} = \sqrt{1 - 2\zeta^2}\,\omega_n \qquad (8\text{-}6.6)$$

To compute the maximum amplitude, Eq. (8-6.6) is substituted into Eq. (8-6.3)

$$\left| \frac{C}{R}(j\omega) \right|_{max} = \frac{\omega_n^2}{[4\zeta^4\omega_n^4 + 4\zeta^2\omega_n^4(1 - 2\zeta^2)]^{1/2}} \qquad (8\text{-}6.7)$$

$$= \frac{1}{(4\zeta^4 + 4\zeta^2 - 8\zeta^2)^{1/2}} \qquad (8\text{-}6.8)$$

and finally

$$\left| \frac{C}{R}(j\omega) \right|_{max} = \frac{1}{2\zeta\sqrt{1 - \zeta^2}} \qquad (8\text{-}6.9)$$

At $\zeta = 0.707$, the maximum amplitude is unity, i.e., the system has no resonance point. This fact is easily demonstrated by substituting directly into either Eq. (8-6.6) or (8-6.9). Choosing the former

$$\omega_{max} = \sqrt{1 - 2\left(\frac{1}{\sqrt{2}}\right)^2}\,\omega_n = 0 \qquad (8\text{-}6.10)$$

$$\zeta = \frac{1}{\sqrt{2}}$$

but, from Eq. (8-6.2), $C/R(j0) = 1$. Thus, the second-order system with $\zeta > 0.707$ has no resonant peak.

The system bandwidth is obtained by substituting the required amplitude ratio value into Eq. (8-6.3)

$$\frac{1}{\sqrt{2}} = \frac{\omega_n^2}{[(\omega_b^2 - \omega_n^2)^2 + 4\zeta^2\omega_n^2\omega_b^2]^{1/2}} \tag{8-6.11}$$

Solving for ω_b

$$(\omega_b^2 - \omega_n^2)^2 + 4\zeta^2\omega_n^2\omega_b^2 = 2\omega_n^4$$

$$\omega_b^4 - 2\omega_n^2(1 - 2\zeta^2)\omega_b^2 + \omega_n^4(1 - 2\zeta^2)^2 = \omega_n^4 + \omega_n^4(1 - 2\zeta^2)^2$$

$$[\omega_b^2 - \omega_n^2(1 - 2\zeta^2)]^2 = \omega_n^4[2 - 4\zeta^2 + 4\zeta^4]$$

$$\omega_b^2 - \omega_n^2(1 - 2\zeta^2) = \omega_n^2\sqrt{2 - 4\zeta^2 + 4\zeta^4}$$

$$\omega_b^2 = \omega_n^2\sqrt{2 - 4\zeta^2 + 4\zeta^4} + \omega_n^2(1 - 2\zeta^2)$$

$$\omega_b = \omega_n[1 - 2\zeta^2 + \sqrt{2 - 4\zeta^2 + 4\zeta^4}]^{1/2} \tag{8-6.12}$$

Thus, given a particular second-order loop, the system bandwidth can be computed directly from Eq. (8-6.12). If two of the three frequency-domain quantities, $\left|\dfrac{C}{R}(j\omega)\right|_{max}$, ω_{max} and ω_b are known, an equivalent second-order system can be easily computed.

As a final consideration, it should be noted that the second-order system bandwidth or cutoff frequency is directly related to system speed of response characteristics, i.e., as the bandwidth increases (for a constant damping ratio), the second-order system rise time and settling time decrease. From this standpoint, the cutoff frequency functions as a transient-response time scale; thus, to increase the speed of response, one need only increase the cutoff frequency.

PROBLEMS

8.1 For each of the following first-order system transfer functions, compute the system time constants and break frequencies.

(a) $\dfrac{\theta}{X}(s) = \dfrac{4}{s + 4}$

(b) $\dfrac{C}{R}(s) = \dfrac{1000}{s + 27}$

(c) $\dfrac{R}{M}(s) = \dfrac{0.25}{6s + 1}$

(d) $\dfrac{L}{F}(s) = \dfrac{0.20}{0.001s + 1}$

8.2 Plot the response of the first-order systems illustrated for (a) a unit step function and (b) a unit ramp function.

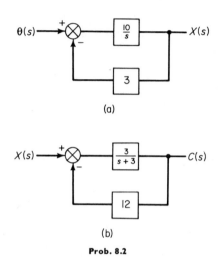

(a)

(b)

Prob. 8.2

8.3 A group of linear "black boxes" are subjected to unit step-function excitations and the system responses are recorded. For each of the following sets of time-domain specifications, deduce the second-order approximation.

(a) Maximum overshoot occurs at $t = 2$ seconds
    Value of maximum overshoot $= 40$ per cent
(b) Maximum overshoot occurs at $t = 10$ milliseconds
    Value of maximum overshoot $= 32$ per cent

8.4 Compute the response of the following second-order system for a combination of initial conditions and input excitations as shown.

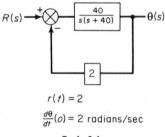

$r(t) = 2$

$\frac{d\theta}{dt}(o) = 2$ radians/sec

Prob. 8.4

8.5 Two physical systems are analyzed in terms of a frequency response with the following results:

	System (A)	System (B)
Maximum amplitude	1.2	2.3
ω_{max}	12 radians/sec	260 radians/sec

Deduce equivalent second-order systems for systems (A) and (B).

8.6 Compute the bandwidth for each of the second-order approximations of Problems 8.3 and 8.5.

BIBLIOGRAPHY

1. D'Azzo, J. J. and C. H. Houpis, *Control System Analysis and Synthesis.* New York: McGraw-Hill Book Company, 1960.

2. Del Toro, V. and S. R. Parker, *Principles of Control System Engineering.* New York: McGraw-Hill Book Company, 1960.

STEADY-STATE ERRORS[1]

9

9-1 INTRODUCTION

It was shown in Chapter 4 that a system containing only negative real-part poles is stable in an absolute sense. Further, it was illustrated that any stable system response could be divided into two separate portions, a transient contribution and a steady-state component. In this chapter, we will investigate the steady-state response characteristics of various

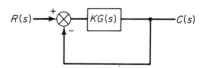

Figure 9-1.1 Unity feedback system.

forms of stable control systems when excited by the common types of polynomial forcing functions, i.e., step, ramp and acceleration inputs. In particular, the steady-state error is often listed as an important design specification; this parameter is applicable to the unity-feedback control system of Fig. 9-1.1, but can also be extended in generalized form to the nonunity feedback loop.

9-2 SYSTEM TYPE NUMBERS

For the unity-feedback control system of Fig. 9-1.1, the complete open-loop transfer function is evidently

$$\frac{C}{E}(s) = KG(s) \qquad \text{(9-2.1)}$$

In general, any open-loop system will consist of stable poles (i.e., poles with negative nonzero real parts), stable or unstable zeros, and open-loop integrations (often referred to as poles at the origin), e.g.,

$$KG(s) = \frac{K(s + \alpha)(s + \beta)(s - \gamma)[(s + \delta)^2 + \psi^2] \cdots}{s^n(s + a)(s + b)(s + c)[(s + d)^2 + e^2] \cdots} \tag{9-2.2}$$

The value of n in Eq. (9-2.2) defines the system type number:

    $n = 0$: Type-0 system; contains no open-loop integrations
    $n = 1$: Type-1 system; contains one open-loop integration
    $n = 2$: Type-2 system; contains two open-loop integrations
    $n = 3$: Type 3 system; contains three open-loop integrations
    $n = 4$: Type-4 system; contains four open-loop integrations etc.

It will be shown that a great deal of useful information concerning steady-state errors can be deduced from a simple knowledge of the loop type number.

9-3　ERROR COEFFICIENTS

With respect to a unity-feedback system, three error constants are conventionally defined as

$$K_o = \text{position constant} = \lim_{s \to 0} KG(s) \tag{9-3.1}$$

$$K_v = \text{velocity constant} = \lim_{s \to 0} sKG(s) \tag{9-3.2}$$

$$K_a = \text{acceleration constant} = \lim_{s \to 0} s^2 KG(s) \tag{9-3.3}$$

where K again represents the constant part and $G(s)$ the variable part of the open-loop transfer function. The definitive expressions of Eqs. (9-3.1), (9-3.2), and (9-3.3) are applicable to any-order control system with any number of open-loop integrations.

If the open-loop transfer function is written in time-constant form, e.g.

$$KG = \frac{K_1(\tau_1 s + 1)(\tau_2 s + 1)}{s^n(\tau_3^2 s^2 + 2\zeta \tau_3 s + 1)(\tau_4 s + 1)} \tag{9-3.4}$$

such that each parenthetical expression approaches unity as $s \to 0$, the *open-loop gain constant* K_1 bears a direct relationship with the system error coefficients. To illustrate, for a Type-1 system (substituting $n = 1$ in Eq. (9-3.4))

$$K_o = \lim_{s \to 0} \frac{K_1}{s} = \infty \qquad (9\text{-}3.5)$$

$$K_v = \lim_{s \to 0} s\left(\frac{K_1}{s}\right) = K_1 \qquad (9\text{-}3.6)$$

$$K_a = \lim_{s \to 0} s^2\left(\frac{K_1}{s}\right) = 0 \qquad (9\text{-}3.7)$$

The results in Table 9-3.1 express the error coefficients as a function of the open-loop gain constant, when applicable, for common type-number open-loop transfer functions

TABLE 9-3.1

System Type No.	Open Loop Gain Constant	K_0	K_v	K_a
0	K_1	K_1	0	0
1	K_1	∞	K_1	0
2	K_1	∞	∞	K_1
3	K_1	∞	∞	∞
4	K_1	∞	∞	∞

We will now compute steady-state errors (in terms of conventional error coefficients) for a variety of type-number systems when excited by step, ramp, and acceleration forcing functions.

9-4 STEADY-STATE ERRORS

The Laplace transformed error variable $\varepsilon(s)$ can be computed directly from Fig. 9-1.1. Since

$$C(s) = KG(s)\varepsilon(s) \qquad (9\text{-}4.1)$$

and

$$\varepsilon(s) = R(s) - C(s) \qquad (9\text{-}4.2)$$

the error quantity is evidently

$$\varepsilon(s) = \frac{R(s)}{1 + KG(s)} \qquad (9\text{-}4.3)$$

To determine the steady state error, i.e., $\lim_{t \to \infty} \varepsilon(t)$, for a generalized time-domain forcing function $r(t)$, where $\mathscr{L}\{r(t)\} = R(s)$, one invokes the final-value theorem of Chapter 4

$$\lim_{t\to\infty} \varepsilon(t) = \lim_{s\to 0} s\varepsilon(s) \qquad (9\text{-}4.4)$$

$$= \lim_{s\to 0} \frac{sR(s)}{1 + KG(s)} \qquad (9\text{-}4.5)$$

Now, if an arbitrary open-loop transfer function

$$KGH(s) = \frac{K(s + a)(s + b)}{s^n[(s + c)^2 + d^2](s + f)} \qquad (9\text{-}4.6)$$

is written in pole-zero format, Eq. (9-4.5) becomes

$$\lim_{t\to\infty} \varepsilon(t) = \lim_{s\to 0} \frac{sR(s)}{1 + \dfrac{K(s + a)(s + b)}{s^n[(s + c)^2 + d^2](s + f)}} \qquad (9\text{-}4.7)$$

We can now investigate Eq. (9-4.7) for various type-number systems and forcing functions.

TYPE-0 SYSTEM

The type-0 system or regulator steady-state error is obtained by substituting $n = 0$ into Eq. (9-4.7), such that

$$\lim_{t\to\infty} \varepsilon(t) = \lim_{s\to 0} \frac{sR(s)}{1 + \dfrac{K(s + a)(s + b)}{[(s + c)^2 + d^2](s + f)}} \qquad (9\text{-}4.8)$$

For a unit step function, $r(t) = u(t)$, $R(s) = \dfrac{1}{s}$, and Eq. (9-4.8) reduces to

$$\lim_{t\to\infty} \varepsilon(t) = \frac{1}{1 + \displaystyle\lim_{s\to 0} \dfrac{K(s + a)(s + b)}{[(s + c)^2 + d^2](s + f)}} \qquad (9\text{-}4.9)$$

But, from Eq. (9-3.1) and Table 9-3.1

$$K_1 = K_o = \lim_{s\to 0} \frac{K(s + a)(s + b)}{[(s + c)^2 + d^2](s + f)} = \frac{Kab}{(c^2 + d^2)f} \qquad (9\text{-}4.10)$$

such that, for a step-input forcing function, the type-0 system steady-state error is simply

$$\lim_{t\to\infty} \varepsilon(t) = \frac{1}{1 + K_o} \qquad (9\text{-}4.11)$$

where the position constant, for a type-0 system, is equal to the open-loop gain constant.

Thus, the regulator exhibits a definite steady-state error when subjected to a step-function excitation. This error quantity is, however, completely specified from open-loop information (the system position constant) only.

Replacing the unit step function of Eq. (9-4.8) by a unit ramp input, i.e., $r(t) = t$, $R(s) = 1/s^2$,

$$\lim_{t \to \infty} \varepsilon(t) = \frac{1}{\lim\limits_{s \to 0} s\left\{1 + \dfrac{K(s+a)(s+b)}{[(s+c)^2 + d^2](s+f)}\right\}} \qquad (9\text{-}4.12)$$

$$= \frac{1}{\lim\limits_{s \to 0} s\left\{\dfrac{K(s+a)(s+b)}{[(s+c)^2 + d^2](s+f)}\right\}}$$

Thus

$$\lim_{t \to \infty} \varepsilon(t) = \frac{1}{K_v} \qquad (9\text{-}4.13)$$

But from Table 9-3.1, $K_v = 0$ for a type-0 system. Hence, the regulator is incapable of following a ramp-input excitation; the error quantity approaches infinity as time becomes large. A similar conclusion can be deduced for the unit acceleration excitation, i.e.

$$\lim_{t \to \infty} \varepsilon(t) = \frac{1}{\lim\limits_{s \to 0} s\left\{1 + \dfrac{K(s+a)(s+b)}{[(s+c)^2 + d^2](s+f)}\right\}}$$

$$= \frac{1}{K_a} = \infty \qquad (9\text{-}4.14)$$

TYPE-I SYSTEM

For a type-1 system, one substitutes $n = 1$ into Eq. (9-4.7) to obtain

$$\lim_{t \to \infty} \varepsilon(t) = \lim_{s \to 0} \frac{sR(s)}{1 + \dfrac{K(s+a)(s+b)}{s[(s+c)^2 + d^2](s+f)}} \qquad (9\text{-}4.15)$$

The unit step-function response is

$$\lim_{t \to \infty} \varepsilon(t) = \frac{1}{1 + \lim\limits_{s \to 0} \dfrac{K(s+a)(s+b)}{s[(s+c)^2 + d^2](s+f)}} = \frac{1}{1 + K_o} \qquad (9\text{-}4.16)$$

Since, from Table 9-3.1, $K_o = \infty$ for a type-1 system

$$\lim_{t \to \infty} \varepsilon(t) = \frac{1}{1 + K_o} = 0 \qquad (9\text{-}4.17)$$

Hence, the type-1 system exhibits no error to a step-function excitation.
    The unit ramp-function response is

$$\lim_{t \to \infty} \varepsilon(t) = \lim_{s \to 0} \frac{1}{s\left(\dfrac{K(s + a)(s + b)}{s[(s + c)^2 + d^2](s + f)}\right)^2} = \frac{1}{K_v} \qquad (9\text{-}4.18)$$

As illustrated in Eq. (9-4.18), the type-1 system unit ramp-function steady-state error is a constant, equal in magnitude to the reciprocal of the open-loop gain constant K_1 of Table 9-3.1.
    The unit acceleration-function response is

$$\lim_{t \to \infty} \varepsilon(t) = \lim_{s \to 0} \frac{1}{s^2\left(\dfrac{K(s + a)(s + b)}{s[(s + c)^2 + d^2](s + f)}\right)} \qquad (9\text{-}4.19)$$

$$= \frac{1}{K_a} = \infty$$

TYPE-2 SYSTEMS

The type-2 system, containing a second-order pole at the origin, is analyzed according to the preceding procedure to yield the following results.
    The unit step-function response is

$$\lim_{t \to \infty} \varepsilon(t) = \lim_{s \to 0} \frac{1}{1 + \lim\limits_{s \to 0} \dfrac{K(s + a)(s + b)}{s^2[(s + c)^2 + d^2](s + f)}} = \frac{1}{1 + K_o} = 0 \qquad (9\text{-}4.20)$$

The unit ramp-function response is

$$\lim_{t \to \infty} \varepsilon(t) = \lim_{s \to 0} \frac{1}{s\left(\dfrac{K(s + a)(s + b)}{s^2[(s + c)^2 + d^2](s + f)}\right)} = \frac{1}{K_v} = 0 \qquad (9\text{-}4.21)$$

TABLE 9-4.1

System Type Number	Open-Loop Gain Constant	K_o	K_v	K_a	Unit Step-Function Steady-State Error	Unit Ramp-Function Steady-State Error	Unit Acceleration-Function Steady-State Error
0	K_1	K_1	0	0	$\dfrac{1}{1+K_o} = \dfrac{1}{1+K_1}$	$\dfrac{1}{K_v} = \infty$	$\dfrac{1}{K_a} = \infty$
1	K_1	∞	K_1	0	$\dfrac{1}{1+K_o} = 0$	$\dfrac{1}{K_v} = \dfrac{1}{K_1}$	$\dfrac{1}{K_a} = \infty$
2	K_1	∞	∞	K_1	$\dfrac{1}{1+K_o} = 0$	$\dfrac{1}{K_v} = 0$	$\dfrac{1}{K_a} = \dfrac{1}{K_1}$
3	K_1	∞	∞	∞	$\dfrac{1}{1+K_o} = 0$	$\dfrac{1}{K_v} = 0$	$\dfrac{1}{K_a} = 0$
4	K_1	∞	∞	∞	$\dfrac{1}{1+K_o} = 0$	$\dfrac{1}{K_v} = 0$	$\dfrac{1}{K_a} = 0$
. . .	. . .	. . .	. . .	. . .	. . .	. . .	. . .

The unit acceleration-function response is

$$\lim_{t \to \infty} \varepsilon(t) = \lim_{s \to 0} \frac{1}{s^2 \left| \dfrac{K(s+a)(s+b)}{s^2[(s+c)^2 + d^2](s+f)} \right|} = \frac{1}{K_a} = \frac{1}{K_1} \qquad (9\text{-}4.22)$$

HIGHER-ORDER SYSTEMS

It can be easily proved that systems with type numbers of 3 and above exhibit no steady-state errors to step-, ramp-, or acceleration-type excitations. The preceding discussion is summarized in Table 9-4.1.

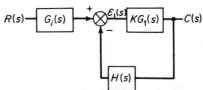

9-5 GENERALIZED STEADY-STATE ERRORS[2]

Figure 9-5.1   Generalized nonunity feedback system.

The typical single-loop feedback control system is not always mechanized in the simplified form of Fig. 9-1.1. In the more realistic configuration of Fig. 9-5.1, the error signal can no longer be considered as the difference between input and output variables. For the system of Fig. 9-5.1

$$\varepsilon_1(s) = G_i R(s) - HC(s) \qquad (9\text{-}5.1)$$

The corresponding error transfer function is

$$\frac{\varepsilon_1}{R}(s) = \frac{G_i(s)}{1 + KG_1 H(s)} \qquad (9\text{-}5.2)$$

Thus, for unit step, velocity, and acceleration inputs, the steady-state driving signals are derived by standard methods as

$$\epsilon'_{step} = \lim_{s \to 0} \frac{sG_i(s)}{s[1 + KG_1 H(s)]} = \lim_{s \to 0} \frac{G_i(s)}{1 + KG_1 H(s)} \qquad (9\text{-}5.3)$$

$$\epsilon'_{velocity} = \lim_{s \to 0} \frac{sG_i(s)}{s^2[1 + KG_1 H(s)]} = \lim_{s \to 0} \frac{G_i(s)}{sKG_1 H(s)} \qquad (9\text{-}5.4)$$

$$\epsilon'_{acceleration} = \lim_{s \to 0} \frac{sG_i(s)}{s^3[1 + KG_1 H(s)]} = \lim_{s \to 0} \frac{G_i(s)}{s^2 KG_1 H(s)} \qquad (9\text{-}5.5)$$

Although the actuating signal ε_1 does not represent the unity-feedback error signal $R(s) - C(s)$, a direct correlation can often be established. For example, the feedback transfer function $H(s)$ may represent a simple gain parameter, which effectively introduces a scale-factor modification in the output variable. Thus, if the feedback transducer consists of a linear-motion potentiometer, then $H(s)$ represents a conversion from inches to electrical voltage, with the value of H a function of the potentiometer excitation voltage and fullscale displacement rating.

PROBLEMS

9.1 Compute the position, velocity, and acceleration constants for the following forward-loop transfer functions (assume a unity-feedback system).

(a) $KG(s) = \dfrac{K_1}{s(s + 11)(s + 400)}$

(b) $KG(s) = \dfrac{K_2}{s^2(s^2 + 3s + 40)(s^2 + 6s + 600)}$

(c) $KG(s) = \dfrac{K_3}{s^2(s^2 + 3s + 40)(s + 420)(s + 460)}$

9.2 The flow-rate feedback controller illustrated here consists of a servoamplifier,

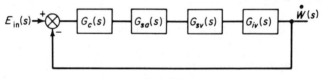

$E_{in}(s) \rightarrow \bigotimes \xrightarrow{+}_{-} G_c(s) - G_{sa}(s) - G_{sv}(s) - G_{iv}(s) \xrightarrow{\dot{W}(s)}$

Prob. 9.2

servovalue, injector valve assembly, and network compensation. What are the unit step function, unit step velocity, and unit step acceleration steady-state errors if:

$$G_{sa}(s) = 10$$

$$G_{sv}(s) = \frac{300}{s(s^2 + 18s + 400)}$$

$$G_{iv}(s) = 1$$

$$G_c(s) = 1$$

9.3 Repeat Problem 9.2 if $G_{iv} = \dfrac{4000}{s^2 + 32s + 4000}$

9.4   Repeat Problem 9.3 if $G_{sa}(s)$ consists of a summing amplifier, a line driver, and incorporates a proportional feature, i.e.

$$G_{sa}(s) = \frac{0.25(s + 40)}{s}$$

9.5   Repeat Problem 9.4 if $G_c(s) = \dfrac{10(s + 12)(s^2 + 18s + 400)}{(s + 120)(s + 10)(s + 40)}$

BIBLIOGRAPHY

1. Truxal, J. C., *Automatic Feedback Control System Synthesis*. New York: McGraw-Hill Book Company, 1955.

2. Savant, C. J., Jr., *Basic Feedback Control System Design*. New York: McGraw-Hill Book Company, 1958.

THE
ROOT-LOCUS[1,2,3,4,5,6,7]

10

10-1 INTRODUCTION

As demonstrated in Chapter 7, the main difficulty associated with a transition from open- to closed-loop systems analysis is that of factoring the closed-loop denominator polynomial. Since a knowledge of all closed-loop pole locations is necessary and sufficient to uniquely define absolute systems stability, it is important that the design engineer be able to obtain this information with a minimum of analytical effort. Although arbitrary polynomials may most certainly be factored through classical mathematical techniques, this process becomes time consuming as the order of the polynomial increases. In addition, the factors obtained through this approach are applicable only to the specific open-loop gain constant used in the analysis. Therefore, employing the classical technique, it would be necessary to choose a particular value of K, determine the zeros corresponding to the resulting denominator polynomial, and evaluate the ensuing system according to some set of design specifications. This over-all procedure is then repeated for any additional choice of gain. Each calculation must necessarily be considered as a separate problem, with very little, if any, correlation existing between successive trials.

The root-locus obviates these inherent difficulties by providing a graphical display of all closed-loop pole positions for all values of open-loop gain between the limits of zero and infinity. The technique is particularly suited to rapid sketching, thus allowing approximate results to be obtained very quickly. And finally, the root-locus is not restricted to variations in gain, but can be effectively employed to evaluate changes in other system parameters.

10-2 THE CHARACTERISTIC EQUATION

In Chapter 7, the closed-loop transfer function $\frac{C}{R}(s)$ is derived in general form as

$$\frac{C}{R}(s) = \frac{KG(s)}{1 + KGH(s)} \tag{10-2.1}$$

If we assume that both $G(s)$ and $H(s)$ consist of ratios of polynomials in s, i.e., $G(s) = \frac{G_N}{G_D}(s)$ and $H(s) = \frac{H_N}{H_D}(s)$, Eq. (10-2.1) is expanded into

$$\frac{C}{R}(s) = \frac{KG_N H_D(s)}{G_D H_D(s) + KG_N H_N(s)} \tag{10-2.2}$$

The *characteristic equation* is formed by equating the closed-loop transfer-function denominator to zero

$$1 + KGH(s) = 0 \tag{10-2.3-a}$$

$$1 + \frac{KG_N H_N}{G_D H_D}(s) = 0 \tag{10-2.3-b}$$

$$G_D H_D(s) + KG_N H_N(s) = 0 \tag{10-2.3-c}$$

The characteristic equation is appropriately named in that it does indeed characterize the closed-loop control-system response. If we consider that $\frac{C}{R}(s)$ arises from the Laplace transformation of some corresponding time-domain differential equation, then the denominator polynomial is precisely that transformed differential equation in the absence of initial conditions and forcing functions. The numerator results from transforming all initial conditions and input functions. Since the stability of any system is determined by the form of governing differential equation (initial conditions and bounded forcing functions do not influence absolute stability), only the closed-loop transfer-function denominator need be investigated. Stated in a slightly different manner, the poles of the closed-loop transfer function $\frac{C}{R}(s)$ and the roots of the characteristic equation, $1 + KGH(s) = 0$, are identical. Hence, if $s = s_i$ is a pole of $\dfrac{C}{R}(s)$, then $s = s_i$ is also a root of $1 + KGH(s) = 0$, and the location of all s_i's upon the complex plane is necessary and sufficient to specify absolute system stability.

10-3 ROOT-LOCUS THEORY

The root-locus provides a procedure for determining the roots of $1 + KGH(s) = 0$ for all values of gain through a graphical trial-and-error-technique. To illustrate the general method which will subsequently be used, consider the trigonometric time-domain expression of Eq. (10-3.1). The problem is now one of solving this equation for positive real values of time.

$$t + \sin t - 1 = 0 \qquad\qquad \textbf{(10-3.1)}$$

Equation (10-3.1) is rearranged so that terms containing the variable t are equated to unity.

$$t + \sin t = 1 \qquad\qquad \textbf{(10-3.2)}$$

Now, to solve Eq. (10-3.2) using the trial-and-error approach, we substitute into the expression a particular value of time such as 3 sec, 0.01 sec, or, in general, t_i sec. The expression formed after making this substitution is no longer an equation, but it is hopefully an identity, for if $t = t_i$ is a root of Eq. (10-3.1), then Eq. (10-3.2) will be satisfied. Thus, at the "test point" $t = t_i$, Eq. (10-3.2) is transformed into the possible identity described symbolically as

$$t_i + \sin t_i \overset{?}{\equiv} 1 \qquad\qquad \textbf{(10-3.3)}$$

The question mark placed above the identity character indicates that Eq. (10-3.3) is not an equation, but that it will be satisfied if $t = t_i$ is a root of Eq. (10-3.2). If t_i is not a root, then a second test point is chosen and the process of trial-and-evaluation repeated.

The root-locus technique is based upon a graphical solution of the characteristic equation $1 + KGH(s) = 0$. The solution is, as in the simple example given previously, a trial-and-error process. However, whereas the variable t was constrained to be positive real, the variable s is by definition a complex quantity. If we substitute a specific test point into the characteristic equation (e.g. $s = s_i$) it will, in general, form a complex number $KGH(s_i)$. Since two complex numbers can be equal if, and only if, their real and imaginary parts are identical, it is necessary that Re $KGH(s_i) = -1$ and

Im $KGH(s_i) = 0$. Equivalently, $KGH(s_i)$ must be a complex quantity with unity amplitude and a phase angle of 180 deg. To investigate the implications of these criteria, consider the generalized open-loop transfer function

$$KGH(s) = \frac{K(s + z_1)(s + z_2)(s + z_3) \cdots}{s(s + p_1)(s + p_2)(s + p_3) \cdots} \quad \text{(10-3.4)}$$

Equation (10-3.4) consists of a ratio of simple first-order zeros and poles, where z_n and p_n can be complex. The characteristic equation corresponding to this open-loop pole-zero array is

$$1 + \frac{K(s + z_1)(s + z_2)(s + z_3) \cdots}{s(s + p_1)(s + p_2)(s + p_3) \cdots} = 0 \quad \text{(10-3.5)}$$

and after rearranging

$$\frac{K(s + z_1)(s + z_2)(s + z_3) \cdots}{s(s + p_1)(s + p_2)(s + p_3) \cdots} = -1 = e^{j180°} \quad \text{(10-3.6)}$$

Let us now choose an arbitrary test point $s = s_i$ and determine if s_i represents a root of Eq. (10-3.5). It should be noted, lest the reader become unduly disturbed, that this process is at this stage of the development akin to searching for the proverbial needle in an infinite haystack. Later in this chapter, however, basic rules are formalized in which the positions of s_i are restricted to lie within only certain areas of the "haystack." Returning to the present, and substituting the test point location $s = s_i$ into Eq. (10-3.6), we form a possible identity

$$\frac{K(s_i + z_1)(s_i + z_2)(s_i + z_3) \cdots}{s_i(s_i + p_1)(s_i + p_2)(s_i + p_3) \cdots} \overset{?}{\equiv} e^{j180°} \quad \text{(10-3.7)}$$

Each component of Eq. (10-3.7) is now evaluated in terms of amplitude and phase. For the initial numerator component, a vector diagram illustrated in Fig. 10-3.1 is employed to sum the complex quantities s_i and z_1. The resulting vector has an amplitude of $|s_i + z_1|$ and a phase angle of

$$\tan^{-1} [\text{Im} \, (s_i + z_1)/\text{Re} \, (s_i + z_1)]$$

In abbreviated form, $s_i + z_1$ is equivalent to the polar-coordinate representation $A_{z_1} e^{j\theta_{z_1}}$.

It will prove convenient, in the further development of the theory, to translate each component vector in such a way that all terminations occur at the test point. Without changing either the vector amplitude or phase characteristics, $A_{z_1} e^{j\theta_{z_1}}$ can be moved horizontally until the arrowhead points to s_i. After accomplishing this reorientation, however, the vector is now observed to originate at the associated open-loop zero location, i.e., at $s = -z_1$. Thus, the quantity $A_{z_1} e^{j\theta_{z_1}}$ can be described by the length and

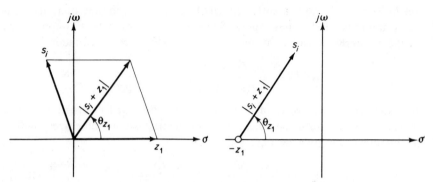

Figure 10-3.1 Summation of s_i and z_1.

Figure 10-3.2 The summation vector of Fig. 10-3.1 is translated to terminate upon the test point.

phase angle of a vector which originates at the corresponding open-loop zero and terminates upon the test point, as illustrated in Fig. 10-3.2. The remaining open-loop numerator-component vector lengths and phase angles are evaluated in an identical manner.

Singularities at the origin are computed without the necessity of any vector translation. For the mth order integration indicated in Fig. 10-3.3, the total amplitude and phase angle contributed to $KGH(s_i)$ is the mth power of the vector length at an angle of m, times the resulting single component phase. Hence

$$\frac{1}{s^m} = \frac{1}{(A_{p_0})^m e^{jm\theta_{p_0}}}$$

Finally, a first-order complex component, characterized by $s_i + p_1$ of

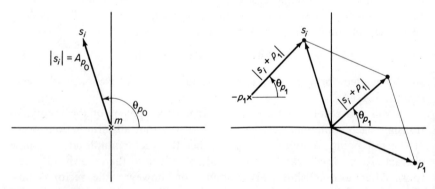

Figure 10-3.3 Singularities at the origin require no vector translation.

Figure 10-3.4 Vector summation and translation.

Fig. 10-3.4 is determined by again constructing a vector from the corresponding open-loop singularity to the test point. Expressing all components of Eq. (10-3.7) in polar coordinates as suggested in the equivalent s-plane vector diagram of Fig. 10-3.5

$$\frac{K(A_{z_1}e^{j\theta_{z_1}})(A_{z_2}e^{j\theta_{z_2}})(A_{z_3}e^{j\theta_{z_3}})\cdots}{(A_{p_0}e^{j\theta_{p_0}})(A_{p_1}e^{j\theta_{p_1}})(A_{p_2}e^{j\theta_{p_2}})(A_{p_3}e^{j\theta_{p_3}})\cdots} \overset{?}{\equiv} e^{j180°} \qquad (10\text{-}3.8)$$

Rearranging the above

$$\frac{KA_{z_1}A_{z_2}A_{z_3}\cdots e^{j(\theta_{z_1}+\theta_{z_2}+\theta_{z_3}+\cdots)}}{A_{p_0}A_{p_1}A_{p_2}A_{p_3}\cdots e^{j(\theta_{p_0}+\theta_{p_1}+\theta_{p_2}+\theta_{p_3}+\cdots)}} \overset{?}{\equiv} e^{j180°} \qquad (10\text{-}3.9)$$

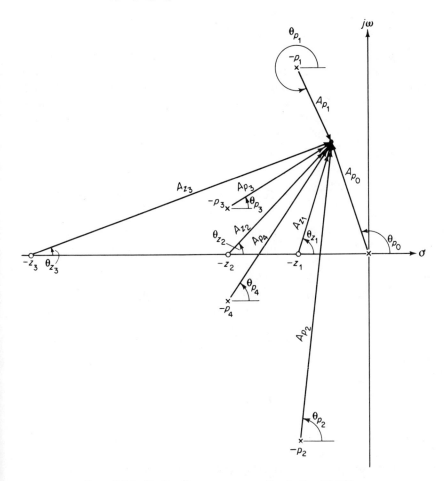

Figure 10-3.5 Vector diagram corresponding to Eq. (10-3.8).

Equation (10-3.9) can be further reduced to

$$\frac{KA_{z_1}A_{z_2}A_{z_3}\cdots}{A_{p_0}A_{p_1}A_{p_2}A_{p_3}\cdots}\, e^{j(\theta_{z_1}+\theta_{z_2}+\cdots-\theta_{p_0}-\theta_{p_1}\cdots)} \overset{?}{\equiv} e^{j180^\circ} \qquad (10\text{-}3.10)$$

For $s = s_i$ to be a root of the characteristic equation and thus satisfy Eq. (10-3.10), it is necessary and sufficient that

$$\theta_{z_1} + \theta_{z_2} + \theta_{z_3} + \cdots - \theta_{p_0} - \theta_{p_1} - \theta_{p_2} - \theta_{p_3} - \cdots = \pm(2n+1)180^\circ$$
$$n = 0, 1, 2, \ldots \qquad (10\text{-}3.11)$$

and

$$\frac{KA_{z_1}A_{z_2}A_{z_3}\cdots}{A_{p_0}A_{p_1}A_{p_2}A_{p_3}\cdots} = 1 \qquad (10\text{-}3.12)$$

Equation (10-3.11) is referred to as the *angle criterion* of root-locus theory, while Eq. (10-3.12) is the *amplitude criterion*. The former states simply that, for the test point s_i to be a root of the characteristic equation, the sum of all open-loop zero vector angles minus the sum of all open-loop pole vector angles must equal 180° (or some multiple of 180°). Equation (10-3.12) provides the method for explicitly calculating the corresponding value of open-loop gain K. Thus, at $s = s_i$

$$K_{s_i} = \frac{1}{A_{z_1}A_{z_2}A_{z_3}\cdots/A_{p_0}A_{p_1}A_{p_2}A_{p_3}\cdots} = \frac{A_{p_0}A_{p_1}A_{p_2}A_{p_3}\cdots}{A_{z_1}A_{z_2}A_{z_3}\cdots} \qquad (10\text{-}3.13)$$

It should be noted that, as stated, Eq. (10-3.13) is valid over the entire s-plane. However, only at those positions where the angle criterion is satisfied does the ensuing gain calculation become meaningful. Consequently, the loci of all roots are first established through an application of Eq. (10-3.11), and the loci are then calibrated for gain by means of Eq. (10-3.12). In the next section, nine specific rules of root-locus construction are described. These rules, when used in conjunction with the Spirule (which will be discussed later in the chapter) greatly facilitate the root-locus generation and render the method attractive as an analytical tool.

10-4 RULES FOR RAPID ROOT-LOCUS SKETCHING

The nine rules developed in this section are presented as a logical step-by-step formula for root-locus sketching. Each rule is a direct consequence of (1) the angle criterion of Eq. (10-3.11), (2) the closed-loop transfer function of Eq. (10-2.2), (3) the theory of polynomials, or (4) intuitive concepts. Rules are first stated, then derived, and, when applicable, applied to an example system. Prior to using the rules, we initiate the root-locus diagram by plotting open-loop singularities upon a sheet of linear graph paper, using equal dimensional spacings along both the real and imaginary axes. Open-loop poles and zeros, designated by **X** and **O** respectively, are then plotted.

RULE 1: *Roots of* $1 + KGH(s) = 0$ *are situated at, and coincide with, the poles of KGH(s) for* $K = 0$

From Eq. (10-2.3-c), when the open-loop gain constant is zero, the characteristic equation degenerates into

$$G_D H_D(s) = 0 \qquad \text{(10-4.1)}$$

Since $G_D H_D(s)$ represents the open-loop transfer-function denominator, all values of s that satisfy this equation lie at the open-loop pole locations. For any physical system, $G_D H_D(s)$ and $1 + KGH(s) = 0$ are of equal order in s. The number of system roots is then equal to the number of poles of $KGH(s)$, so that a starting point for each of the roots of $1 + KGH(s) = 0$ is specified.

RULE 2: *The roots of* $1 + KGH(s) = 0$ *terminate upon the zeros of KGH(s) for* $K = \infty$. *Each root-locus branch is a unique single-valued function of gain*

Dividing each term of Eq. (10-2.3-c) by the gain factor K

$$\frac{G_D H_D(s)}{K} + G_N H_N(s) = 0 \qquad \text{(10-4.2)}$$

As K approaches infinity, the first term of Eq. (10-4.2) approaches zero, and the characteristic equation is reduced to

$$G_N H_N(s) = 0 \qquad \text{(10-4.3)}$$

Thus, as the open-loop gain tends to infinity, the roots of $1 + KHG(s) = 0$ will exist at each open-loop transfer-function zero. Since $KGH(s)$ will, in general, contain more poles than zeros, all of the root-locus branches can not terminate upon finite zeros. Hence, some of the roots must terminate at infinity, or more appropriately, upon zeros located at infinity.

Trajectories followed by each root in traversing the s-plane are single-valued functions of gain, as witnessed by the linearity (with respect to K) exhibited by Eq. (10-2.3-a). Uniqueness is a direct consequence of the fact that both the amplitude and angle criteria must be satisfied simultaneously.

RULE 3:   *The root-locus exists at any point on the real axis which lies to the left of an odd number of singularities*

For an intuitive proof of Rule 3, consider the open-loop pole-zero array of Fig. 10-4.1. As illustrated, the phase angle contributed by each singularity situated to the right of the test point is $\pm 180°$. Singularities lying to the left of the test point result in a zero contribution, and the phase angle associated

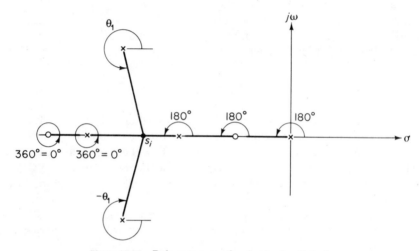

Figure 10-4.1   Pole-zero array for developing Rule 3.

with a complex singularity is cancelled by the complex-conjugate vector angle. Thus, only singularities lying to the right of the test point need be considered in evaluating the angle criterion. Since each pole or zero to the right of s_i contributes 180° (positive for a zero and negative for a pole), an odd number must exist if s_i is to be a point on the locus.

Many problems in root-locus sketching can be solved through applying only the rules stated thus far. As an example, assume the open-loop transfer function

$$KGH(s) = \frac{K(s+2)(s+10)}{s(s+20)^2} \qquad \textbf{(10-4.4)}$$

To prepare for root-locus sketching, we plot the open-loop poles and zeros of Eq. (10-4.4) on linear graph paper, using identical real and imaginary coordinate spacings as shown in Fig. 10-4.2. From Rule 1, the roots of $1 + KGH(s) = 0$ coincide with the three open-loop poles for $K = 0$. Since the number of poles is one greater than the number of zeros, two of the roots terminate upon finite zeros (at $s = -2$ and -10) and the third root terminates at infinity. The locus occurs on the real axis between the origin and the zero

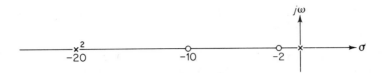

Figure 10-4.2 Pole-zero format corresponding to Eq. (10-4.4).

at $s = -2$, because only one singularity is observed to the right of this path. Similarly, the locus is present between the zero at $s = -10$ and negative infinity. Each system root trajectory fulfills the requirements of Rules 1 and 2, therefore Fig. 10-4.3 represents a complete root-locus sketch. This example also defines the manner in which multiple-order singularities are considered. The fact that a second-order system pole occurs at $s = -20$ (indicated by the X^2 designation of Fig. 10-4.2) allows the root-locus to exist on either side of the singularities. Thus, nth order poles (or zeros) are treated as n first-order poles (or zeros) separated by an infinitely small distance.

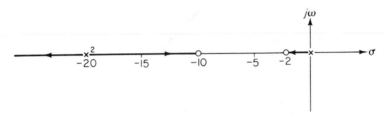

Figure 10-4.3 Complete root-locus diagram.

Consider now the pole-zero array of Eq. (10-4.5), comprised of a second-order open-loop integration with lead-lag compensation.

$$KGH(s) = \frac{K(s + 12)}{s^2(s + 20)} \qquad (10\text{-}4.5)$$

The corresponding root-locus plot of Fig. 10-4.4 is, in this case, not complete, since both roots originating at the origin must terminate at infinity, whereas real-axis paths to infinity are not legitimate portions of the locus. Thus, additional rules are required before a system of this type can be sketched.

RULE 4: *For values of K approaching infinity, the locus is asymptotic to the angles*

$$\frac{\pm(2n + 1)180°}{\#P - \#Z}$$

$$(10\text{-}4.6)$$

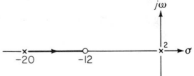

Figure 10-4.4 The root-locus diagram corresponding to Eq. (10-4.5) is not complete.

where n = 0, 1, 2, 3, . . . and #P − #Z represents the excess of poles over zeros in the open loop

Rule 4 is easily proved by considering a test point s_i situated at infinity, as symbolically illustrated in Fig. 10-4.5. Because of the great distances involved, all finite open-loop singularities will appear to be located at the

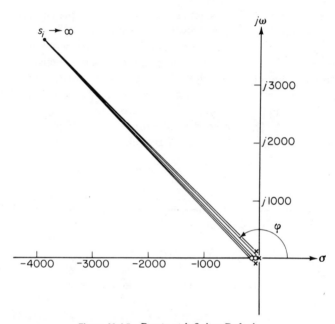

Figure 10-4.5   Roots at infinity: Rule 4.

origin when viewed from the test point; hence, each vector connecting the open-loop poles and zeros with the test point is of equal magnitude and phase. Thus, for large values of gain, the open-loop array can be replaced by a pole at $s = 0$ of multiplicity M, where $M = \#P - \#Z$. Returning again to the angle criterion of Eq. (10-3.11), s_i will be located on the root-locus if, and only if

$$-\varphi(\#P - \#Z) = (2n + 1)180° \qquad \textbf{(10-4.7)}$$

Solving Eq. (10-4.7) for the vector angle φ

$$\varphi = \frac{-(2n + 1)180°}{\#P - \#Z} \qquad \textbf{(10-4.8)}$$

In any physical system, a complex singularity must be accompanied by a complex-conjugate member, so that both positive and negative asymptotes are present. Combining this consideration with Eq. (10-4.8) yields the required proof.

One might conclude from Fig. 10-4.5 that all asymptotic lines intersect at the origin; this observation only appears true in that for an infinite gain, the entire pole-zero array has been collapsed to a point at the origin. For accurate root-locus sketching, the true real-axis intercept must be computed, and this subject will be considered in Rule 5. Before proceeding, however, let us investigate asymptotic angles corresponding to some typical open-loop systems. If $\#P - \#Z = 0$, no asymptotes exist, because each root terminates upon a finite open-loop zero. For $\#P - \#Z = 1$, one need only substitute $n = 0$ into Eq. (10-4.6) to observe that the single asymptotic angle is 180°. If any other value of n is employed, the identical angle will again be obtained. This computation has already been verified in the root-locus sketch of Fig. 10-4.3.

To summarize, the number of unique asymptotic angles is equal to $\#P - \#Z$. In calculating these angles, it is only necessary to substitute into Eq. (10-4.6) a sufficient number of integers n to determine the total number of possible asymptotes. The substitution of higher values of n will result in a repetition of the original angles, and will yield only redundant information. Figure 10-4.6 presents the asymptotes occurring for various values of the quantity $\#P - \#Z$.

RULE 5: *All asymptotic lines intersect the real axis at the center of gravity of the roots defined as*

$$CG = \frac{\sum \text{poles} - \sum \text{zeros}}{\#P - \#Z} \qquad \textbf{(10-4.9)}$$

From the theory of equations it can be shown that, with respect to polynomial-type equations, the second-highest power coefficient is equal to the negative sum of all roots. This general principle is illustrated in Eq. (10-4.10); the two roots $s = -a$, and $-b$, when summed negatively, form the coefficient of the s^1 power term.

$$s^2 + (a + b)s + ab = 0 \qquad \textbf{(10-4.10)}$$

Although Eq. (10-4.10) by no means proves this principle, one can consider an any-order polynomial equation with a similar result. The open-loop transfer function consists, in general, of ratios of polynomials in s. Although the characteristic equation of Eq. (10-2.3-c) is conventionally written in factored form, an alternative approach is to expand both $G_N H_N(s)$ and $G_D H_D(s)$ into polynomials, i.e.

$$s^l + a_d s^{l-1} + b_d s^{l-2} + \cdots + K(s^m + a_n s^{m-1} + b_n s^{m-2} + \cdots) = 0$$

$$\textbf{(10-4.11)}$$

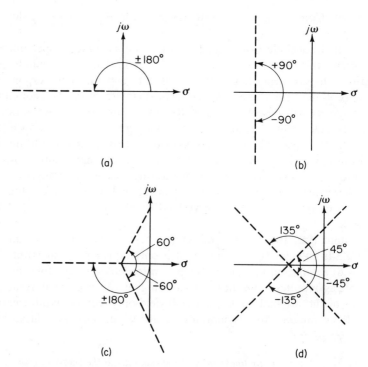

Figure 10-4.6   Asymptotic angles for various values of $\#P - \#Z$. (a) $\#P - \#Z = 1$, (b) $\#P - \#Z = 2$, (c) $\#P - \#Z = 3$, (d) $\#P - \#Z = 4$.

where $a_d, b_d, \ldots$ and $a_n, b_n, \ldots$ are coefficients of the denominator and numerator polynomials respectively. Dividing both sides of the equation by the numerator polynomial

$$s^{l-m} + (a_d - a_n)s^{l-m-1} + \cdots + K = 0 \qquad (10\text{-}4.12)$$

If $\#P - \#Z \geqslant 2$ or, equivalently, $l - m \geqslant 2$, then the open-loop gain constant K does not appear in either the highest- or second-highest power coefficient. Under these circumstances, the sum of all roots of the characteristic equation are constant. Hence, if one branch of the locus moves to the left, another must move to the right so that the total sum of all roots remains invariant. If $\#P - \#Z < 2$, the center-of-gravity location is of academic interest only, since the asymptote will lie along the negative real axis for $\#P - \#Z = 1$, and no asymptotic lines will occur for $\#P - \#Z = 0$.

As the value of s becomes large, Eq. (10-4.12) is an $(l - m)$th-order polynomial equation and, for $l - m \geqslant 2$, the sum of all system roots is constant, equal in magnitude to $-(a_d - a_n)$. Thus, each asymptote intersects the real axis at a point

$$CG = \frac{-(a_d - a_n)}{l - m} \qquad \text{(10-4.13)}$$

But, from Eq. (10-4.11), a_d must be the negative sum of all zeros of $G_D H_D(s)$, or the open-loop poles. Similarly, a_n represents the sum of all open-loop zeros. Thus, Eq. (10-4.13) is transformed into Eq. (10-4.9) and this completes the proof.

Returning to the pole-zero array of Fig. 10-4.4, and applying Rules 4 and 5, the resulting asymptotic angles are, for $n = 0$

$$\pm \frac{180°}{2} = \pm 90°$$

while the asymptotes originate at a *CG* location of

$$CG = \frac{-20 + 12}{2} = -4$$

The locus of Fig. 10-4.7 is still not totally described, however, since the behavior of branches which break from the real axis have not been defined. One additional rule is therefore required.

RULE 6: *Dual root-locus branches depart from, or arrive on, the real axis at angles of* $\pm 90°$

Rule 6 is proved by referring to the pole-zero array of Fig. 10-4.8. Consider a circle of infinitely small diameter drawn about the second-order open-loop poles as illustrated. To determine which specific points on the circumference satisfy the angle criterion of Eq. (10-3.11), an intuitive analysis is conducted as follows: Since the entire circle lies an infinitely small distance from the real axis, all real-axis singularities contribute either $0°$ or $\pm 180°$ to $KGH(s_i)$. By definition, however, an even number of singularities occur to

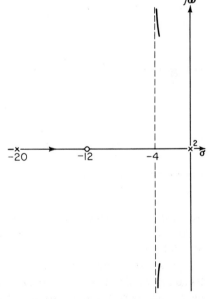

Figure 10-4.7 Root-locus diagram of Fig. 10-4.4 after incorporation of Rules 4 and 5.

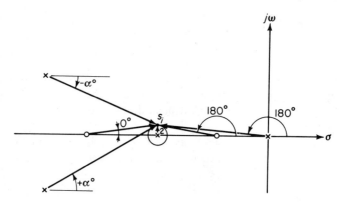

Figure 10-4.8   Pole-zero array used to develop Rule 6.

the right of the double poles, for if an odd number existed, the locus would remain upon the real axis. The net phase angle resulting from all poles and zeros lying to the right of the test point is then zero, while the contribution of all singularities lying to the left is similarly zero. Complex pole and zero angles, when summed with the complex-conjugate vector phase likewise yield an over-all contribution of zero. Hence, the angle criterion must be satisfied by the phase angles associated with the double poles, which are evidently $\pm 90°$.

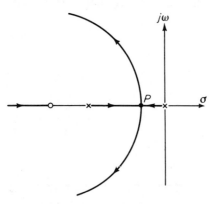

Figure 10-4.9   Double roots break from the real axis at $\pm 90°$.

Although Rule 6 has been proved for double poles of $KGH(s)$, the proof is general. For the open-loop transfer function plotted in Fig. 10-4.9, system roots are observed to meet or *coalesce* at a particular value of open-loop gain. At this point, a second-order real-axis pole is produced. If the gain constant is now reset to zero and a new root-locus plotted, the general shape of the two loci will be the same. Thus, the roots depart from the real axis at angles of $\pm 90°$. A similar analysis demonstrates that roots also arrive on the real axis at $\pm 90°$.

Occasionally one encounters a situation in which three roots are observed to coalesce. The angles of arrival and departure for the two possible configurations corresponding to this condition are indicated in Fig. 10-4.10. Similarly, fourth-order roots depart at angles of $0°$, $\pm 90°$, and $180°$, or $\pm 45°$ and $\pm 135°$, depending upon the particular open-loop array.

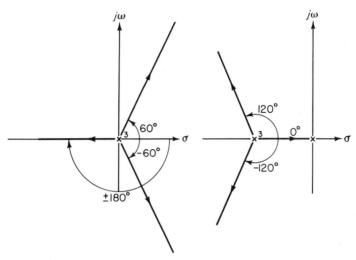

Figure 10-4.10 Angles of departure from third-order real-axis roots.

With the generation of Rule 6, the root-locus of Fig. 10-4.7 can now be concluded. The locus has been drawn without explicitly computing the angle criterion. Although the results as pictured in Fig. 10-4.11 are only approximate, the entire system-transient character has been developed with a minimum of analytical calculations.

RULE 7: *The breakaway point (the point at which roots coalesce and depart from the real axis) is determined from the equation*

$$\sum \frac{1}{|z_L - s_b|} - \sum \frac{1}{|p_L - s_b|}$$
$$= \sum \frac{1}{|s_b - z_R|} - \sum \frac{1}{|s_b - p_R|}$$

(10-4.14)

where s_b is the position of the breakaway point, subscripts L and R represent singularities to the left and right of the breakaway point respectively, and $|s_b - z_i|$ is the length of the vector from an arbitrary zero, located upon the real axis, to the breakaway point

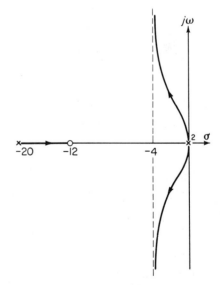

Figure 10-4.11 Original root-locus diagram of Fig. 10-4.4 can now be completed.

As indicated by Rule 6, two real-axis roots, after coalescing, depart from the real axis asymptotic to the angles of $\pm 90°$. Thus, at a very small distance from the point of coalescence (the breakaway point) and perpendicular to the real axis, the angle criterion must still be satisfied. This is equivalent to stating that the net change in angle of $KGH(s)$ is zero. Rule 7 will now be proved through an illustrative example. If all poles and zeros of $KGH(s)$

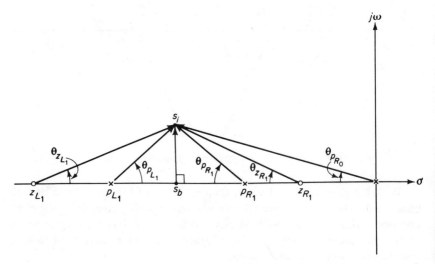

Figure 10-4.12   Breakaway-point calculation.

are located upon the real axis as shown in Fig. 10-4.12, and if the changes in phase contribution calculated for each singularity are equated to zero, with zero-vector phase considered positively and pole-vector phase negatively

$$\theta_{z_{L_1}} - \theta_{p_{L_1}} + \theta_{p_{R_1}} - \theta_{z_{R_1}} + \theta_{p_{R_0}} = 0 \qquad (10\text{-}4.15)$$

or equivalently

$$\theta_{z_{L_1}} - \theta_{p_{L_1}} = \theta_{z_{R_1}} - \theta_{p_{R_1}} - \theta_{p_{R_0}} \qquad (10\text{-}4.16)$$

Substituting the small-angle approximation $\theta_i = \tan \theta_i$ into the above

$$\frac{s_i - s_b}{|z_{L_1} - s_b|} - \frac{s_i - s_b}{|p_{L_1} - s_b|} = \frac{s_i - s_b}{|z_{R_1} - s_b|} - \frac{s_i - s_b}{|p_{R_1} - s_b|} - \frac{s_i - s_b}{|p_{R_0} - s_b|} \qquad (10\text{-}4.17)$$

Dividing Eq. (10-4.17) by $s_i - s_b$ yields the expression predicted in Eq. (10-4.14). The presence of complex open-loop singularities tends to complicate the breakaway point calculation; as stated, Rule 7 no longer applies to this general configuration. If, however, the complex quantities have imaginary parts lying far from the real axis in comparison to the open-loop singularities (a rule of thumb measure of six times the greatest real-axis distance is often used), the breakaway point can be based upon only real-axis considerations. If this is not the case, the net change in angle from the complex-conjugate pair is given by

$$\frac{\pm 2(s_i - s_b)\,|s_b - \alpha|}{|(s_b - \alpha)^2 + \beta^2|}$$

(10-4.18)

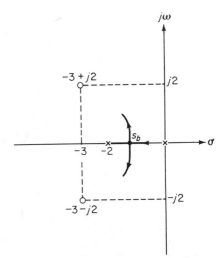

Figure 10-4.13 Breakaway-point calculation for Eq. (10-4.19).

where α and β are the real and imaginary components of the complex singularity with poles taken negatively and zeros positively. As an example of a typical breakaway-point calculation consider the root-locus diagram of Fig. 10-4.13 derived from the open-loop transfer function

$$KGH(s) = \frac{K(s + 3 + j2)(s + 3 - j2)}{s(s + 2)}$$

(10-4.19)

For this particular array, the breakaway equation becomes

$$\frac{2(s_i - s_b)\,|s_b + 3|}{|(s_b + 3)^2 + 2^2|} - \frac{s_i - s_b}{|s_b + 2|} = \frac{-(s_i - s_b)}{|s_b|}$$

(10-4.20)

Dividing Eq. (10-4.20) by the quantity $s_i - s_b$, and substituting a test point $s_b = -1$

$$\frac{2(2)}{(2)^2 + (2)^2} - \frac{1}{1} \stackrel{?}{=} -\frac{1}{1}$$

(10-4.21)

$$0.5 - 1 \neq -1$$

For $s_b = -1.5$

$$\frac{2(1.5)}{(1.5)^2 + (2)^{2\cdot}} - \frac{1}{0.5} \stackrel{?}{=} -\frac{1}{1.5}$$

(10-4.22)

$$0.48 - 2.0 \neq -0.667$$

In comparing these calculations, it is observed that the two test points bracket the true breakaway point. Further refinements in the assumed breakaway point would decrease the resulting inequalities to some acceptable

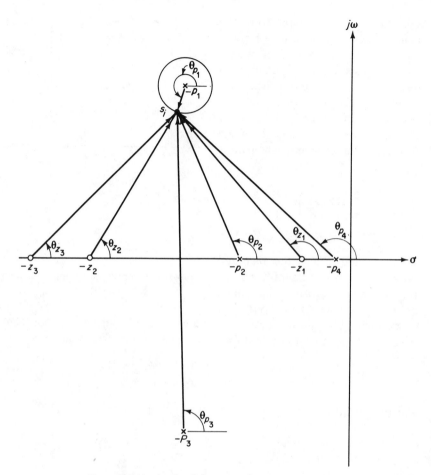

Figure 10-4.14 Angle of departure from complex pole.

value. Since the breakaway calculation is, by definition, a trial-and-error process, the precise point is often not determined explicitly, but rather, it is estimated from visual examination of the root-locus paths.

> RULE 8: *The angle of departure from complex poles, or the angle of arrival to complex zeros are determined by summing the angular contributions of vectors originating at the open loop singularities and terminating upon the complex pole or zero, and subtracting 180° from this total*

The proof of Rule 8 follows directly from the angle criterion expression. If, as in Fig. 10-4.14, a circle of small diameter is drawn about the complex singularity (shown as an open-loop pole), then only one point on the circumference will similarly exist as a point on the root-locus. To determine the location of this point, a test point s_i is considered as shown. If, at $s = s_i$, the angle criterion is satisfied, then

$$\theta_{z_1} + \theta_{z_2} + \theta_{z_3} - \theta_{p_1} - \theta_{p_2} - \theta_{p_3} - \theta_{p_4} = 180° \qquad \text{(10-4.23)}$$

Solving for θ_{p_1}

$$\theta_{p_1} = \theta_{p_2} + \theta_{p_3} + \theta_{p_4} - \theta_{z_1} - \theta_{z_2} - \theta_{z_3} - 180° \qquad \text{(10-4.24)}$$

As the circle diameter shrinks to zero, the angle of departure is calculated as stated. For complex zeros, the angle of arrival is determined in an identical manner, with the exception that the vector angle sign conventions are reversed.

RULE 9: *The point at which the root-locus crosses the imaginary axis is determined from Routh's stability criterion*

Routh's stability criterion allows a rapid and accurate calculation of both the open-loop gain and resulting oscillational frequency that exist at the point of system instability. The Routh array is described in Appendix B of this volume; in addition, some problems are presented that illustrate the required calculations.

10-5 SECOND-ORDER SYSTEM

In Chapter 8, the typical second-order closed-loop system was discussed in terms of transient- and frequency-response characteristics. Let us now consider the same second-order transfer function as pictured upon the root-locus diagram and, from this approach, derive a graphical interpretation of the system damping ratio and undamped natural frequency parameters.

Assuming a unity-feedback system with an open-loop transfer function

$$KGH(s) = \frac{K}{s(s + \alpha)} \qquad \text{(10-5.1)}$$

the corresponding closed-loop transfer function is

$$\frac{C}{R}(s) = \frac{\omega_n^2}{s^2 + 2\zeta\omega_n s + \omega_n^2} \qquad \text{(10-5.2)}$$

where $\omega_n = \sqrt{K}$ and $\zeta = \alpha/2\sqrt{K}$. Applying the rules of construction generated in the previous section, we sketch the complete root-locus diagram corresponding to the open-loop array of Eq. (10-5.1) as illustrated in

Fig. 10-5.1. Rules 1, 2, and 3 require that the root-locus originate at the open-loop system poles ($s = 0, -\alpha$) and exist upon the negative real axis between these singularities. Furthermore, both locus branches terminate upon zeros located at infinity. Since $\#P - \#Z = 2$, the high-frequency asymptotic angles are calculated as $\pm 90°$, while the center of gravity is evidently at

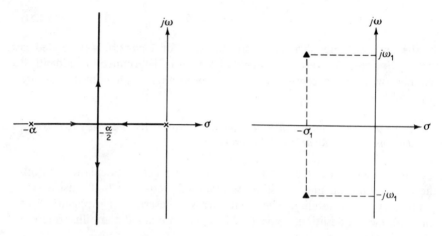

Figure 10-5.1   Root-locus diagram for second-order system.

Figure 10-5.2   Typical underdamped closed-loop poles for second-order system of Fig. 10-5.1.

$s = -\alpha/2$. Rules 6 and 7 indicate that the breakaway point and center of gravity coincide, while the breakaway angles and asymptotic angles are also identical. Thus, the second-order system root-locus is as described in Fig. 10-5.1.

For very low values of open-loop gain, the roots of $1 + KGH(s) = 0$ are negative real-axis quantities, resulting in an overdamped system state. As K increases, the roots migrate together, finally coalescing at the point $s = -\alpha/2$; this configuration represents a critically-damped condition. And finally, for any additional increase in gain the roots depart from the real axis, exhibiting the characteristic oscillatory nature of an underdamped system. From this root-locus diagram, one can determine the poles of $\frac{C}{R}(s)$ for any chosen value of K. In particular, let us choose a value of gain such that the resulting roots lie away from the real axis. As shown in Fig. 10-5.2, the complex-conjugate pole positions are at $s = -\sigma_1 + j\omega_1$ and $-\sigma_1 - j\omega_1$, so that the closed-loop transfer function becomes

$$\frac{C}{R}(s) = \frac{K_o}{(s + \sigma_1 + j\omega_1)(s + \sigma_1 - j\omega_1)} \qquad (10\text{-}5.3)$$

where K_0 is the specific value of gain. From a comparison of Eqs. (10-5.3) and (10-5.2), it is apparent that

$$(s + \sigma_1 + j\omega_1)(s + \sigma_1 - j\omega_1) = s^2 + 2\zeta\omega_n s + \omega_n^2 \qquad \text{(10-5.4)}$$

Equivalently

$$s^2 + 2\sigma_1 s + (\sigma_1^2 + \omega_1^2) = s^2 + 2\zeta\omega_n s + \omega_n^2 \qquad \text{(10-5.5)}$$

Equating like coefficients of s

$$\omega_n^2 = \sigma_1^2 + \omega_1^2$$
$$\omega_n = \sqrt{\sigma_1^2 + \omega_1^2} = |\sigma_1 + j\omega_1| \qquad \text{(10-5.6)}$$

and

$$2\sigma_1 = 2\zeta\omega_n$$

$$\zeta = \frac{\sigma_1}{\omega_n} = \frac{\sigma_1}{|\sigma_1 + \omega_1|} = \cos\theta \qquad \text{(10-5.7)}$$

The calculations suggested in Eqs. (10-5.6) and (10-5.7) are graphically displayed in Fig. 10-5.3. Instead of describing ζ in the form of Eq. (10-5.7), however, a simple geometrical transformation is employed to produce the situation exhibited in Fig. 10-5.4. Thus, once the second-order system closed-loop poles have been established, the system damping ratio and

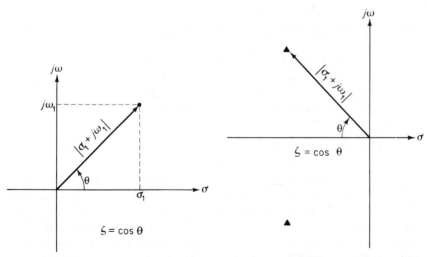

Figure 10-5.3 Graphical significance of damping-ratio and undamped natural-frequency parameters.

Figure 10-5.4 Equivalent geometrical damping-ratio and undamped natural-frequency calculations.

undamped natural frequency can be measured directly from the root-locus plot. Note also that the imaginary axis component of $-\sigma_1 + j\omega_1$ has a value $\sqrt{1 - \zeta^2}\,\omega_n$. This is the system damped natural frequency, i.e., the frequency at which the closed-loop system will oscillate when subjected to a transient excitation. This verifies the conclusion previously reached in Eq. (8-5.4) of Chapter 8.

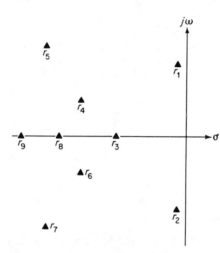

Although the second-order system is rarely encountered in practice, higher-order systems are often adequately represented in terms of a second-order approximation. Higher-order systems are characterized by dominant closed-loop poles (or control poles) and, as such, behave approximately as equivalent second-order loops. Thus, the transient response of the closed-loop system of Fig. 10-5.5 will, in general, be controlled by the location of roots r_1 and r_2. Roots which are near the $j\omega$ axis yield a slowly decaying oscillatory time-response contribution which will exist long after all other transient effects have been subdued.

Figure 10-5.5   Typical closed-loop pole array with control poles r_1 and r_2.

10-6   APPLICATION OF ROOT-LOCUS SKETCHING

As with the second-order system of Section 10.5, many simple control loops can be sketched through applying some or all of the nine rules for root-locus construction. Figure 10-6.1 presents a selected group of root-locus diagrams corresponding to various simple control systems.

10-7   USE OF THE SPIRULE

Root-locus construction is based upon the designer's ability to find those values of s which satisfy the angle criterion of Eq. (10-3.11). Once these points have been established, the resulting locus is then calibrated for gain according to the magnitude criterion. The most accurate, but also the most time consuming, method of evaluating these criteria involves a desk-calculator and standard trigonometric function-table approach; one calculates the distances from each open-loop singularity to the test point analytically, computes sines or cosines of the resulting angle using the desk calculator, and

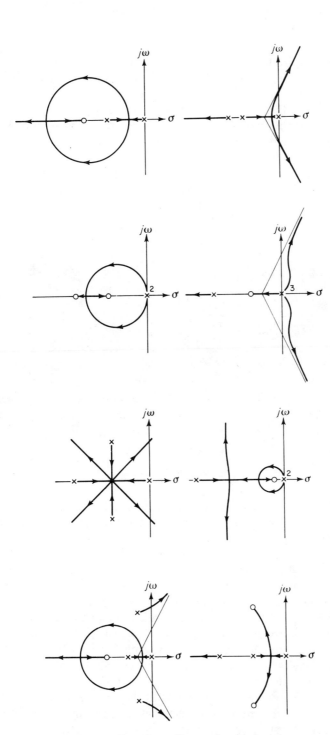

Figure 10-6.1 Root-locus diagram for simple systems.

refers to the standard tables to ascertain the precise value of all vector angles. A simplified but approximate technique is that of using a protractor and ruler to graphically determine angles and distances. An engineering device, the *Spirule*, combines the protractor and ruler into a single tool, the use of which greatly expedites root-locus construction. A combination of Spirule determination of angles and accurate ruler (or divider) and slide-rule gain calibration is also widely employed.

The Spirule of Fig. 10-7.1 consists of a circular protractor or disk attached to a ruler or arm by means of an eyelet. Both elements are of transparent

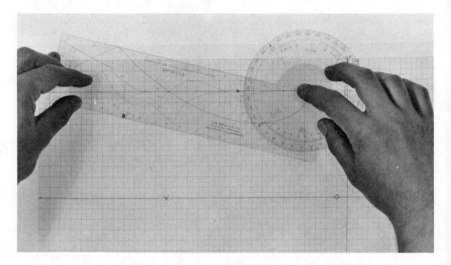

Figure 10-7.1   Spirule.

plastic construction. The upper disk face is provided with a small amount of friction so that both arm and disk can be rotated simultaneously about the eyelet without slippage. To sum the angles, the eyelet is placed atop the test point and the disk and arm are progressed through a repetitive step-by-step rotational procedure. The final angle summation is then read directly from the protractor scale. Values of open-loop gain existing at points previously defined as being on the locus are obtained by the multiplication and division of vector lengths. For this purpose, the Spirule is equipped with a logarithmic scale such that vector lengths can be manipulated by again employing a step-by-step procedure. Similarly, breakaway angles from complex poles and complex-zero angles of arrival are obtained graphically; in addition, the Spirule contains scales for measuring damping ratios.

A test point is evaluated with respect to the angle criterion as follows: The Spirule is first oriented in such a way that the eyelet appears immediately over the required test point. The disk is aligned so that the reference line (the R line as shown in Fig. 10-7.1) passes through the 0° disk mark. We now choose an open-loop pole and align the reference through the pole. The disk is then held firmly to the paper while the arm alone is rotated until the reference coincides with an open-loop zero. Both arm and disk are now rotated to the next pole, and the process continued until all open-loop singularities have been considered. For systems containing an excess of poles over zeros, angles corresponding to the excess poles are subtracted by revolving the arm and disk from the horizontal (with the reference line lying horizontally along the negative real axis) to the additional pole, followed by returning the arm alone back to the horizontal position. The final angle sum is read from the intersection of the reference line and the protractor scale. If this angle is 180°, the test point $s = s_i$ lies on the locus; if the angle is other than 180°, the particular value is marked on the paper adjacent to the test point, and another point is chosen. Once 180° has been bracketed, however, one can usually interpolate with a single additional test.

The Spirule permits the multiplication and division of vector lengths graphically (logarithmically). The device is constructed in such a way that the angles between the arm and a specially designed logarithmic curve (located upon the arm) are directly proportional to the logarithms of vectors originating at the eyelet and terminating upon the curve. Open-loop gain-constant values along the locus are determined according to the following procedure: The disk is first turned until the 0° mark coincides with the reference line R. With the eyelet placed upon the particular calibration point, both disk and arm are rotated until the reference passes through a pole. The disk is firmly held and the arm moved until the pole coincides with the spiral S curve (see Fig. 10-7.1). Both arm and disk are now rotated to the next pole, and the process continued. For zeros, the arm and disk are rotated simultaneously until the zero coincides with the S curve. The disk is now held while the arm alone is rotated until the zero coincides with the reference. By repetitive application of these steps, the total gain constant is obtained in normalized form. Once all singularities have been considered, the final normalized vector length is obtained by reading the arm logarithmic curve with either the X–.1, X–1, or X–10 pointer (corresponding to 270°, 0°, and 90° respectively). A scale factor must be applied to achieve the final gain value, and it is obtained from the formula

$$SF = y^{\#P - \#Z} \qquad (10\text{-}7.1)$$

where $\#P - \#Z$ is the excess of poles over zeros in the open loop, and y is the value of real-axis dimensional spacing corresponding to 1.0 on the linear arm scale. Thus, the final gain parameter is computed from the equation

$$K = (\text{logarithmic scale reading})(X\text{- reading})(SF) \qquad (10\text{-}7.2)$$

The angles of departure from complex poles and the angles of arrival at complex zeros can be determined rapidly through using the Spirule as an angle-summing device. For complex poles, the eyelet is placed directly over the pole, and all singularity angles summed in the normal sense; 180° is then subtracted from the resulting reading. For complex zeros, an identical procedure is employed, with the exception that pole and zero conventions are reversed, and 180° is again subtracted from the total.

A special scale is supplied over one quadrant of the disk to permit the direct reading of complex-singularity damping ratios. With the eyelet located at the origin, the arm reference is aligned with the 180° protractor mark and the negative real axis. The arm is then rotated until the reference passes through the complex singularity. The corresponding damping ratio is read directly from the appropriate scale.

10-8 ROOT-LOCUS ANALYSIS OF A REPRESENTATIVE SYSTEM

To illustrate the root-locus approach as applied to representative systems, consider the unity feedback open loop transfer function of Eq. (10-8.1), corresponding to a missile attitude control autopilot with cancellation compensation.

$$KG(s) = \frac{K(s + 0.1)}{s(s + 2.97 + j5.2)(s + 2.97 - j5.2)(s + 0.4)(s + 10.4)} \tag{10-8.1}$$

The problem is that of adjusting the gain constant to yield dominant roots with a 0.4 damping ratio. The rules of construction are applied in the order of their presentation:

1 & 2. Open-loop poles and zeros are plotted as shown in Fig. 10-8.1.
3. The root-locus exists between the origin and -0.1, and between -0.4 and -10.4. The low-frequency real-axis branch is complete, while the high-frequency roots must break from the real axis.
4. High-frequency asymptotic lines are obtained by substituting the values $n = 0$ and $n = 1$ into Eq. (10-4.6). Since $\#P - \#Z = 4$

for $n = 0$

$$\varphi = \frac{\pm 180°}{4} = \pm 45°$$

for $n = 1$

$$\varphi = \frac{\pm 540°}{4} = \pm 135°$$

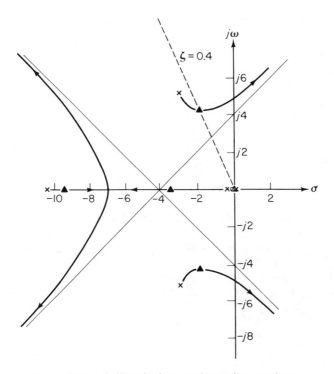

Figure 10-8.1   Missile attitude control autopilot root-locus.

5. The center of gravity of the roots is calculated from Eq. (10-4.13)

$$CG = \frac{-2.97 - 2.97 - 0.4 - 10.4 + 0.1}{4}$$

$$= -4.16$$

6 & 7. Between the real-axis positions of -0.4 and -10.4, the roots coalesce and break from the real axis at angles of $\pm 90°$. The breakaway point is computed by trial and error from the diagram of Fig. 10-8.2.

$$\frac{1}{\alpha} = \frac{1}{\gamma} + \frac{1}{\eta} - \frac{1}{\delta} + \frac{2\beta}{\beta^2 + 5.2^2} \tag{10-8.2}$$

Equation (10-8.2) is solved to yield the result, $s_b \cong -7.0$

8. The angle of departure from the complex pole located at $s = -2.9 - j5.2$ is determined by conventional methods to be 298°.

9. Roots of $1 + KGH(s) = 0$ cross the imaginary axis at a frequency of 4.9 radians/sec (see Appendix B).

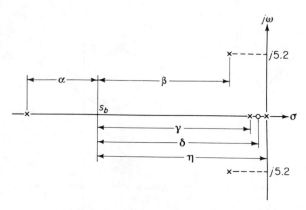

Figure 10-8.2 Geometrical representation of Eq. (10-8.2).

The finalized root-locus plot of Fig. 10-8.1 is prepared through use of the spirule. A 0.4 control-pole damping ratio occurs for an open-loop gain $K = 607$. Calibrating the remaining branches for gain, the additional root locations are found to be $s = -0.083$, -3.5, and -9.5. The closed-loop transfer function is thus

$$\frac{C}{R}(s) = \frac{607(s + 0.1)}{(s + 0.083)(s + 3.5)(s + 9.5)[(s + 1.9)^2 + 4.3^2]} \qquad \textbf{(10-8.3)}$$

10-9 POLYNOMIAL FACTORING

In control systems analysis, the root-locus provides a graphical method for factoring the closed-loop denominator polynomial. This same technique is applicable, however, to the solution of any polynomial-type equation; the only requirement is that the equation can be arranged in the form $1 + \frac{KA}{B}(s) = 0$, where $A(s)$ and $B(s)$ are polynomials in s, and K is a parameter independent of s. To illustrate, consider the polynomial

$$s^5 + 18s^4 + 105s^3 + 296s^2 + 500s + 400 \qquad \textbf{(10-9.1)}$$

The first step required in factoring this expression is to equate the polynomial to zero, thus forming an equation similar to the characteristic equation of Eq. (10-2.3-c).

$$s^5 + 18s^4 + 105s^3 + 296s^2 + 500s + 400 = 0 \qquad \textbf{(10-9.2)}$$

This equation is now organized into two sub groups

$$s^3(s^2 + 18s + 105) + 296(s^2 + \tfrac{500}{296}s + \tfrac{400}{296}) = 0 \qquad \textbf{(10-9.3)}$$

Dividing Eq. (10-9.3) by the sub group containing the higher order of s, i.e., $s^3(s^2 + 18s + 105)$

$$1 + \frac{296(s^2 + 1.689s + 1.351)}{s^3(s^2 + 18s + 105)} = 0 \qquad \textbf{(10-9.4)}$$

Both the numerator and denominator of Eq. (10-9.4) are now factored into a pole-zero format. This operation presents no special difficulties because the polynomials involved are of second order only.

$$1 + \frac{296(s + 0.845 + j0.798)(s + 0.845 - j0.798)}{s^3(s + 9 + j4.9)(s + 9 - j4.9)} = 0 \qquad \textbf{(10-9.5)}$$

Thus, Eq. (10-9.2) has been transformed into an expression analogous to the form of the characteristic equation in Eq. (10-2.3-b), where the open-loop gain constant K has been assigned the specific numerical value of 296. The root-locus corresponding to Eq. (10-9.5) is constructed for a variable gain, the results of which are presented in Fig. 10-9.1. Calibrating the loci for the particular gain constant $K = 296$, the root locations are determined as $s = -2, -4, -10, -1 + j2,$ and $-1 - j2$. Hence, the original polynomial of Eq. (10-9.1) contains zeros at these locations.

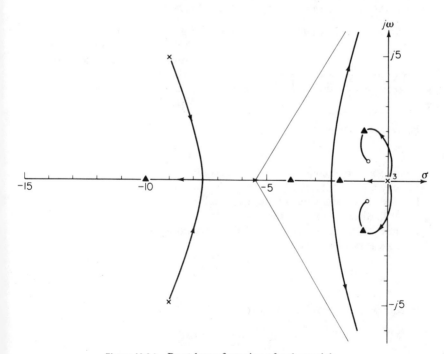

Figure 10-9.1   Root-locus factoring of polynomials.

If, in employing this graphical factoring procedure, the numerator and denominator polynomials of Eq. (10-9.4) are of high order (as would be the case for an original tenth-order polynomial), the intermediate polynomials are first factored by means of root-locus construction; the resulting poles and zeros then constitute the *open-loop* singularities of Eq. (10-9.5).

To summarize, the root-locus is amenable to the factoring of any arbitrary polynomial. Viewing the approach from this over-all vantage, we see that the usefulness of root-locus plotting is not restricted to an investigation of gain changes; variations in other parameters may similarly be evaluated as demonstrated in the following section.

10-10 OTHER APPLICATIONS OF ROOT-LOCUS CONSTRUCTION

In this section the root-locus method is applied to systems in which the effects of parameter variations other than open-loop gain values are of interest. These analyses are possible because of the inherent ability of the root-locus to function in an arbitrary polynomial-solving capacity.

EXAMPLE 1: *Optimum Location of Lead Compensation*

Consider the system block diagram of Fig. 10-10.1, consisting of an unalterable plant with unity feedback. The system open-loop transfer is

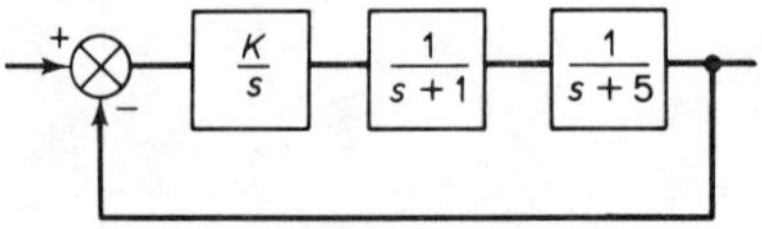

Figure 10-10.1 Original system block diagram.

$$KGH(s) = \frac{K}{s(s + 1)(s + 5)}$$

(10-10.1)

From both bandwidth and steady-state error considerations, it is required that the system exhibit a velocity constant $K_v = 10$. Equivalently, the root-locus gain constant K is evidently set at a value of 50. The resulting root-locus diagram of Fig. 10-10.2, when calibrated for $K = 50$, yields an unstable closed loop. Because of the real-axis nature of the plant poles, a lead compensation network is proposed, i.e.

$$G_c(s) = \frac{(s/0.1\omega_b) + 1}{(s/\omega_b) + 1}$$

(10-10.2)

or equivalently, in pole-zero form

$$G_c(s) = \frac{10(s + 0.1\omega_b)}{s + \omega_b}$$

(10-10.3)

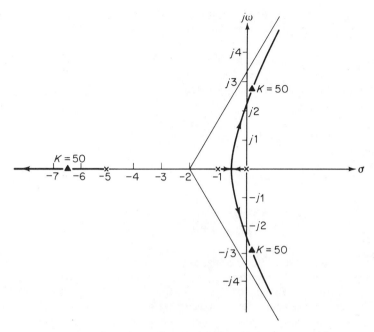

Figure 10-10.2   Root-locus diagram for Fig. 10-10.1 for $K_v = 10$.

where ω_b is the lag-term break frequency. The compensated open-loop transfer function is

$$KGH(s) = \frac{500(s + 0.1\omega_b)}{s(s + 1)(s + 5)(s + \omega_b)} \qquad (10\text{-}10.4)$$

In Eq. (10-10.4), the open loop velocity constant is observed to be 10, and is independent of ω_b. The specific positioning of the lead-lag pair should have a definite effect upon closed-loop stability. As $\omega_b \to \infty$, the original unstable closed loop is produced. Similarly, if $\omega_b \to 0$, the compensation will not influence systems operation within the frequency range of interest. For intermediate values, however, the compensation will produce a stabilizing effect. The root-locus is now employed to determine an optimum position for ω_b and the corresponding closed-loop transfer function. In unfactored form

$$\frac{C}{R}(s) = \frac{500(s + 0.1\omega_b)}{s(s + 1)(s + 5)(s + \omega_b) + 500(s + 0.1\omega_b)} \qquad (10\text{-}10.5)$$

The poles of $\dfrac{C}{R}(s)$ are identical to the roots of the characteristic equation

$$s(s + 1)(s + 5)(s + \omega_b) + 500(s + 0.1\omega_b) = 0 \qquad (10\text{-}10.6)$$

Expanding Eq. (10-10.6), and arranging into two sub groups (one that contains the parameter ω_b and one that is independent of ω_b)

$$s^4 + 6s^3 + 5s^2 + 500s + \omega_b(s^3 + 6s^2 + 5s + 50) = 0 \quad \text{(10-10.7)}$$

Equation (10-10.7) is now organized into a conventional root-locus diagram format, i.e.

$$1 + \frac{\omega_b(s^3 + 6s^2 + 5s + 50)}{s(s^3 + 6s^2 + 5s + 500)} = 0 \quad \text{(10-10.8)}$$

The resulting numerator and denominator polynomials are factored to yield

$$1 + \frac{\omega_b(s + 6.43)(s - 0.215 + j2.78)(s - 0.215 - j2.78)}{s(s + 10.27)(s - 2.135 + j6.65)(s - 2.135 - j6.65)} \quad \text{(10-10.9)}$$

From Eq. (10-10.9), a normal root-locus diagram can be generated. The open-loop gain parameter has, in this instance, been replaced by the new parameter ω_b. Except for this distinction, all rules of locus construction are applicable, and the over-all diagram significance remains unaltered. As illustrated in Fig. 10-10.3, the root locations for $\omega_b = \infty$ coincide with the

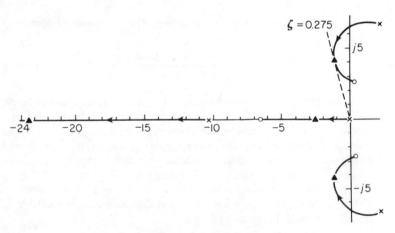

Figure 10-10.3 Root-locus for variable-lag break frequency.

poles of the uncompensated system. Similarly, for $\omega_b = 0$, the roots are situated at right half-plane open-loop poles so that the system is again unstable. For intermediate values, however, a stable root configuration exists. Assuming that the optimum system is one in which the dominant-pole damping ratio is maximized, the lead-lag pair should evidently be designed with $\omega_b = 22.2$, i.e.

$$G_c(s) = \frac{10(s + 2.22)}{s + 22.2} \qquad \text{(10-10.10)}$$

The resulting closed-loop transfer function is written by inspection

$$\frac{C}{R}(s) = \frac{500(s + 2.2)}{[s^2 + 2.26s + 18.3](s + 2.61)(s + 23.33)} \qquad \text{(10-10.11)}$$

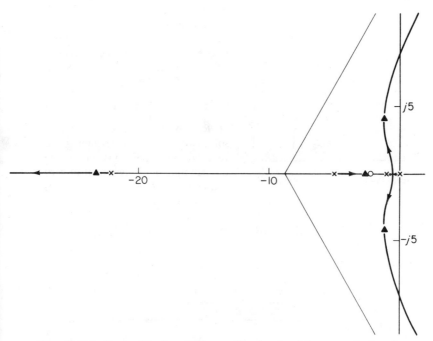

Figure 10-10.4 Conventional root-locus verifies the closed-loop transfer function of Eq. (10-10.11).

The results of this analysis are verified by constructing the conventional root-locus diagram of Fig. 10-10.4, in which the open-loop transfer function consists of the original plant singularities, together with the lead network specified in Eq. (10-10.10). The closed-loop transfer function derived from Fig. 10-10.4 is identical to that of Eq. (10-10.11).

EXAMPLE 2: *Effects of Output Loading on a Compensation-Network Transfer Function*

The passive-element compensation network of Fig. 10-10.5 has been designed to generate a required transfer function (see Appendix C of

Advanced Control Systems Engineering, Volume II) for a 1-megohm resistive load impedance.

$$\frac{E_2}{E_1}(s) =$$

$$\frac{R_L[1 + (R_1C_1 + R_2C_2)s + R_1R_2C_1C_2s^2]}{R_1 + R_L + [R_1R_LC_1 + (R_1R_2 + R_1R_L + R_2R_L)C_2]s + R_1R_2R_LC_1C_2s^2}$$

$$(10\text{-}10.12)$$

It is now desired to consider the effects of a varying load and, in particular, to calculate the network transfer function for various values of load resistance between 100 K-ohms and 2 megohms. From Eq. (10-10.12), it is observed that the zeros of $\frac{E_2}{E_1}(s)$ are independent of R_L, so that the problem is resolved into one of determining the varying pole positions. Equating the denominator polynomial to zero and combining into two sub groups as previously described

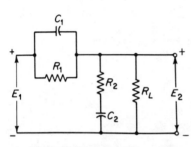

Figure 10-10.5 Passive-element filter network.

$$R_1 + R_1R_2C_2s + R_L[1 + (R_1C_1 + R_1C_2 + R_2C_2)s + R_1R_2C_1C_2s^2] = 0$$

$$(10.10\text{-}13)$$

Rearranging the preceding

$$1 + \frac{R_1R_2C_1C_2}{R_1R_2C_2}R_L\frac{\left[s^2 + \dfrac{R_1C_1 + R_1C_2 + R_2C_2}{R_1R_2C_1C_2}s + \dfrac{1}{R_1R_2C_1C_2}\right]}{s + \dfrac{1}{R_2C_2}} = 0$$

$$(10\text{-}10.14)$$

Substituting the specific network-element values $R_1 = 0.1$ megohms, $R_2 = 0.2$ megohms, $C_1 = 0.5$ μf, and $C_2 = 0.1$ μf

$$1 + 0.5R_L\frac{(s^2 + 80s + 1000)}{s + 50} = 0 \qquad (10\text{-}10.15)$$

where R_L is now expressed in megohms. Factoring the numerator polynomial again produces the required root-locus format

$$1 + 0.5R_L\frac{(s + 64.5)(s + 15.5)}{s + 50} = 0 \qquad (10\text{-}10.16)$$

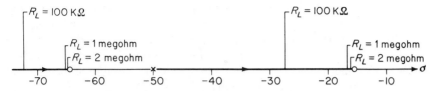

Figure 10-10.6   Root-locus for variable filter-network loading.

The corresponding root-locus diagram of Fig. 10-10.6 differs from those considered to this point in that the open-loop expression contains an excess of zeros over poles. Hence, a root of $1 + KGH(s) = 0$ exists at infinity for a short-circuited output load, but migrates to the right as R_L increases. The root-locus is now calibrated for R_L. Note that the gain parameter includes the factor 0.5; a ratio of pole to zero vector distances thus corresponds to a particular value of the over-all parameter $0.5\,R_L$, from which R_L is obtained by simple division.

10-11 POSITIVE-FEEDBACK SYSTEMS

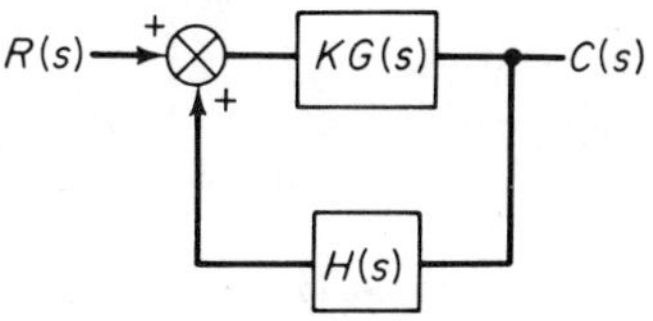

In dealing with complex control systems, one occasionally encounters an interior positive-feedback loop, stabilized by outer loops. As indicated in Chapter 7, the typical positive-feedback system of Fig. 10-11.1 is described by the closed-loop transfer function

Figure 10-11.1   Positive-feedback system.

$$\frac{C}{R}(s) = \frac{KG(s)}{1 - KGH(s)} \qquad (10\text{-}11.1)$$

The equivalent characteristic equation is

$$1 - KGH(s) = 0 \qquad (10\text{-}11.2)$$

Similarly, for a conventional unity-feedback system, the open-loop transfer function $KG(s)$ is related to the closed loop through the expression

$$KG(s) = \frac{(C/R)(s)}{1 - (C/R)(s)} \qquad (10\text{-}11.3)$$

If, in Eq. (10-11.3), the closed-loop transfer function is known, a corresponding open-loop transfer function and gain constant can be generated.

This technique can be employed as an important step in the analysis and synthesis of certain simple control systems by means of Guillemin's method[7].

The characteristic equation of Eq. (10-11.2) can be solved through the application of root-locus techniques. The angle criterion and some of the rules of root-locus construction are altered, however, because of the negative polarity of $KGH(s)$. Thus, rearranging Eq. (10-11.2)

$$KGH(s) = 1 = e^{j0°} \qquad (10\text{-}11.4)$$

Equation (10-11.4) demonstrates that the angle criterion, as applied to positive-feedback systems, requires that the summation of all pole and zero

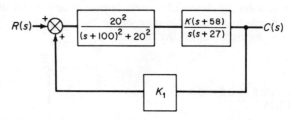

Figure 10-11.2   Representative positive-feedback system block diagram.

vector phase angles must equal 0°. The magnitude criterion, however, remains unaltered.

The rules of construction are now considered. Rules 1 and 2 are unchanged since the roots of $1 - KGH(s) = 0$ begin at the open-loop poles and terminate upon open-loop zeros as before. With respect to Rule 3, the locus exists at any point along the real axis which lies to the left of an even number (including zero) of singularities. Rule 4 is restated such that, as $K \rightarrow \infty$, the locus becomes asymptotic to the angles $\pm n\,360°/(\#P - \#Z)$, where $n = 0, 1, 2, \ldots$ and $\#P - \#Z$ represents, as before, the excess of poles over zeros. The center of gravity defined in Rule 5, and the angles of departure from, and arrival to, the real axis (Rule 6) are unchanged. Similarly, Rule 7 remains the same. Rule 8 is modified such that, when calculating complex-singularity breakaway angles, 180° is no longer subtracted from the total vector-angle summation. And finally, Rule 9 is still valid; Routh's criterion applies to positive- as well as negative-feedback systems.

Consider, now, the sample positive-feedback system block diagram of Fig. 10-11.2 with the open-loop transfer function

$$KGH(s) = \frac{K(s + 58)}{s(s + 27)[(s + 100)^2 + 20^2]} \qquad (10\text{-}11.5)$$

The modified rules of root-locus construction are applied as follows:

1. The roots of the characteristic equation are located at open-loop pole positions ($s = -27$, $-100 + j20$, $-100 - j20$) for $K = 0$.

2. For $K = \infty$, one branch of the root-locus terminates at the open-loop zero ($s = -58$).

3. The root-locus exists upon the real axis between the origin and positive infinity, and between $s = -27$ and $s = -58$.

4. As $K \to \infty$, the root-locus branches become asymptotic to the angles $\pm 0°/3 = 0°$ and $\pm 360°/3 = \pm 120°$.

5. The system center of gravity is calculated as

$$CG = \frac{-27 - 200 + 58}{3} = -56.3$$

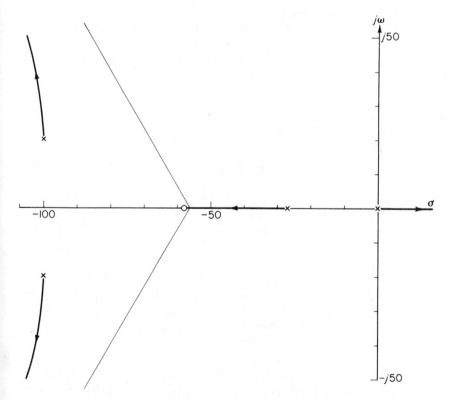

Figure 10-11.3   Root-locus diagram for positive-feedback system.

6 & 7. No roots break from or arrive at, the real axis.

8. Breakaway angles from the two complex poles are calculated as 93°.

9. Rule 9 does not apply, since complex roots do not cross the $j\omega$ axis.

Figure 10-11.3 illustrates the final root-locus diagram. Note that for any value of gain, an unstable system is produced due to the root originating at the origin. This system must, then, be stabilized with an outer loop.

An additional possible closed-loop system is indicated in the block diagram of Fig. 10-11.4. Although the feedback signal is summed positively, a negative gain constant appears in the open-loop transfer function. A system of this type is governed by the closed-loop transfer expression

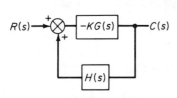

Figure 10-11.4 Negative-feedback system.

$$\frac{C}{R}(s) = \frac{-KG(s)}{1 + KGH(s)} \quad \text{(10-11.6)}$$

The characteristic equation associated with Eq. (10-11.6) is identical to that of Eq. (10-2.3-a). Thus, the root-locus diagram is constructed as for the conventional negative-feedback system.

10-12 CLOSED-LOOP TRANSIENT-RESPONSE MEASUREMENTS[8,9]

In the conventional design of linear feedback control systems, the root-locus represents a powerful and well-defined graphical procedure. Once all system parameters have been determined, however, it is usually necessary to verify that the final design does indeed meet all required time-domain specifications. The suggested sequence of design, analysis, and evaluation may have to be repeated many times before a completely satisfactory transient response is obtained. The process of translating a closed-loop pole-zero array into meaningful time-domain information requires an inverse Laplace transformation which can be both tedious and time-consuming when attacked by the classical partial-fraction expansion methods of Chapter 4. This is particularly true if a large number of singularities are involved. The purpose of this section is to present a straightforward graphical procedure, based upon ruler and protractor measurements, for obtaining an inverse Laplace transformation directly from an s-plane closed-loop pole-zero array. The method is applicable to systems containing real, imaginary and complex first-order poles when excited by a step-input forcing function.

Graphical inverse Laplace transform calculations are based upon the following three relationships

$$\mathscr{L}^{-1}\left[\frac{1}{s+\alpha}\right] = Ae^{-\alpha t} \qquad \alpha = \sigma + j\omega \qquad \text{(10-12.1)}$$

$$Ae^{j\theta} + Ae^{-j\theta} = 2 \operatorname{Re} Ae^{j\theta} = 2 \operatorname{Re} Ae^{-j\theta} \qquad \text{(10-12.2)}$$

$$\operatorname{Re} Ae^{j\theta} = \operatorname{Re} Ae^{-j\theta} = A \cos \theta \qquad \text{(10-12.3)}$$

The first equation states simply that the inverse Laplace transformation of a first-order lag (with a break frequency of α, where α is, in general, complex) is a decaying exponential time function with a time constant of $1/\alpha$. The second equation expresses the well-known fact that the sum of a complex number and its complex conjugate is equal to twice the real part of either quantity. Equation (10-12.3) defines the real part of a complex number by means of polar coordinates. Let us now consider an arbitrary closed-loop control system, whose transfer function is

$$\frac{C}{R}(s) = \frac{s+a}{(s+b)[(s+c)^2 + d^2]}$$

$$\text{(10-12.4)}$$

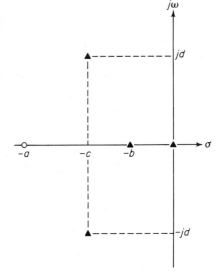

For a unit step-function input, i.e., $R(s) = 1/s$, Eq. (10-12.4) becomes

$$C(s) = \frac{s+a}{s(s+b)[(s+c)^2 + d^2]}$$

$$\text{(10-12.5)}$$

Figure 10-12.1 Arbitrary closed-loop transfer function pole-zero array.

The pole-zero array corresponding to Eq. (10-12.5) is plotted in Fig. 10-12.1. In applying the conventional inverse Laplace transform techniques of Chapter 4, the following procedure would normally be employed.

1. Equation (10-12.5) is expanded into partial fractions through the introduction of arbitrary coefficients

$$\frac{s+a}{s(s+b)[(s+c)^2 + d^2]} = \frac{A}{s} + \frac{B}{s+b} + \frac{Cs+D}{(s+c)^2 + d^2} \qquad \text{(10-12.6)}$$

2. To determine the first coefficient A, Eq. (10-12.6) is multiplied by s, and the resulting expression is evaluated for $s = 0$, i.e.

$$A = sC(s)\Big|_{s=0}$$

and similarly

$$B = (s + b)C(s)\Big|_{s=-b}$$

3. To calculate C and D, Eq. (10-12.6) is multiplied by the quadratic $(s + c)^2 + d^2$. We then employ the substitution $s = -c + jd$ and define C and D by equating real and imaginary parts of the resulting expression. With all coefficients now determined, the inverse transform is obtained by referring to standard transform tables.

This over-all procedure becomes involved for high-order systems, and may readily lead to algebraic or arithmetic error. These difficulties can be obviated to a great extent through applying a graphical approach which is now formalized.

In applying the graphical inverse Laplace transformation, a slightly different partial-fraction expansion is employed. Each quadratic expression is decomposed into first-order complex poles so that the resulting partial-fraction expansion appears as indicated in Eq. (10-12.7)

$$\frac{s + a}{s(s + b)[(s + c)^2 + d^2]} = \frac{A}{s} + \frac{B}{s + b} + \frac{C}{s + c - jd} + \frac{D}{s + c + jd}$$

(10-12.7)

Once the arbitrary coefficients A, B, C, and D have been computed, the inverse transformation can be written directly, without referring to tables, since each factor is in the form of Eq. (10-12.1). In computing the coefficient B by classical means, we multiply $C(s)$ by the quantity $(s + b)$ and evaluate $(s + b)C(s)$ for $s = -b$ as described previously. This is equivalent, geometrically, to constructing vectors from each s-plane singularity to the pole associated with B (i.e., $1/(s + b)$), measuring the length and subtended angle of each vector, and evaluating the coefficient B according to the following generalized expression

$$B = \frac{Z_1 e^{j\theta_{z_1}} Z_2 e^{j\theta_{z_2}} \cdots Z_n e^{j\theta_{z_n}}}{P_1 e^{j\theta_{p_1}} P_2 e^{j\theta_{p_2}} \cdots P_n e^{j\theta_{p_n}}}$$

$$= \frac{Z_1 Z_2 \cdots Z_n e^{j(\theta_{z_1} + \theta_{z_2} + \cdots + \theta_{z_n})}}{P_1 P_2 \cdots P_n e^{j(\theta_{p_1} + \theta_{p_2} + \cdots + \theta_{p_n})}}$$

(10-12.8)

where $Z_1 Z_2 \cdots Z_n$ is the product of vector lengths from the system zeros to the pole in question

$P_1 P_2 \cdots P_n$ is the product of the vector lengths from the system poles to the pole in question

$\theta_{z_1} + \theta_{z_2} + \cdots + \theta_{z_n}$ is the sum of the angles subtended by all zero vectors

$\theta_{p_1} + \theta_{p_2} + \cdots + \theta_{p_n}$ is the sum of the angles subtended by all pole vectors

Returning to the final s-plane pole-zero array of Fig. 10-12.1, we now compute the coefficient B as indicated in Fig. 10-12.2. To generalize, the coefficient corresponding to any real-axis pole will be a real quantity (either positive or negative), since each complex pole or zero exists as one-half of a complex-conjugate pair. The coefficients C and D are determined in an identical manner. For complex poles, however, the coefficients are also complex in nature, representing a complex-conjugate pair, as demonstrated In Fig. 10-12.3. Assuming that the coefficients A, B, C, and D have been determined numerically as A_1, B_1, $\Delta e^{j\varphi}$, and $\Delta e^{-j\varphi}$, the inverse Laplace transform of Eq. (10-12.7) is

$$c(t) = A_1 + B_1 e^{-bt} + \Delta e^{j\varphi} e^{-(c-jd)t}$$
$$+ \Delta e^{-j\varphi} e^{-(c+jd)t}$$

(10-12.9)

Rearranging,

$$c(t) = A_1 + B_1 e^{-bt} + \Delta e^{-ct} e^{j(dt+\varphi)}$$
$$+ \Delta e^{-ct} e^{-j(dt+\varphi)}$$

(10-12.10)

Since the quantities $e^{j(dt+\varphi)}$ and $e^{-j(dt+\varphi)}$ form a complex-conjugate pair, Eqs. (10-12.2) and (10-12.3) can be applied to yield the final result

$$c(t) = A_1 + B_1 e^{-bt}$$
$$+ 2\Delta e^{-ct} \cos(dt + \varphi)$$

(10-12.11)

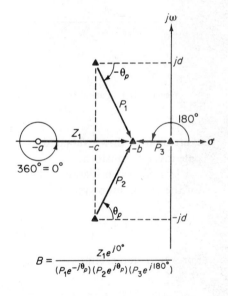

$$B = \frac{Z_1 e^{j0°}}{(P_1 e^{-j\theta_p})(P_2 e^{j\theta_p})(P_3 e^{j180°})}$$

$$= \frac{Z_1}{P_1 P_2 P_3} e^{-j180°} = \frac{-Z_1}{P_1 P_2 P_3}$$

Figure 10-12.2 Computing the partial-fraction coefficient corresponding to a real-axis pole.

Thus, it is not necessary to measure both coefficients associated with any set of complex poles. Only one of the coefficients need be calculated; the total corresponding time-domain

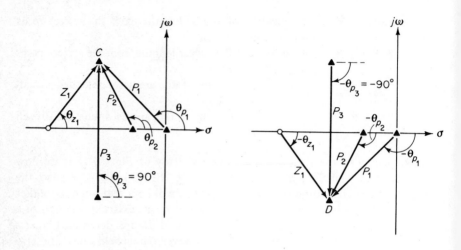

$$C = \frac{Z_1 e^{j\theta_{z_1}}}{P_1 P_2 P_3 e^{j(\theta_{p_1} + \theta_{p_2} + \theta_{p_3})}}$$

$$= \frac{Z_1}{P_1 P_2 P_3} e^{j\varphi}$$

$$D = \frac{Z_1 e^{-j\theta_{z_1}}}{P_1 P_2 P_3 e^{-j(\theta_{p_1} + \theta_{p_2} + \theta_{p_3})}}$$

$$= \frac{Z_1}{P_1 P_2 P_3} e^{-j\varphi}$$

Figure 10-12.3 Partial-fraction expansion coefficients for conjugate roots are observed to be conjugate quantities.

expression is then evaluated as twice the real part of the resulting single-pole inverse transform.

As a final consideration, let us compute the unit step-function response for the closed-loop system

$$\frac{C}{R}(s) = \frac{250(s + 2)(s + 5)}{(s + 1)(s + 6)[(s + 2)^2 + 3^2][(s + 4)^2 + 4^2]} \qquad \text{(10-12.12)}$$

For a unit step excitation, the transformed output variable $C(s)$ becomes

$$C(s) = \frac{250(s + 2)(s + 5)}{s(s + 1)(s + 6)[(s + 2)^2 + 3^2][(s + 4)^2 + 4^2]} \qquad \text{(10-12.13)}$$

Expanding into first-order partial fractions

$$C(s) = \frac{A}{s} + \frac{B}{s + 1} + \frac{C}{s + 6} + \frac{D}{s + 2 - j3} + \frac{E}{s + 2 + j3}$$

$$+ \frac{F}{s + 4 - j4} + \frac{G}{s + 4 + j4} \qquad \text{(10-12.14)}$$

The arbitrary coefficients A, B, C, D, and F are now computed graphically. The partial-fraction expansion coefficients associated with each pole of Eq. (10-12.14) are now computed. The geometrical solution for the coefficient F is illustrated in Fig. 10-12.4. Note that E and G need not be calculated, since these coefficients contain only redundant information.

$$A = \frac{(2.0e^{j0^\circ})(5.0e^{j0^\circ})}{(1.0e^{j0^\circ})(6.0e^{j0^\circ})(3.6e^{j\theta_1})(3.6e^{-j\theta_1})(5.65e^{j\psi_1})(5.65e^{-j\psi_1})}$$

$$= \frac{(2.0)(5.0)e^{j0^\circ}}{(1.0)(6.0)(3.6)(3.6)(5.65)(5.65)} = 0.0040$$

Since, at any point along the real axis, the phase angle contributed by a complex-pole vector is cancelled by the complex-conjugate vector angle, it is not actually necessary to measure the subtended angles explicitly. Thus, in

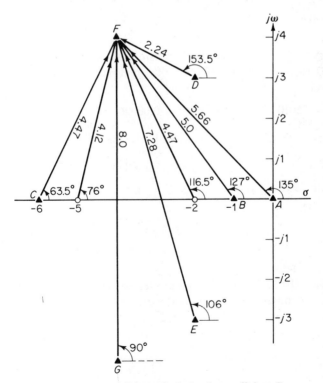

Figure 10-12.4   Graphical calculation for coefficient F.

the preceding, the quantities θ_1 and ψ_1 need not be defined numerically.

$$B = \frac{(1.0e^{j0°})(4.0e^{j0°})}{(1.0e^{j180°})(5.0e^{j0°})(3.17e^{j\theta_2})(3.17e^{-j\theta_2})(5.0e^{j\psi_2})(5.0e^{-j\psi_2})}$$

$$= -0.0032$$

$$C = \frac{(4.0e^{j180°})(1.0e^{j180°})}{(6.0e^{j180°})(5.0e^{j180°})(5.0e^{j\theta_3})(5.0e^{-j\theta_3})(4.47e^{j\psi_3})(4.47e^{-j\psi_3})}$$

$$= 0.000266$$

$$D = \frac{(3.0e^{j90°})(4.25e^{j45°})}{(3.6e^{j123.5°})(3.17e^{j108.5°})(6.0e^{j90°})(5.0e^{j37°})(2.24e^{j333.5°})(7.28e^{j74°})}$$

$$= 0.00228e^{-j271.5°}$$

$$F = \frac{(4.47e^{j116.5°})(4.12e^{j76°})}{(2.24e^{j153.5°})(5.66e^{j135°})(5.0e^{j127°})(4.47e^{j63.5°})(7.28e^{j106°})(8.0e^{j90°})}$$

$$= 0.00111e^{-j123°}$$

Applying the inverse Laplace transformation of Eq. (10-12.1) to Eq. (10-12.14) and considering only twice the real part of each complex pole

$$c(t) = 250\{0.0040 - 0.0032e^{-t} + 0.000266e^{-6t}$$

$$+ 2 \text{ Re } [0.00228e^{-j271.5°}e^{(-2+j3)t}]$$

$$+ 2 \text{ Re } [0.00111e^{-j123°}e^{(-4+j4)t}]\} \qquad \textbf{(10-12.15)}$$

which reduces to

$$c(t) = 1 - 0.8e^{-t} + 0.0665e^{-6t} + 1.39e^{-2t} \cos (3t - 271.5°)$$

$$+ 0.555e^{-4t} \cos (4t - 123°) \qquad \textbf{(10-12.16)}$$

Equation (10-12.16) can now be plotted to yield the system step-function response. Although certainly not a requirement, the graphical transient-response measurement is ideally suited for use in conjunction with the root-locus diagram. For nonunity-feedback systems, poles of $H(s)$ become zeros of $\frac{C}{R}(s)$, and zeros of $H(s)$ do not appear explicitly in $\frac{C}{R}(s)$. These facts must be reflected in the closed-loop pole-zero array prior to the initiation of graphical measurements. Multiple-order pole systems are also amenable to transient analysis by this procedure, but not in a simple or straightforward manner. Thus, the technique essentially is restricted to systems containing simple first-order poles exclusively.

10-13 FREQUENCY-RESPONSE MEASUREMENTS

It has been demonstrated in the previous section, that a direct correspondence exists between an s-plane pole-zero array and the associated time-domain transient-response characteristics. The purpose of this section is to derive a similar relationship between the system s-plane array and corresponding frequency-response characteristics. As described in Chapter 5, the frequency response of a generalized closed-loop transfer function

$$\frac{C}{R}(s) = \frac{K(s + z_1)(s + z_2)}{(s + p_1)(s + p_2)(s + p_3)} \tag{10-13.1}$$

can be obtained by substituting $s = j\omega$, and evaluating the resulting expression for various values of ω, i.e.

$$\frac{C}{R}(j\omega) = \frac{K(j\omega + z_1)(j\omega + z_2)}{(j\omega + p_1)(j\omega + p_2)(j\omega + p_3)} \tag{10-13.2}$$

Each of the numerator and denominator components of Eq. (10-13.2) is now expressed in polar coordinates. As illustrated in Fig. 10-13.1, $\frac{C}{R}(j\omega)$ is graphically calculated by constructing vectors from each closed loop s-plane singularity to the imaginary-axis test point $j\omega_i$. The resulting amplitude ratio and phase angle are evaluated from the equations

$$\left|\frac{C}{R}(j\omega)\right| = \frac{K[\Pi \text{ (length of closed-loop zero vectors)}]}{\Pi \text{ (length of closed-loop pole vectors)}} \tag{10-13.3}$$

$$\tan^{-1}\frac{\text{Im }(C/R)(j\omega)}{\text{Re }(C/R)(j\omega)} = \frac{\sum \text{(closed-loop zero-vector phase angle)}}{\sum \text{(closed-loop pole-vector phase angle)}} \tag{10-13.4}$$

As the test point is translated up the imaginary axis and Eqs. (10-13.3) and (10-13.4) computed, an equivalent system frequency response is easily generated. Thus, the root-locus represents a universal procedure, the results of which can be directly correlated with both time and frequency-response considerations.

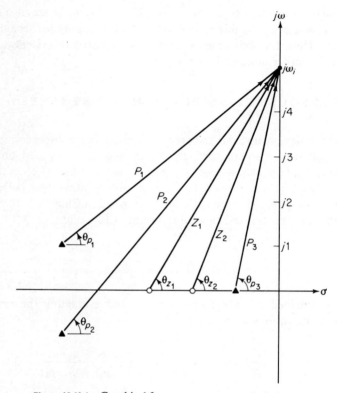

Figure 10-13.1 Graphical frequency-response calculation.

PROBLEMS

In the problems to follow, $KG(s)$ is the forward open-loop transfer function, $H(s)$ is the feedback transfer function, and $KGH(s)$ is the complete system open-loop function.

10.1 For each of the following open loop transfer functions, plot the pole-zero array and sketch all *real axis* root-locus branches.

(a) $KGH(s) = \dfrac{K(s+2)}{s(s+4)(s+10)}$

(b) $KGH(s) = \dfrac{K(s+2)(s+5)}{s(s+7)(s+11)}$

(c) $KGH(s) = \dfrac{K[(s+2)^2 + 3^2]}{s^2(s+5)(s+11)}$

(d) $KGH(s) = \dfrac{K(s + 20)^2}{s(s + 6)(s + 10)(s + 30)}$

(e) $KGH(s) = \dfrac{K(s + 1)(s + 5)}{s[(s + 2)^2 + 4^2](s + 6)}$

10.2 $KGH(s) = K(s + 6)/s(s+10)$

(a) Plot the root-locus for a variable K
(b) Determine the closed-loop pole positions for $K = 100$

10.3 $KGH(s) = K/s(s + 60)$

(a) Plot the root-locus for a variable K
(b) What value of gain corresponds to a critically damped system?
(c) Discuss the stability of a second-order system in terms of the open-loop gain constant

10.4 For each of the following open-loop systems, determine the value of gain which results in marginal stability (closed-loop poles situated upon the imaginary axis) and indicate the steady-state oscillational frequency.

(a) $KGH(s) = \dfrac{K}{s(s + 4)(s + 7)}$

(b) $KGH(s) = \dfrac{K(s + 7)}{s^2(s + 12)(s + 17)}$

(c) $KGH(s) = \dfrac{K(s + 1)}{s[(s + 2)^2 + 3^2](s + 11)}$

10.5 $KG(s) = K_1(s + 6)/s^2(s + 10)$ and $H(s) = 3(s + 1)/(s + 3)$

(a) Plot the root-locus for a variable K
(b) What are the closed-loop pole positions for $K_1 = 30$?
(c) Construct the system closed-loop transfer function for part (b)

10.6 For each of the following unity-feedback systems ($H = 1$), plot the root-locus and determine the closed-loop transfer function for a 0.3 control-pole damping ratio.

(a) $KG(s) = \dfrac{K}{s(s + 10)(s + 30)}$

(b) $KG(s) = K\dfrac{(s + 6)}{s(s^2 + 2s + 12)(s + 18)}$

(c) $KG(s) = \dfrac{K}{s(s + 10)(s + 21)^2}$

10.7   Plot the root-locus diagrams for the following functions.

(a) $KGH(s) = \dfrac{K(s + 6)}{s^3(s + 60)}$

(b) $KGH(s) = \dfrac{K(s + 1)}{s(s - 2)(s + 6)}$

(c) $KGH(s) = \dfrac{K(s - 2)^2}{s^2(s + 31)}$

10.8   Complete the root-locus sketches of Problem 10.1 and, in particular, indicate

(a)   Center of gravity locations
(b)   Asymptotic angles
(c)   Angles of departure from complex poles
(d)   Angles of arrival at complex zeros
(e)   Frequency at which root-locus crosses imaginary axis

10.9   A unity-feedback system block diagram is illustrated here. All forward

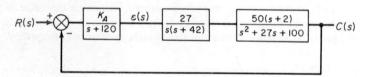

Prob. 10.9

element gain parameters are fixed with the exception of the summing amplifier. Determine the amplifier gain K_A such that the system control poles have a damping ratio of 0.6.

10.10   The following process-controller block diagram consists of a summing amplifier, compensator, and hydraulic actuator in the forward loop. The output flow rate is sensed by a turbine-type flow transducer (pulsed output), and is converted to a d-c voltage by an electronic filter network.

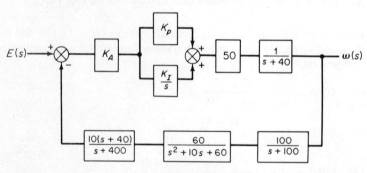

Prob. 10.10

(a) For $K_P = 1$, what value of K_I will produce a system zero at $s = -20$?

(b) What amplifier gain K_A yields a closed-loop pole at $s = -10$, assuming the condition of (a)

(c) Determine the system closed-loop transfer function for the system as specified in (a) and (b)

10.11 The regulator $KG(s) = K(s + 7)/(s + 2)(s + 6)$ is modified by the introduction of a phase-shift network $N(s) = (s - 3)/(s + 3)$ as illustrated in the accompanying figure.

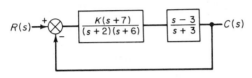

$$R(s) \longrightarrow \boxed{\dfrac{K(s+7)}{(s+2)(s+6)}} \boxed{\dfrac{s-3}{s+3}} \longrightarrow C(s)$$

Prob. 10.11

(a) What loop gain results in the formation of a closed-loop pole at the origin?

(b) What is the resulting closed-loop transfer function?

(c) Discuss the merits of this technique

10.12 $KG(s) = \dfrac{K(s + 16)}{s(s + 10)^2(s + 30)}$ and $H(s) = \dfrac{114(s + 6)}{(s + 11)(s + 26)}$

(a) Plot the root-locus for a variable K

(b) Determine the closed-loop pole positions for $K = 1000$

(c) What is the closed-loop transfer function?

(d) Compute the closed-loop system step-function response graphically

10.13 Employ root-locus techniques to factor the following polynomials

(a) $s^4 + 13s^3 + 60s^2 + 56s + 80$

(b) $s^5 + 32s^4 + 57s^3 + 126s^2 + 208s + 1076$

(c) $s^5 + 16s^4 - 132s^3 + 162s^2 + 1045s + 1672$

(d) $s^6 + 6s^5 + 27s^4 + 122s^3 + 286s^2 + 1265s + 4269$

10.14 For each of the following closed-loop transfer functions, compute (1) the step-function response, (2) amplitude and phase shift at $s = j1$, (3) amplitude and phase shift at $s = j5$.

(a) $\dfrac{C}{R}(s) = \dfrac{100(s + 2)(s + 7)}{(s + 14)(s + 100)}$

(b) $\dfrac{C}{R}(s) = \dfrac{2400(s + 16)}{[(s + 16)^2 + 32^2](s + 12)}$

(c) $\dfrac{C}{R}(s) = \dfrac{10(s - 2)(s + 2)}{(s + 1)(s + 4)(s + 5)}$

(d) $\dfrac{C}{R}(s) = \dfrac{1000[(s + 2)^2 + 16^2]}{(s + 3)[(s + 6)^2 + 9^2][(s + 14)^2 + 7^2]}$

10.15 Plot the frequency response from 1 to 50 cycles per second for the following closed-loop transfer functions

(a) $\dfrac{C}{R}(s) = \dfrac{42(s+1)}{(s+6)(s+7)}$

(b) $\dfrac{C}{R}(s) = \dfrac{(s+7)(s+9)}{[(s+2)^2 + 16^2](s+21)}$

(c) $\dfrac{C}{R}(s) = \dfrac{14(s+13)[(s+2)^2 + 11^2]}{[(s+4)^2 + 16^2][(s+9)^2 + 18^2]}$

10.16 Proportional and derivative compensation is provided to stabilize the fixed plant dynamics of the following illustration. Plot a root-locus diagram for a variable time constant τ to determine the optimum zero location (control poles with the highest damping ratio).

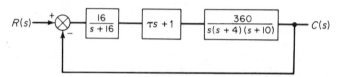

Prob. 10.16

10.17 A particular electronic circuit has the following open-loop transfer function

$$\frac{E_0}{E_i} = \frac{s^3 + 2s^2 + 13s + 27}{s^4 + (3 + R_D)s^3 + (16 + 4R_D)s^2 + (37 + 2R_D)s + (20 + 6R_D)}$$

Show, by root-locus techniques, the open-loop pole locations for various dropping-resistor values ($R_D = 1, 5, 10$).

10.18 Plot the root-locus diagrams for the following positive-feedback systems

(a) $KGH(s) = \dfrac{K}{s(s+2)}$

(b) $KGH(s) = \dfrac{K(s+4)}{s(s+5)(s+16)}$

(c) $KGH(s) = \dfrac{K(s+10)}{s^2(s+4)[(s+6)^2 + 10^2]}$

(d) $KGH(s) = \dfrac{K[(s+2)^2 + 3^2]}{s(s+9)(s+14)}$

10.19 The multiloop block diagram of the accompanying figure illustrates a positive-feedback loop stabilized by an outer loop. For this system,

(a) Determine the value of K_1 which produces an inner-loop pole at $s = +1$

(b) Compute the inner loop closed-loop transfer function $\theta_o/\theta_i(s)$

(c) Using the results of (b) as an open-loop transfer function for the outer loop, compute the value of K_2 required to produce a marginally stable system.

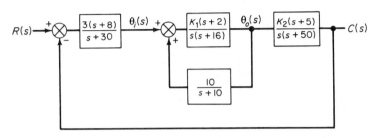

Prob. 10.19

10.20 A system closed-loop transfer function is determined experimentally as

$$\frac{C}{R}(s) = \frac{100(s + 20)(s + 30)}{[(s + 10)^2 + 10^2](s + 5)(s + 6)(s + 10)}$$

The open-loop system contains a single integration, and it is known to have a unity feedback. From Eq. (10-11.3), determine the original open-loop transfer function.

BIBLIOGRAPHY

1. D'Azzo, J. J. and C. H. Houpis, *Control System Analysis and Synthesis*. New York: McGraw-Hill Book Company, 1960.

2. Del Toro, V. and S. R. Parker, *Principles of Control System Engineering*. New York: McGraw-Hill Book Company, 1960.

3. Evans, W. R., *Control-System Dynamics*. New York: McGraw-Hill Book Company, 1954.

4. Langill, A. W., "Root-locus Systems Analysis," *Electro-Technology*, October 1963.

5. Savant, C. J., Jr., *Basic Feedback Control System Design*. New York: McGraw-Hill Book Company, 1958.

6. Seifert, W. W. and C. W. Steeg, *Control Systems Engineering*. New York: McGraw-Hill Book Company, 1960.

7. Truxal, J. G., *Automatic Feedback Control System Synthesis*. New York: McGraw-Hill Book Company, 1955.

8. Langill, A. W., "Measuring Step Function Response," *Electronic Industries*, May 1962.

9. Smith, O. J. M., *Feedback Control Systems*. New York: McGraw-Hill Book Company, 1958.

NYQUIST STABILITY CRITERION[1,2,3,4]

11-1 INTRODUCTION

Root-locus construction equips the designer with a technique for locating all poles of the closed-loop transfer function, thus specifying the system in terms of absolute stability. An application of the *Nyquist stability criterion* yields similar quantitative information regarding over-all loop stability but without indicating the corresponding pole positions. The root-locus achieves its desired objectives by providing a graphical solution to the characteristic equation $(1 + KGH(s) = 0)$ for all values of open-loop gain K. Conversely, in employing Nyquist's criterion, the gain parameter is first assigned a specific value. The existence of unstable zeros of $1 + KGH(s)$ resulting from this particular choice of gain is then deduced, again by a graphical technique. Since

$$\frac{C}{R}(s) = \frac{KG(s)}{1 + KGH(s)} = \frac{KG_N H_D(s)}{G_D H_D(s) + KG_N H_N(s)}$$

(11-1.1)

where, as before, $G(s) = \dfrac{G_N}{G_D}(s)$, $H(s) = \dfrac{H_N}{H_D}(s)$, and K is the open-loop gain constant

$$1 + KGH(s) = 1 + \frac{KG_N H_N(s)}{G_D H_D(s)}$$

$$= \frac{G_D H_D(s) + KG_N H_N(s)}{G_D H_D(s)}$$

(11-1.2)

238

Observe that the zeros of $1 + KGH(s)$ and the poles of $\dfrac{C}{R}(s)$ are identical.

If $1 + KGH(s)$ contains one or more right half-plane zeros, an unstable closed loop arises. Since the polynomial-type equation solved by the root-locus is

$$G_D H_D(s) + K G_N H_N(s) = 0 \qquad \text{(11-1.3)}$$

it follows directly that

$$\text{zeros of } 1 + KGH(s) \equiv \text{poles of } \frac{C}{R}(s) \equiv \text{roots of } 1 + KGH(s) = 0 \qquad \text{(11-1.4)}$$

In keeping with the terminology developed in Chapter 10, we can define $1 + KGH(s)$ as the *characteristic polynomial ratio*, or simply CPR. The zeros of this ratio characterize the closed-loop control system in terms of absolute stability. Note that the poles of $1 + KGH(s)$ are identical to the poles of the open-loop transfer function $KGH(s)$.

Nyquist's stability criterion is founded in complex-variable theory, but it can be derived both in terms of formal and intuitive concepts. With respect to the latter, the development is based upon the theory of conformal transformations. A particular closed s-plane contour is mapped into the $1 + KGH(s)$ plane and, from an evaluation of the resulting CPR-plane contour, absolute closed-loop stability is deduced. Accordingly, certain features of conformal mapping must be investigated before we can use the criterion.

11-2 CONFORMAL MAPPING

Conformal mapping is the process by which certain regions of a complex-variable plane (s-plane) are transformed into corresponding portions of a function plane (e.g., $1 + KGH(s)$ plane). In this section, a few simple CPR functions are constructed, and the associated conformal transformations are investigated. As an initial example, consider the function

$$1 + KGH(s) = s - 2 \qquad \text{(11-2.1)}$$

Equation (11-2.1) describes a CPR which, when plotted upon the s-plane, consists of a simple zero located at $s = 2$. In the previous chapter, an open-loop system zero location was designated by the **O** symbol, while a closed-loop pole position was denoted by a triangle ▲. It will be less confusing if we conform to this familiar format. Thus, the CPR zero described in Eq. (11-2.1) is illustrated in Fig. 11-2.1 as a triangle; this singularity is equivalent to a closed-loop system pole as indicated in Eq. (11-1.4), and it bears no resemblance to any open-loop zero.

Let us now evaluate the conformal transformations of various s-plane points and contours onto the $1 + KGH(s)$ plane. To begin, the s-plane origin maps into the $1 + KGH(s)$ plane as a point Re $[1 + KGH(s)] = -2$, Im $[1 + KGH(s)] = 0$ as follows: In general, $s = \sigma + j\omega$. For the particular CPR in question, substituting $s = \sigma + j\omega$ into Eq. (11-2.1) yields

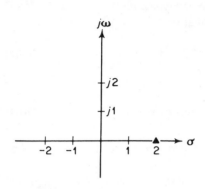

$$\text{Re } [1 + KGH(s)] = \sigma - 2$$

$$\text{Im } [1 + KGH(s)] = \omega \qquad \text{(11-2.2)}$$

Figure 11-2.1 A zero of $1 + KGH(s)$ is plotted upon the s-plane as a pole of $C/R(s)$.

Hence, for $\sigma = \omega = 0$, the equivalent CPR-plane coordinates are Re CPR $= -2$, Im CPR $= 0$. Similarly, the s-plane zero location $s = 2 + j0$ maps into the origin of the $1 + KGH(s)$ plane.

Now consider the closed s-plane contours of Fig. 11-2.2. As constructed, contour No. 2 encircles the s-plane zero, while contour No. 1 does not encircle the zero. Applying the same analytical mapping techniques derived in Eq. (11-2.2), we see that contour No. 2 encircles the origin of the CPR plane, while contour No. 1 does not encircle the origin. This result is not unexpected, since the s-plane zero has been shown to map into the CPR plane at the origin. Hence, any closed contour which encircles the s-plane zero must similarly enclose the CPR-plane origin. Furthermore, the direction of rotation has been maintained through this conformal transformation. For a clockwise encirclement of the s-plane zero, a net clockwise encirclement of the CPR-plane origin results. Thus, as shown in Fig. 11-2.2-b, the net change in phase of $1 + KGH(s)$, as s takes on all values required to traverse a closed contour about the s-plane zero, is -2π for contour No. 2 and zero for contour No. 1. A vector,

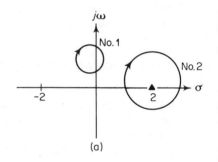

(a)

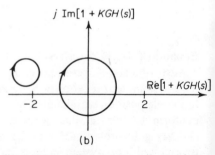

(b)

Figure 11-2.2 s-plane contours that encircle the CPR zero will encircle the $1 + KGH(s)$ plane origin.

originating at the CPR-plane origin and terminating upon the closed contour $1 + KGH(s)$, sweeps through a clockwise angle of 2π as contour No. 2 circles the s-plane zero; but an equivalent vector exhibits no net change in phase when following contour No. 1. These results are not affected by any gain associated with Eq. (11-2.1). If a new CPR, $1 + KGH(s) = K(s - 2)$, is chosen, all of the preceding comments are still valid. Although the CPR contour will be expanded for $K > 1$ and contracted for $1 > K$, both the polarity and magnitude of the net CPR-plane phase contributions remain invariant.

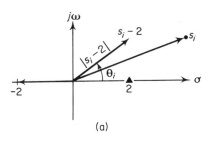

(a)

Let us review the conformal transformation of Eq. (11-2.1) from a standpoint of vector addition. As discussed in Section 10-3, Chapter 10, the CPR function $s - 2$ can be expressed, for any s-plane test point s_i, as the vector summation of two complex quantities, i.e., s_i and -2. The resultant is indicated geometrically as a vector with magnitude $|s_i - 2|$ and a phase angle of $\theta = \tan^{-1} \operatorname{Im}(s - 2)/ \operatorname{Re}(s - 2)$. This summation vector, when translated so that the arrowhead terminates upon the test point, originates at the associated right half-plane zero location, $s = 2$. Since $1 + KGH(s) = |s_i - 2| e^{j\theta}$, the conformal transformation of Eq. (11-2.1) for any s-plane test point s_i is obtained by constructing a vector from the CPR zero to the required test point, by measuring the vector length and phase angle upon the s-plane, and by transferring this vector into the CPR plane. This geometrical process is described in Fig. 11-2.3.

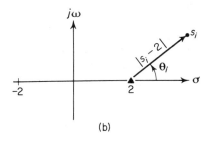

(b)

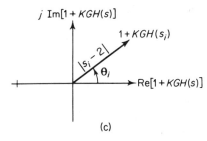

(c)

Figure 11-2.3 Conformal transformation: (a) vector summation of $s_i - 2$, (b) equivalent s-plane vector, (c) transformation to $1 + KGH(s)$ plane.

Consider, now, a CPR consisting of a positive real-axis pole, i.e.

$$1 + KGH(s) = \frac{1}{s - 5} \qquad\qquad \textbf{(11-2.3)}$$

As described in Fig. 11-2.4, a closed s-plane contour that encircles the pole will again encircle the origin of the CPR plane. (Note in the corresponding s-plane diagram of Fig. 11-2.4 that a pole of $1 + KGH(s)$ is designated by the familiar **X** symbol, since this singularity is identical to a pole of $KGH(s)$.) Conversely, a closed contour that does not encircle the pole will not encircle the function-plane origin. It is noted, however, that the direction of rotation has been reversed. If the s-plane pole is encircled in a clockwise direction, a

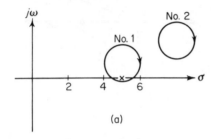

(a)

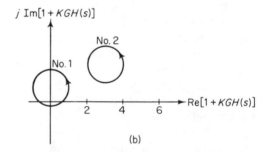

(b)

Figure 11-2.4   Transformations of closed contours from the s-plane to the CPR plane for $1 + KGH(s) = 1/(s - 5)$.

net counterclockwise encirclement of the CPR-plane origin is produced. This phase reversal is easily visualized by considering the particular s-plane test point s_i, illustrated in Fig. 11-2.5.

A vector representing the summation of s_i and -5, when translated so as to originate at the s-plane pole, has a magnitude $|s_i - 5|$ and a phase angle $\theta = \tan^{-1} \operatorname{Im}(s_i - 5)/\operatorname{Re}(s_i - 5)$. In exponential polar coordinates, $s_i - 5 = Ae^{j\theta}$. Since $1 + KGH(s_i) = 1/(s_i - 5)$, then

$$1 + KGH(s) = \frac{1}{A} e^{-j\theta} \tag{11-2.4}$$

Thus, the conformal transformation corresponding to Eq. (11-2.3) is obtained by constructing a vector from the s-plane pole to the test point, by measuring

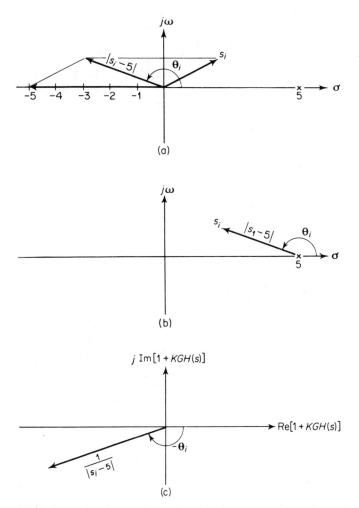

Figure 11-2.5 Conformal transformation: (a) vector summation of $s_i - 5$, (b) equivalent s-plane vector, (c) transformation to $1 + KGH(s)$ plane.

the resulting vector length and included angle, and by transforming this information into a CPR-plane vector as follows: The CPR-plane vector has a length equal to the reciprocal of the s-plane vector magnitude, while the CPR-plane phase is a reflection of the s-plane vector argument across the axis of reals.

To summarize, the phase angle of an s plane vector from a right half-plane pole to an arbitrary point s_i is negative with respect to the phase of the transformed $1 + KGH(s)$-plane vector directed from the origin. As the phase angle θ becomes more and more negative in the s-plane (clockwise rotation), the transformed phase angle becomes more and more positive. This consideration is illustrated in Fig. 11-2.5.

The magnitude of the s-plane vector length A will not influence the transformation phase characteristics. As the s-plane vector magnitude tends to zero, the transformed CPR-plane contour approaches infinity, but the net encirclement characteristics remain unaltered.

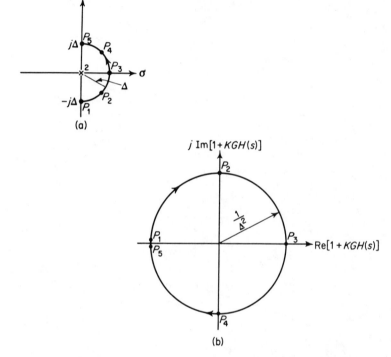

Figure 11-2.6   Conformal transformation: (a) very small-diameter semicircle about the s-plane origin, (b) $1 + KGH(s)$ plane transformation.

To further develop this situation, consider the second-order pole at $s = 0$, illustrated in Fig. 11-2.6. Assume an s-plane contour consisting of a counterclockwise-directed semicircle, extending from $s = 0 - j\Delta$ to $s = 0 + j\Delta$, where Δ approaches zero. The CPR corresponding to this double-pole configuration is

$$1 + KGH(s) = \frac{1}{s^2} \qquad \text{(11-2.5)}$$

Since any point s_i lying upon this semicircle is expressed in polar coordinates as $\Delta e^{j\theta}$, the transformed CPR-plane representation is evidently

$$1 + KGH(s_i) = \frac{1}{\Delta^2 e^{j2\theta}} = \frac{1}{\Delta^2} e^{-j2\theta} \qquad \text{(11-2.6)}$$

As the s-plane vector angle θ varies from $-90°$ to $90°$ in a counterclockwise direction, the transformed $1 + KGH(s)$-plane contour forms a circle of infinitely large diameter, varying in phase angle from $180°$ to $-180°$ in a clockwise direction. One may generalize the preceding to the extent that, for a CPR consiting of an nth-order pole at the origin, the conformal map of a counterclockwise-directed semicircle from $s = 0 - j\Delta$ to $s = 0 + j\Delta$ is clockwise-directed circular segment of infinite diameter with a net change in phase of $n\pi$ radians.

To this point, only singular pole and zero CPR structures have been investigated. Consider now a normal open-loop transfer function,

$$KGH(s) = \frac{K(s + z_1)(s + z_2)}{s(s - p_1)(s + p_2)(s + p_3)} \qquad \text{(11-2.7)}$$

If we assume that z_1, z_2, $-p_1$, p_2, and p_3 are real-axis quantities, a root-locus diagram corresponding to Eq. (11-2.7) might well appear as illustrated in Fig. 11-2.7. For a particular open-loop gain constant K_0, the closed-loop

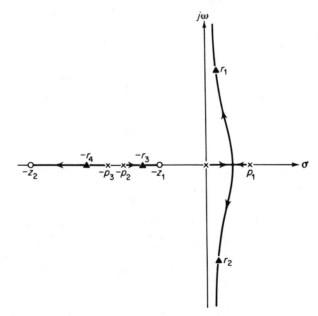

Figure 11-2.7 Possible root-locus diagram corresponding to Eq. (11-2.7).

poles are located at r_1, r_2, $-r_3$, and $-r_4$ as shown. As stated previously, the zeros of $1 + KGH(s)$ and the roots of $1 + KGH(s) = 0$ coincide, while, the poles of $1 + KGH(s)$ are the poles of $KGH(s)$. Thus, the resulting CPR pole-zero array

$$1 + KGH(s) = \frac{(s - r_1)(s - r_2)(s + r_3)(s + r_4)}{s(s - p_1)(s + p_2)(s + p_3)} \qquad \text{(11-2.8)}$$

can be plotted as shown in Fig. 11-2.8. A number of closed s-plane contours are now constructed. Specifically, contour No. 1 encircles a CPR zero only,

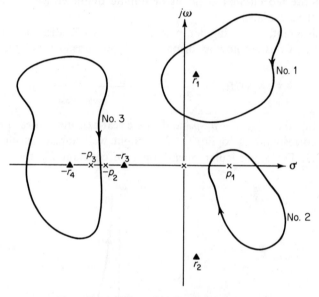

Figure 11-2.8 Three closed s-plane contours.

contour No. 2 encloses only an s-plane pole, and contour No. 3 surrounds both a pole and a zero. All closed s-plane contours are directed in a clockwise sense.

Choosing a point $s = s_i$ located upon contour No. 1, and directing vectors from each CPR singularity to the test point as described in Fig. 11-2.9, we obtain

$$1 + KGH(s_i) = \frac{(A_{r_1}e^{j\theta_{r_1}})(A_{r_2}e^{j\theta_{r_2}})(A_{r_3}e^{j\theta_{r_3}})(A_{r_4}e^{j\theta_{r_4}})}{(A_{p_0}e^{j\theta_{p_0}})(A_{p_1}e^{j\theta_{p_1}})(A_{p_2}e^{j\theta_{p_2}})(A_{p_3}e^{j\theta_{p_3}})} \qquad \text{(11-2.9)}$$

As the test point s_i takes on all values required to traverse the closed contour

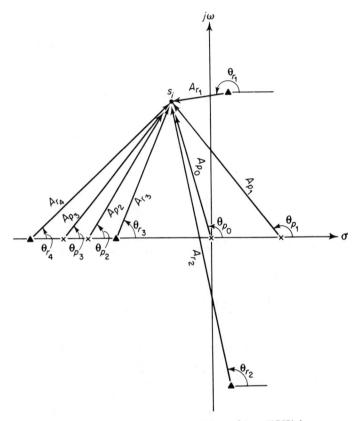

Figure 11-2.9   Graphical computation of $1 + KGH(s_i)$.

No. 1, a calculation of the type indicated in Eq. (11-2.9) provides a conformal transformation onto the $1 + KGH(s)$ plane. Quantitatively, the angle contribution of each individual pole vector is zero, since the closed contour does not encircle and CPR pole. Similarly, vectors associated with the CPR zeros located at r_2, $-r_3$, and $-r_4$ produce no net change in the phase angle of $1 + KGH(s)$; these singularities are also outside the limits of contour No. 1. The fact that contour No. 1 does enclose the zero at r_1, however, results in the net change in phase of -2π about the CPR-plane origin as illustrated in Fig. 11-2.10. In a like manner, contour No. 2 yields a net counterclockwise encirclement of the $1 + KGH(s)$-plane origin since one CPR pole is enclosed. Contour No. 3 results in no net encirclements; the phase contribution of the enclosed s-plane pole and zero are observed to cancel. It is upon these considerations that the Nyquist stability criterion is based.

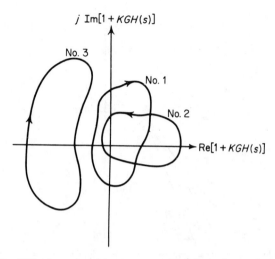

$j\ \text{Im}[1 + KGH(s)]$

No. 3

No. 1

No. 2

$\text{Re}[1 + KGH(s)]$

Figure 11-2.10 CPR-plane closed contours resulting from the conformal transformation of Fig. 11-2.8 contours.

11-3 DERIVATION OF THE CRITERION

In this section, the Nyquist criterion is developed from an intuitive point of view, reflecting the theory of conformal mapping derived in the previous discussion. Consider, initially, the CPR function

$$1 + KGH(s) = \frac{(s + r_1)(s + r_2)(s + r_3)(s - r_4)(s - r_5)}{s(s + p_1)(s + p_2)(s - p_3)(s - p_4)} \tag{11-3.1}$$

containing right half-plane poles at $s = p_3$ and p_4, right half-plane zeros at $s = r_4$ and r_5, and an open-loop integration, together with additional left half-plane singularities. In general, the CPR zero positions would be unknown, since the express purpose of the Nyquist criterion is to deduce the existence or nonexistence of right half-plane zeros. Due to the properties associated with conformal transformations, any s-plane contour that encircles a right half-plane singularity produces a known angular effect upon the transformed $1 + KGH(s)$-plane contour. Accordingly, an s-plane contour is chosen such that the entire right half-plane is enclosed. The resulting s-plane contour is illustrated in Fig. 11-3.1. Note that the pole at $s = 0$ is constrained to lie in the left half-plane by traversing a small counterclockwise semicircle about this singularity, from $s = 0 - j\Delta$ to $s = 0 + j\Delta$. The over-all s-plane contour is directed in the clockwise direction; each zero enclosed within the contour will contribute a clockwise encirclement of the CPR-plane origin, while each enclosed pole contributes a counterclockwise rotation. Thus

$$N_{ccw} = \#P - \#Z \qquad (11\text{-}3.2)$$

where N_{ccw} is the net counterclockwise encirclements of the CPR-plane origin, while $\#P$ and $\#Z$ represent the number of right half-plane poles and zeros of $1 + KGH(s)$ respectively.

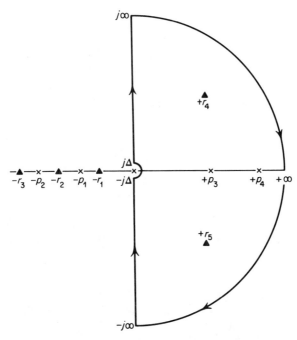

Figure 11-3.1 Closed contour employed in the Nyquist criterion encircles the entire right half-plane.

In mapping the s-plane line consisting of the positive imaginary axis of Fig. 11-3.1 into the CPR plane, we generate an equation similar to Eq. (11-2.9) by substituting $s = j\omega$ for all values of ω between the limits of 0^+ and positive infinity. The resulting relationship is exactly equivalent, however, to the expression $1 + KGH(j\omega)$, which is nothing more than the open-loop system frequency response $KGH(j\omega)$, encountered in Chapter 5, summed with unity. The conformal transformation corresponding to the positive imaginary s-plane axis is illustrated in Fig. 11-3.2. It is not actually necessary to compute the transformation corresponding to the negative imaginary axis, since the points $1 + KGH(j\omega_1)$ and $1 + KGH(-j\omega_1)$ are complex-conjugate quantities. Thus, once $1 + KGH(j\omega)$ has been computed, the transformation of $1 + KGH(-j\omega)$ is sketched by inspection. For an open-loop transfer function containing an excess of poles over zeros, the infinite semicircle of Fig. 11-3.1 maps into the CPR plane as the point at $+1$. Finally, the small semicircle traversing the s-plane origin is transformed into an infinite $1 + KGH(s)$ contour, with a net angular contribution of a clockwise 180°. This final observation is based upon the considerations

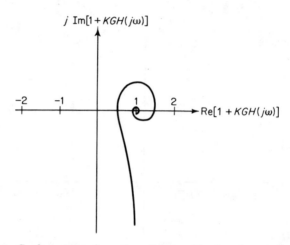

Figure II-3.2 Conformal transformation of the positive imaginary axis of Fig. 11-3.1.

pictured in Fig. 11-2.6; additional CPR singularities do not invalidate this result because the net change in angle contributed by singularities other than open-loop integrations are zero.

The complete $1 + KGH(s)$ contour is presented in Fig. 11-3.3. To determine the number of net counterclockwise encirclements, we draw a radial line from the CPR-plane origin. The angular direction associated with this radial line is unimportant because the same information is obtained from any line configuration; hence, the least complicated line is chosen. The number of net counterclockwise encirclements is determined by noting the polarity of all $1 + KGH(s)$ branches that intersect the radial line. From Fig. 11-3.3, for any of the three radial lines illustrated, $N_{ccw} = 0$. Accordingly Eq. (11-3.2) is written

$$\#Z - \#P = 0 \qquad \text{(11-3.3)}$$

In Eq. (11-3.3), $\#P$ represents the number of right half-plane poles of $1 + KGH(s)$ or, equivalently, the number of unstable open-loop poles. From

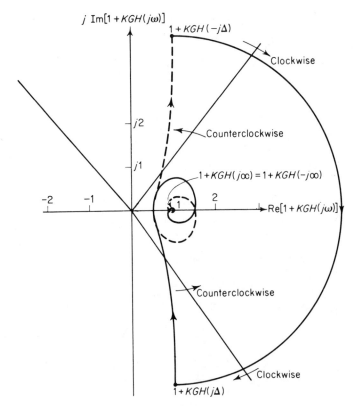

Figure 11-3.3 Complete transformation of the closed contour of Fig. 11-3.1. The number of net counterclockwise encirclements of the origin is determined by summing the direction of intersections between the diagram and any of the three radial lines.

Eq. (11-3.1), $\#P = 2$ (i.e., $1 + KGH(s)$ contains unstable poles at p_3 and P_4). Hence, Eq. (11-3.3) is solved for $\#Z$ as

$$\#Z = 2 - 0 = 2 \qquad \textbf{(11-3.4)}$$

Thus, right-half plane poles of $\dfrac{C}{R}(s)$ exist, and the closed loop is judged unstable.

In practice, the CPR function is rarely plotted. Rather, the open-loop frequency response $KGH(j\omega)$ is obtained and plotted directly, instead of $1 + KGH(j\omega)$. Since $KGH(j\omega)$ is obtained from $1 + KGH(j\omega)$ by the subtraction of unity from the CPR for all values of ω, the Nyquist criterion is applicable for net counterclockwise encirclements of the transformed origin, $-1 + j0$. This final conformal transformation is illustrated in Fig. 11-3.4.

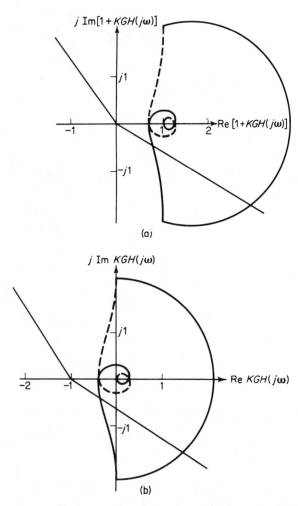

Figure II-3.4 Final transformation allows the open-loop frequency response $KGH(j\omega)$ to be plotted directly. The origin in (a) is shifted to the equivalent point, $-1 + j0$, in (b).

II-4 A RIGOROUS DERIVATION

In the preceding section, Nyquist's criterion was developed by means of an intuitive approach. The same conclusion can be derived by referring directly to basic complex-variable theory, notably, the residue theorem. Since the residue theorem is applicable to a system consisting exclusively of single-order poles, it is first necessary to transform a general CPR function into this form. Consider initially the CPR consisting of an ath order zero at $s = z_1$, together with additional left half-plane singularities.

$$\text{CPR}(s) = (s - z_1)^a U(s) \qquad (11\text{-}4.1)$$

$U(s)$ is constrained to be analytic within the right half-plane. Differentiating Eq. (11-4.1) with respect to s

$$\frac{d\text{CPR}(s)}{ds} = a(s - z_1)^{a-1} U(s) + (s - z_1)^a \frac{dU(s)}{ds} \qquad (11\text{-}4.2)$$

Dividing Eq. (11-4.2) by Eq. (11-4.1), and denoting the resulting function as $W(s)$,

$$W(s) = \frac{d\text{CPR}(s)/ds}{\text{CPR}(s)} = \frac{a}{s - z_1} + \frac{dU(s)/ds}{U(s)} \qquad (11\text{-}4.3)$$

Since $U(s)$ is, by definition, analytic in the right half-plane, then the component $\dfrac{U'}{U}(s)$ is also analytic within this region. Assume a closed contour C, taken in a clockwise direction, and enclosing the entire right half-plane. Then, from the residue theorem

$$\oint_C W(s)\, ds = \oint_C \frac{a}{s - z_1}\, ds = j2\pi a \qquad (11\text{-}4.4)$$

Thus, a multiple-order zero of $1 - KGH(s)$ is transformed into a simple pole of $W(s)$, with the residue of that pole being the order of multiplicity of the original CPR zero. The same technique, when applied to multiple-order CPR poles leads to a similar conclusion. These features allow the residue theorem to be applied directly to the auxiliary function $W(s)$. To illustrate, consider the function

$$\text{CPR}(s) = \frac{(s - z_1)^{a_1}(s - z_2)^{a_2} \cdots (s - z_n)^{a_n}}{(s - p_1)^{b_1}(s - p_2)^{b_2} \cdots (s - p_m)^{a_m}} U(s) \qquad (11\text{-}4.5)$$

where $U(s)$ is again analytic in the region of the right half-plane. Differentiating Eq. (11-4.5) and obtaining $W(s)$ as before

$$W(s) = \left(\frac{a_1}{s - z_1} + \frac{a_2}{s - z_2} + \cdots + \frac{a_n}{s - z_n} \right)$$

$$- \left(\frac{b_1}{s - p_1} + \frac{b_2}{s - p_2} + \frac{b_m}{s - p_m} \right) + \frac{U'}{U}(s) \qquad (11\text{-}4.6)$$

Using the residue theorem

$$\oint_C W(s) = j2\pi[(a_1 + a_2 + \cdots + a_n) - (b_1 + b_2 + \cdots + b_m)]$$

(11-4.7)

and introducing the quantities

$$\#P_R = b_1 + b_2 + b_3 + \cdots + b_m$$

$$\#Z_R = a_1 + a_2 + a_3 + \cdots + a_n$$

$$\oint_C W(s) = -j2\pi(\#P_R - \#Z_R)$$

(11-4.8)

Let us now establish a relation between $1 + KGH(s)$ and $W(s)$. At any point $s = s_i$, where s_i lies upon the closed contour C

$$\mathrm{CPR}(s) = re^{j\theta}$$

(11-4.9)

Differentiating

$$\frac{d\mathrm{CPR}(s)}{ds} = e^{j\theta}\frac{dr}{ds} + jre^{j\theta}\frac{d\theta}{dr}$$

(11-4.10)

$$W(s) = \frac{d\mathrm{CPR}(s)/ds}{\mathrm{CPR}(s)} = \frac{1}{r}\frac{dr}{ds} + j\frac{d\theta}{ds}$$

(11-4.11)

Now, from Eq. (2-4.9) of Chapter 2

$$\log_e \mathrm{CPR}(s) = \mathrm{Log}_e\, r + j\theta$$

(11-4.12)

Therefore

$$\frac{d[\log_e \mathrm{CPR}(s)]}{ds} = \frac{1}{r}\frac{dr}{ds} + j\frac{d\theta}{ds}$$

(11-4.13)

Since Eqs. (11-4.13) and (11-4.11) are identical, it follows that

$$W(s) = \frac{d[\log_e \mathrm{CPR}(s)]}{ds}$$

(11-4.14)

Hence

$$\oint_C W(s)\, ds = \oint_C \frac{d[\log_e \mathrm{CPR}(s)]}{ds}\, ds$$

$$= \oint_C d(\mathrm{Log}_e\, r) + j\oint_C d\theta$$

(11-4.15)

The integral $\oint_C d(\text{Log}_e r)$ is zero because C is a closed contour. Thus, combining Eqs. (11-4.15) and (11-4.8)

$$j \oint_C d\theta = j2\pi(\#P_R - \#Z_R) \qquad \text{(11-4.16)}$$

or

$$(\theta_2 - \theta_1) = 2\pi(\#P_R - \#Z_R) \qquad \text{(11-4.17)}$$

where $\theta_2 - \theta_1$ is the difference in the phase angle of $1 + KGH(s)$ as s takes on all values required to traverse the closed contour C. Hence

$$N_{ccw} = \#P - \#Z \qquad \text{(11-4.18)}$$

This equation is identical to Eq. (11-3.2) of the previous section and thus completes the proof.

II-5 SAMPLE PROBLEM ANALYSIS

To illustrate the application of Nyquist's stability criterion, we will consider the open-loop transfer function

$$KGH(s) = \frac{10(s + 2)}{s(s + 1)(s + 4)} \qquad \text{(11-5.1)}$$

The corresponding Nyquist diagram is plotted in Fig. 11-5.1. Since a radial line drawn from the point $-1 + j0$ does not intersect any branch of the diagram, the number of counterclockwise encirclements of the transformed origin is evidently zero. Similarly, no open-loop unstable poles are observed to exist in Eq. (11-5.1), so that $\#P = 0$. Substituting these data into Eq. (11-3.2) or Eq. (11-4.18) yields

$$\#Z = 0 \qquad \text{(11-5.2)}$$

Hence, the closed-loop system corresponding to Eq. (11-5.1) is stable.

II-6 A SIMPLIFIED APPROACH TO THE STABILITY CRITERION

Nyquist's stability criterion as discussed to this point entails a closed s-plane contour that surrounds all unstable CPR singularities. An alternative approach is possible, however, if one assumes a contour that is not closed, but rather, consists of the entire positive $j\omega$ axis, from 0^+ to $+j\infty$. Employing this contour results in a simplified procedure for establishing closed-loop stability in that it is no longer necessary to close the resulting CPR-plane

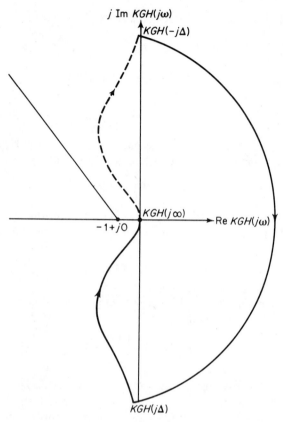

Figure 11-5.1 Nyquist diagram for example problem.

contour or to compute net counterclockwise encirclements. The simplified criterion is based upon a knowledge of the net change in phase of $1 + KGH(j\omega)$, written $\Delta/1 + KGH(j\omega)$, by stable and unstable CPR singularities as the input frequency varies from zero to infinity.

To illustrate this approach, let us consider a generalized CPR function

$$1 + KGH(s) = \frac{(s + r_1)(s + r_2)(s - r_3)(s - r_4)(s - r_5)(s + r_6)}{s^2(s + p_1)(s + p_2)(s - p_3)(s - p_4)} \quad \textbf{(11-6.1)}$$

consisting of unstable zeros at r_3, r_4, and r_5, stable zeros at $-r_1$, $-r_2$, and $-r_6$, right half-plane poles at p_3 and p_4, left half-plane poles at $-p_1$ and $-p_2$, and a second-order open-loop integration. It is now necessary to calculate the change in phase of $1 + KGH(j\omega)$ contributed by each singularity for the particular contour shown in Fig. 11-6.1.

Let us initially assume a test frequency ω_1. The value of $1 + KGH(j\omega_1)$, that results from substituting $s = j\omega_1$ into Eq. (11-6.1), is

$$1 + KGH(j\omega_1)$$

$$= \frac{(j\omega_1 + r_1)(j\omega_1 + r_2)(j\omega_1 - r_3)(j\omega_1 - r_4)(j\omega_1 - r_5)(j\omega_1 + r_6)}{(j\omega_1)^2(j\omega_1 + p_1)(j\omega_1 + p_2)(j\omega_1 - p_3)(j\omega_1 - p_4)} \qquad \text{(11-6.2)}$$

Each component of Eq. (11-6.2) can be expressed in polar coordinates as

$$1 + KGH(j\omega_1) = \frac{(R_1 e^{j\theta_{r_1}})(R_2 e^{j\theta_{r_2}})(R_3 e^{j\theta_{r_3}})(R_4 e^{j\theta_{r_4}})(R_5 e^{j\theta_{r_5}})(R_6 e^{j\theta_{r_6}})}{(P_o e^{j\theta_{p_0}})^2(P_1 e^{j\theta_{p_1}})(P_2 e^{j\theta_{p_2}})(P_3 e^{j\theta_{p_3}})(P_4 e^{j\theta_{p_4}})} = A_1 e^{j\psi_1}$$

$$\text{(11-6.3)}$$

where R_1, R_2, . . . , R_6 and P_o, P_1, . . . , P_4 are vector distances and θ_{r_1}, θ_{r_2}, . . . , θ_{r_6} and θ_{p_0}, θ_{p_1}, . . . , θ_{p_4}, are vector angles computed from the s-plane diagram of Fig. 11-6.2.

The total angle (ψ_1) of $1 + KGH(j\omega_1)$ is a combination of all pole- and zero-vector angles, with zero angles summed positively and pole angles summed negatively. Thus, the net change in the angle of $1 + KGH(j\omega)$ as ω varies from 0^+ to infinity is similarily the sum of net phase contributions from vectors originating at each CPR singularity. The problem is now resolved into one of determining these component phase contributions as a function of position.

For a right half-plane CPR zero, the test-point vector of Fig. 11-6.3 sweeps through an angle of $-(\pi/2)$ radians (clockwise rotation) as the frequency increases from 0^+ to infinity. Thus, $\Delta/1 + KGH(j\omega) = -(\pi/2)$ for each right half-plane zero. Conversely, the left half-plane zero vector rotates through $\pi/2$ radians (counterclockwise direction). As can be seen, Fig. 11-6.3 considers only real-axis zeros. Complex zeros,

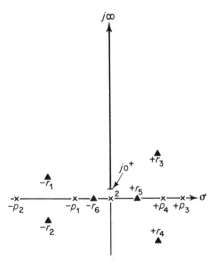

Figure 11-6.1 Pole-zero array associated with Eq. (11-6.1). The s-plane contour consists of the positive imaginary axis from $s = j0^+$ to $s = j\infty$.

however, when treated in an analogous manner, yield identical results; since a complex singularity is always accompanied by a complex-conjugate companion, the net change in angle contributed by the conjugate pair is π radians. This condition is demonstrated in Fig. 11-6.4.

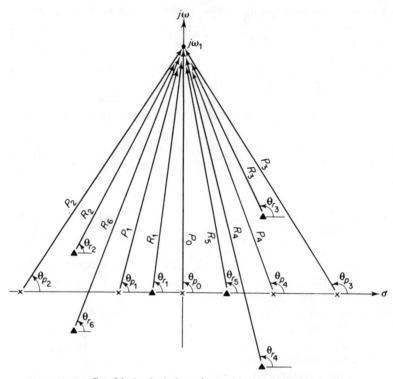

Figure II-6.2 Graphical calculation of magnitude and phase at $s = j\omega_1$.

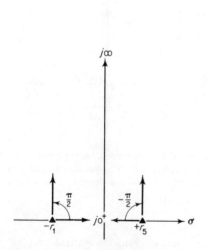

Figure II-6.3 *CPR* zero contributions.

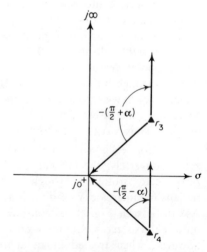

Figure II-6.4 Complex right half-plane zeros contribute a change in phase angle of π radians.

Pole-vector phase angles behave in an equivalent manner, i.e., right half-plane pole vectors sweep through $-(\pi/2)$ radians, while the left half-plane pole-vector angle increases by $\pi/2$ radians. The resulting contributions to $\Delta\!\!\not{/}1 + KGH(j\omega)$ are reversed, however, because these quantities appear in the denominator of Eq. (11-6.3).

CPR poles at the origin of the s-plane produce no contributions to $\Delta\!\!\not{/}1 + KGH(j\omega)$. As described in Fig. 11-6.5, the open-loop integration vectors do not change position as frequency increases, but are directed along the positive imaginary axis for all values of ω.

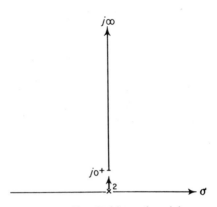

Figure 11-6.5 Singularities at the origin contribute no net change in phase.

Combining the above considerations

$$\Delta\!\!\not{/}1 + KGH(j\omega) = \frac{\pi}{2}(\#Z_L + \#P_R - \#Z_R - \#P_L) \qquad \textbf{(11-6.4)}$$

where subscripts L and R represent left and right half-plane locations respectively.

Let us now introduce two new quantities, N and M where

$$N = \#Z_L + \#Z_R \qquad \textbf{(11-6.5)}$$

$$M = \#P_L + \#P_R + \#P_o \qquad \textbf{(11-6.6)}$$

As defined, N and M represent the order of s existing in the numerator and denominator polynomials of $1 + KGH(s)$ respectively. $\#P_o$ is the number of open-loop system integrations. Solving Eqs. (11-6.5) and (11-6.6) for $\#Z_L$ and $\#Z_R$ and substituting into Eq. (11-6.4)

$$\Delta\!\!\not{/}1 + KGH(j\omega) = \frac{\pi}{2}[N - 2\#Z_R - M + 2\#P_R + \#P_o] \qquad \textbf{(11-6.7)}$$

For any physical system, the open-loop transfer function $KGH(s)$ contains an excess of poles over zeros. If $\#P \geqslant \#Z$ in $KGH(s)$, then the power of s in the CPR numerator and denominator are of the same order; hence $N = M$. Combining this result of physical reasoning with Eq. (11-6.7)

$$\Delta\!\!\not{/}1 + KGH(j\omega) = \pi\left(\#P_R - \#Z_R + \frac{\#P_o}{2}\right) \qquad \textbf{(11-6.8)}$$

which is rearranged into final form to yield

$$\#P_R - \#Z_R = \frac{\Delta/1 + KGH(j\omega)}{\pi} - \frac{\#P_o}{2} \qquad (11\text{-}6.9)$$

In employing Eq. (11-6.9), the open-loop system frequency response $KGH(j\omega)$ is computed, and $1 + KGH(j\omega)$ is plotted. Note that in Fig. 11-6.6 it is necessary to consider only positive frequencies, i.e., no negative frequency

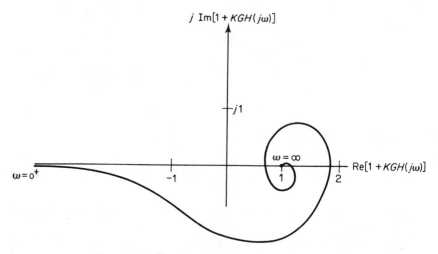

Figure 11-6.6 Frequency response of Eq. (11-6.1).

branch or contour closure is required. The quantity $\Delta/1 + KGH(j\omega)$ is determined by observing the total change in phase of a vector originating at the CPR-plane origin and following the transformed $1 + KGH(j\omega)$ contour as ω varies from 0^+ to infinity. Both $\#P_o$ and $\#P_R$ are obtained from a knowledge of the open-loop transfer function.

Again, it is usually convenient to plot only the open-loop frequency response $KGH(j\omega)$ and compute $\Delta/1 + KGH(j\omega)$ as the angle subtended by a vector originating at the point $-1 + j0$. Returning to the illustrative example of Eq. (11-6.1), it can be shown that the open-loop frequency-response diagram of Fig. 11-6.7 reflects an unstable system by the following procedure: From Eq. (11-6.1), $\#P_o = 2$ and $\#P_R = 2$. The $\Delta/1 + KGH(j\omega)$ derived from Fig. 11-6.7 is evidently π radians. Thus

$$2 - \#Z_R = \frac{\pi}{\pi} - 1$$

from which $\#Z \neq 0$

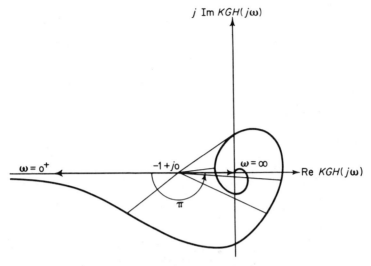

Figure 11-6.7 $\Delta \underline{/1 + KGH(j\omega)} = \pi.$

11-7 AN ADDITIONAL PROBLEM

As a final example, consider the open-loop transfer function

$$KGH(s) = \frac{2500(2s + 1)(0.025s + 1)^2}{s^2(0.1s - 1)(0.2s - 1)(0.0025s + 1)} \tag{11-7.1}$$

This system is now analyzed by using the simplified criterion of Eq. (11-6.9). From Fig. 11-7.1, $\Delta \underline{/1 + KGH(j\omega)} = 3\pi$, and from Eq. (11-7.1),

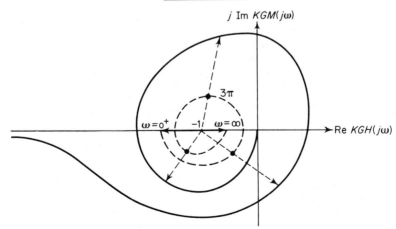

Figure 11-7.1 Final example yields a net change in phase of 3π radians.

$\#P_R = \#P_o = 2$. Substituting into Eq. (11-6.9)

$$2 - \#Z_R = \frac{3\pi}{\pi} - 1$$

$$\#Z_R = 0$$

Accordingly, the closed-loop system is stable.

PROBLEMS

11.1 For the following open-loop Nyquist plots, deduce the stability of the corresponding closed-loop systems. (No unstable open-loop poles are present.)

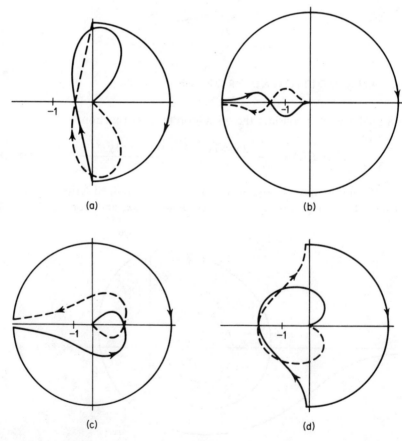

(a)

(b)

(c)

(d)

Prob. 11.1

11.2 Using the simplified criterion of Section 11.6, determine whether the following open-loop systems give rise to unstable closed loops. The number of right half-plane open-loop poles and poles at the origin are as indicated.

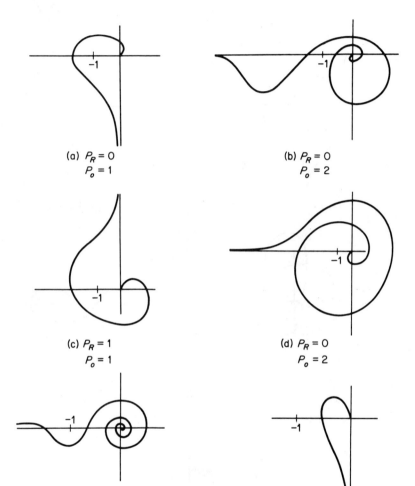

(a) $P_R = 0$
$P_o = 1$

(b) $P_R = 0$
$P_o = 2$

(c) $P_R = 1$
$P_o = 1$

(d) $P_R = 0$
$P_o = 2$

(e) $P_R = 0$
$P_o = 2$

(f) $P_R = 2$
$P_o = 1$

Prob. 11.2

11.3 Determine the number of unstable open-loop poles that are required to provide stable closed-loop configurations for each of the following. (The number of open-loop integrations are stated for each figure.)

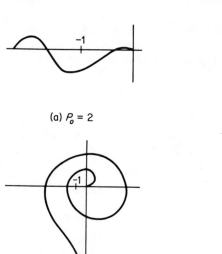

(a) $P_o = 2$

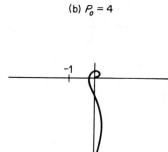

(b) $P_o = 4$

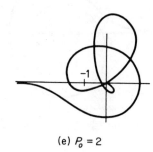

(c) $P_o = 1$

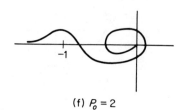

(d) $P_o = 3$

(e) $P_o = 2$

(f) $P_o = 2$

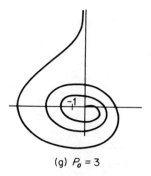

(g) $P_o = 3$

Prob. 11.3

11.4 Using the techniques of Chapter 5, plot the frequency response for each of the following open-loop transfer functions, and deduce closed loop stability.

(a) $KGH(s) = \dfrac{10}{s(s + 2)}$

(b) $KGH(s) = \dfrac{100(s + 4)}{s^3(s + 10)}$

(c) $KGH(s) = \dfrac{4}{s(s - 2)}$

(d) $KGH(s) = \dfrac{40(s + 1)}{s(s + 2)(s + 10)}$

(e) $KGH(s) = \dfrac{1000}{s[(s + 10)^2 + 10^2]}$

11.5 Derive a simplified criterion, similar to that of Eq. (11-6.9) if, instead of the positive imaginary axis, the negative imaginary axis is chosen as the s-plane contour.

11.6 The position servomechanism of the accompanying figure has been designed as an inner loop of a multiple-loop autopilot. Is this inner loop stable?

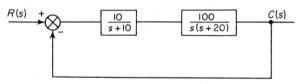

Prob. 11.6

BIBLIOGRAPHY

1. Bower, J. L. and P. M. Schultheiss, *Introduction to the Design of Servomechanisms.* New York: John Wiley & Sons, Inc., 1958.

2. Gille, J. C., M. J. Pelegrin, and P. Decaulne, *Feedback Control Systems.* New York: McGraw-Hill Book Company, 1959.

3. Langill, A. W., "Stability of Closed Loop Control Systems," *Electro-Technology*, February, 1964.

4. Savant, C. J., Jr., *Basic Feedback Control System Design.* New York: McGraw-Hill Book Company, 1958.

POLAR
PLOTS[1,2]

12

12-1 INTRODUCTION

In addition to defining the existence or non-existence of absolute systems stability, the polar plot (Nyquist diagram) can also be employed to determine many important open- and closed-loop frequency-response characteristics. Specifically, closed-loop quantities such as gain margin, phase margin, maximum-frequency resonance, bandwidth, etc. are easily computed from a polar plot of $KGH(j\omega)$. In this chapter, these concepts, together with additional auxiliary topics, are considered. The Nyquist diagram forms an important historical factor in control systems theory, and it will be again encountered in Chapters 14, 15, 21, and 22 of Volume II.

12-2 PHASE AND GAIN MARGINS

The root-locus, developed in Chapter 10, was often employed to compute the increase in open-loop gain required to generate a marginally stable system. For example, the generalized root-locus diagram of Fig. 12-2.1, when calibrated for gain, would suggest systems that were stable, marginally stable, and unstable for open-loop gains of K_1, K_2, and K_3 respectively.

In an analogous manner, corresponding polar diagrams, plotted for gains of K_1, K_2, and K_3 would appear as indicated in Fig. 12-2.2. Thus, a direct correlation exists between the s-plane imaginary axis closed-loop pole configuration (for $K = K_2$) of Fig. 12-2.1 and the $-1 + j0$ contour of Fig. 12-2.2. Similarly, the *margin of stability* exhibited by the system for a loop gain of K_1 can be deduced from both root-locus and polar diagrams. In particular, the *gain margin* is defined as the factor by which the loop gain must be multiplied, for a phase shift of 180°, to produce marginal stability. The concept of gain margin is illustrated in Fig. 12-2.3; the gain margin is evidently d^{-1}.

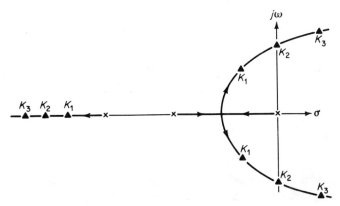

Figure 12-2.1   Root-locus diagram calibrated for open-loop gain constants K_1, K_2, and K_3.

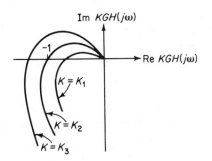

Figure 12-2.2 Nyquist diagram corresponding to root-locus of Fig. 12-2.1.

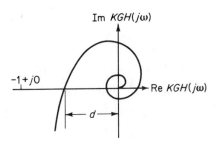

Figure 12-2.3 Graphical description of gain margin.

The *phase margin* is defined as 180° minus the phase lag that occurs at a unity loop gain. In Fig. 12-2.4, it is observed that, if the system were subjected to an additional ϕ degrees of phase lag with no variation in amplitude, a marginally stable system would result.

The frequency, associated with the point on the polar plot at which the phase margin is computed is termed the *unit crossover frequency*. This particular frequency is of special interest in the design of passive-element compensators, and will receive additional attention in Chapter 14 of Volume II.

12-3 M AND N CIRCLES

For unity-feedback systems, i.e., $H(s) = 1$, the closed-loop frequency response can be expressed as

$$\frac{C}{R}(j\omega) = \frac{KG(j\omega)}{1 + KG(j\omega)} = M\angle\tan^{-1} N \qquad (12\text{-}3.1)$$

where

$$M = \left| \frac{KG(j\omega)}{1 + KG(j\omega)} \right| \qquad (12\text{-}3.2)$$

and

$$N = \frac{\text{Im}\ (C/R)(j\omega)}{\text{Re}\ (C/R)(j\omega)} \qquad (12\text{-}3.3)$$

Thus, M contours are lines along which the closed-loop frequency-response amplitude ratio remains invariant. Similarly, constant N contours imply that the closed-loop phase shift remains invariant. We can now prove that, on the $KG(j\omega)$ polar diagram, both M and N contours appear as circles.

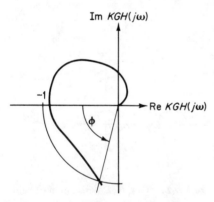

Since, in general, $KG(j\omega)$ is a complex variable, then

$$KG(j\omega) = x + jy \qquad (12\text{-}3.4)$$

Substituting Eq. (12-3.4) into Eq. (12-3.2), and taking the square of the resulting expression

$$M^2 = \frac{x^2 + y^2}{(1 + x)^2 + y^2} \qquad (12\text{-}3.5)$$

Figure 12-2.4   Phase margin calculation.

Simplifying, we obtain

$$y^2 + x^2 + 2x\frac{M^2}{M^2 - 1} + \frac{M^2}{M^2 - 1} = 0 \qquad (12\text{-}3.6)$$

or

$$y^2 + \left(x + \frac{M^2}{M^2 - 1}\right)^2 = \frac{M^2}{(M^2 - 1)^2} \qquad (12\text{-}3.7)$$

Equation (12-3.7) describes a circle, with center located at

$$y_0 = 0 \qquad x_0 = \frac{-M^2}{M^2 - 1} \qquad (12\text{-}3.8)$$

and radius of

$$R = \frac{M}{M^2 - 1} \qquad (12\text{-}3.9)$$

To compute the form of N-contour character, we first substitute Eq. (12-3.4) into Eq. (12-3.1) to obtain

$$\frac{C}{R}(j\omega) = \frac{x + jy}{(1 + x) + jy} = \frac{(x + jy)[(1 + x) - jy]}{(1 + x)^2 + y^2}$$
$$= \frac{x^2 + x + y^2 + jy}{(1 + x)^2 + y^2} \qquad (12\text{-}3.10)$$

Substituting the real and imaginary parts of Eq. (12-3.10) into Eq. (12-3.3)

$$N = \frac{y}{x^2 + x + y^2} \qquad (12\text{-}3.11)$$

or

$$(x^2 + x) + \left(y^2 - \frac{y}{N}\right) = 0 \qquad (12\text{-}3.12)$$

Completing the square

$$\left(x^2 + x + \frac{1}{4}\right) + \left(y^2 - \frac{y}{N} + \frac{1}{4N^2}\right) = \frac{1}{4} + \frac{1}{4N^2} \qquad (12\text{-}3.13)$$

which reduces to

$$\left(x + \frac{1}{2}\right)^2 + \left(y - \frac{1}{2N}\right)^2 = \frac{1}{4}\left(1 + \frac{1}{N^2}\right) \qquad (12\text{-}3.14)$$

Thus, Eq. (12-3.14) is again observed to describe a family of circles with center coordinates

$$x = -\frac{1}{2} \qquad y = \frac{1}{2N} \qquad (12\text{-}3.15)$$

and a radius of

$$R = \frac{1}{2N}\sqrt{1 + \frac{1}{N^2}} \qquad (12\text{-}3.16)$$

Families of constant M and N circles are illustrated in Fig. 12-3.1.

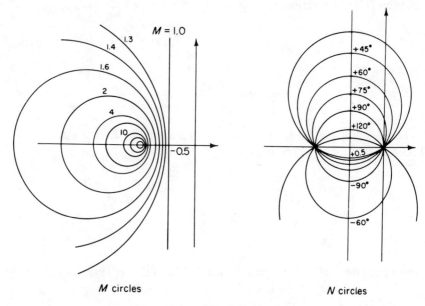

M circles   N circles

Figure 12-3.1   *M* and *N* contours.

Note that, with the use of the concept of *M* circles, the unity-feedback system resonant frequency and associated maximum-amplitude response is determined by the tangency of the polar-plot contour and the highest-valued *M* circle. This condition is suggested in Fig. 12-3.2.

As a final consideration, let us determine the closed-loop system bandwidth by again considering a particular *M* circle contour, By definition, the bandwidth is that frequency at which the closed-loop response has a value of

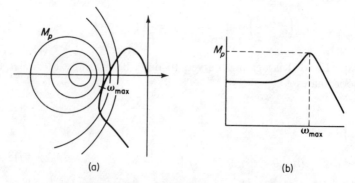

(a)   (b)

Figure 12-3.2   Closed-loop frequency response from Nyquist diagram. (a) Nyquist diagram; (b) closed-loop frequency response.

0.707 compared to a d-c response of unity, i.e., $M = 0.707$. Thus, from Eqs. (12-3.8) and (12-3.9)

$$y_0 = 0$$

$$x_0 = -\frac{M^2}{M^2 - 1} = -\frac{0.5}{0.5 - 1} = +1.0 \text{ (right half-plane)} \qquad \textbf{(12-3.17)}$$

and

$$R = \frac{M}{M^2 - 1} = \frac{0.707}{0.5 - 1} = 1.414 \qquad \textbf{(12-3.18)}$$

Hence, the closed-loop bandwidth, for a unity-feedback system, is the frequency at which the circle described by Eqs. (12-3.17) and (12-3-18) intersects the Nyquist-diagram contour.

12-4 POLAR PLOTS ON THE ANALOG COMPUTER

During the course of an analog simulation study, the requirement for implementing an accurate frequency-response capability often arises, e.g., (1) from the standpoint of a dynamic check solution, it is normally much simpler to analytically compute a system-frequency response than to calculate the corresponding transient response, and (2) once a satisfactory transient response has been established, a knowledge of the finalized system frequency response is desirable. A straightforward technique is that of introducing a unit-amplitude sinusoid at the appropriate point in the loop and recording the resulting steady-state output response. A comparison of input and output sinusoids then allows a direct observation of system phase-shift and amplitude-attenuation characteristics. For this application, the analog oscillator described in Chapter 6 is employed. The direct method suffers from an inherent disadvantage, however, because, as the input frequency increases, it becomes increasingly difficult to determine phase-shift characteristics accurately. A second technique that allows an accurate computation of both amplitude attenuation and phase shift or, equivalently, the real and imaginary portions of the response, is illustrated in Fig. 12-4.1.

If a unit cosine function of arbitrary frequency is employed as the system forcing function, the output sinusoid can be expressed as $A \cos (\omega t + \phi)$, where A represents the system amplitude ratio and ϕ represents the phase. By trigonometric transformation

$$A \cos (\omega t + \phi) = A \cos \phi \cos \omega t - A \sin \phi \sin \omega t \qquad \textbf{(12-4.1)}$$

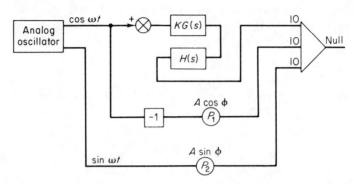

Figure 12-4.1 Frequency response calculations on the analog computer.

Two potentiometers, designated as the real-part potentiometer ($A \cos \phi$) and the imaginary-part potentiometer ($A \sin \phi$), are adjusted, in the steady state, until the output of the summing amplifier is nulled to zero. At this point, the real and imaginary parts of $GH(j\omega)$ are read directly from potentiometers P_1 and P_2 respectively. A simple calculation then yields amplitude ratio and phase.

Occasionally one is confronted with a system in which the open-loop transfer function $GH(s)$ is unstable, but the closed loop $\dfrac{C}{R}(s)$ is stabilized by the application of degenerative feedback. This situation is suggested by the root-locus sketch of Fig. 12-4.2.

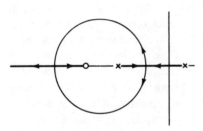

Figure 12-4.2 System with unstable open loop but stable closed loop.

In this case, a mechanization of the type described in Fig. 12-4.1 would not apply, since no stable steady-state condition would exist. However, the open-loop frequency response for such a system can be computed in the manner illustrated in Fig. 12-4.3.

For $e_s = \cos \omega t$, i.e., an input consisting of a unity real part and a zero imaginary part, the real part of e_i is equal to unity plus the real part of $-e_o$, and the imaginary part of e_i is equal to the imaginary part of $-e_o$. Thus, since

$$\frac{e_i}{e_s}(j\omega) = e_i(j\omega) = c + jd \qquad (12\text{-}4.2)$$

and

$$-e_o = c - 1 + jd \qquad (12\text{-}4.3)$$

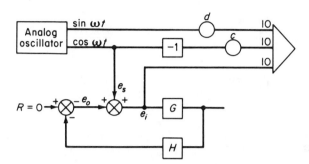

Figure 12-4.3 Open-loop frequency response calculation for an open-loop unstable system.

where c and d are determined on the computer, it follows directly that

$$\text{Re} \frac{e_o}{e_i} (j\omega) = -1 + \frac{c}{c^2 + d^2} \qquad (12\text{-}4.4)$$

$$\text{Im} \frac{e_o}{e_i} (j\omega) = \frac{-d}{c^2 + d^2} \qquad (12\text{-}4.5)$$

Amplitude and phase characteristics are now computed from Eqs. (12-4.4) and (12-4.5).

12-5 INVERSE POLAR PLOTS

Prior to the development of graphical s-plane methods, the frequency-response analysis technique was employed almost exclusively for purposes of servo systems design, and had attained a very advanced stature. Hence, even at this late date, a variety of separate frequency-response formats exist. The Bode plot, which will be investigated in Chapter 13, is a useful graphical tool when employed in conjunction with Nyquist diagram analysis, as it facilitates a rapid polar-plot construction. Other formats, including the inverse Nyquist diagram, the Nichols chart, M and N contour plots, etc., represent only slight variations of the basic polar plot, and yield no additional information. The inverse polar plot will be encountered again in Chapter 22 of Volume II (describing function analysis methods) however, and thus deserves mention at this time. Basically, as the name implies, the inverse polar diagram is a plot of the function $1/KGH(j\omega)$. As developed in Chapter 11, Nyquist's criterion was applied to the conventional polar plot of $KGH(j\omega)$. In the present case, the criterion is still applicable, but a number of qualifications are required. Hence, for the inverse plot, if

$$\frac{1}{KGH(s)} = \frac{G_D H_D}{K G_N H_N} (s) \qquad (12\text{-}5.1)$$

then

$$1 + \frac{1}{KGH(s)} = \frac{G_D H_D + KG_N H_N}{G_N H_N} \qquad \textbf{(12-5.2)}$$

Thus, the relationship

$$N = \#P - \#Z \qquad \textbf{(12-5.3)}$$

is valid, where N is the number of counterclockwise encirclements of the $-1 + j0$ point (if $1/KGH(j\omega)$ is plotted directly instead of the $1 + [1/KGH(j\omega)]$ function), $\#P$ is the number of unstable *zeros* of $KGH(s)$, and $\#Z$ is the number of unstable poles of $C/R(s)$. Hence, the significance of the $-1 + j0$ point remains unaltered.

An additional variation exists: whereas the conventional Nyquist diagram is closed through a clockwise $n\pi$ radians, where n is the number of free integrations, the inverse polar plot is closed through a clockwise $n\pi$ radians, where n is *the excess of poles over zeros in $KGH(s)$*, i.e., the so-called high-frequency type number. To illustrate, the inverse Nyquist diagram of the open-loop transfer function

$$\frac{1}{KGH(s)} = \frac{s(s+1)(s+4)}{16} \qquad \textbf{(12-5.4)}$$

is depicted in Fig. 12-5.1.

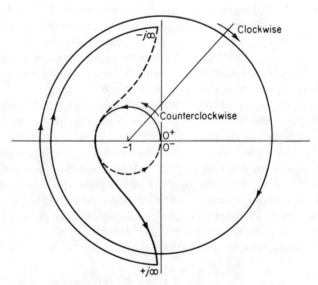

Figure 12-5.1 Inverse polar plot of Eq. (12-5.4).

PROBLEMS

12.1 For the following Nyquist diagrams (assuming that they represent stable systems), compute the gain margins.

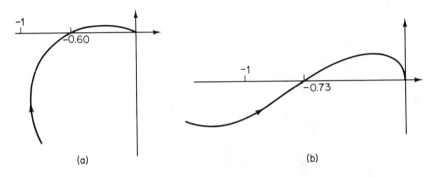

(a)

(b)

Prob. 12.1

12.2 The polar plot of this problem corresponds to a conditionally stable system. What are the high- and low-frequency gain margins?

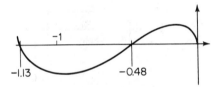

Prob. 12.2

12.3 What type number systems are plotted in each of the following polar diagrams (assuming no right half-plane open-loop poles)?

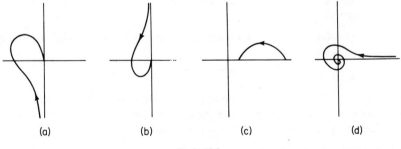

(a)   (b)   (c)   (d)

Prob. 12.3

12.4 From the polar diagrams for each of the following transfer functions, determine absolute systems stability by means of Nyquist's stability criterion (or the simplified criterion). For those systems that are observed to be stable, compute the gain and phase margins and the unity crossover frequencies.

(a) $G(s) = \dfrac{10}{s(0.5s + 1)}$

(b) $G(s) = \dfrac{100}{s^2(s + 10)}$

(c) $G(s) = \dfrac{1}{s(0.5s + 1)(2s + 1)}$

12.5 Plot Nyquist diagrams corresponding to the open-loop transfer functions and deduce the closed-loop stability.

(a) $K_1GH(s) = \dfrac{5}{s[(s/5) + 1][(s/16) + 1](4s + 1)}$

(b) $K_2GH(s) = \dfrac{1}{s[(s/5) + 1][(s/16) + 1](4s + 1)}$

12.6 A radar control loop has the approximate block diagram

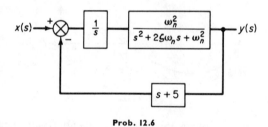

Prob. 12.6

Compute the Nyquist diagram, $KGH(j\omega)$, for $\zeta = 0.6$ and $\omega_n = 6$ radians per second. What is the system phase and gain margins, and unity crossover frequency?

12.7 The open-loop response of a mechanical follower servomechanism is given by

$$KG(s) = \dfrac{K}{s(s + 1)(s/4 + 1)}$$

Compute the value of K such that the maximum closed-loop amplitude ratio has a value of 2.2. What is the phase margin, gain margin, unity crossover frequency, bandwidth, and resonant frequency?

12.8 Compute the maximum-amplitude ratio response for each of the following.

(a) $KG(s) = \dfrac{10}{s(s + 10)}$

(b) $KG(s) = \dfrac{10(s+1)}{s^2(s+5)}$

(c) $KG(s) = \dfrac{18}{s(s^2+2s+10)}$

BIBLIOGRAPHY

1. Nixon, F. E., *Principles of Automatic Controls*. Englewood Cliffs, N.J.: Prentice-Hall, Inc., 1953.

2. Savant, C. J., Jr., *Basic Feedback Control System Design*. New York: McGraw-Hill Book Company, 1958.

LOG
FREQUENCY
PLOTS[1,2]

13

13-1 DERIVATION OF THE LOG FREQUENCY

The log frequency plot (more commonly referred to as the Bode diagram) is a graphical presentation of a system transfer function. The technique is based upon the logarithm of frequency, i.e., both amplitude ratio and phase are plotted against logarithmic frequency. In particular, the amplitude ratio is expressed in decibels where, for an input magnitude A_{in} and an output magnitude A_{out}

$$db = 20 \log_{10} \frac{A_{out}}{A_{in}} \qquad (13\text{-}1.1)$$

The Bode plot obviates the need for a tedious and time-consuming point-by-point polar-plot computation of $KGH(j\omega)$. Applying log frequency techniques, a continuous plot of $KGH(j\omega)$ is generated by a process of simple addition and subtraction of component curves. Further, the component curves are obtained by standard template techniques. Once the amplitude ratio and phase characteristics are known as a function of frequency, the information can be transformed into a standard polar plot by referring to a conversion table for db and amplitude ratio. Such a conversion chart is illustrated in Table 13-1.1.

In general, the arbitrary transfer function consists of a ratio of polynomials in s, that is decomposed into first- and second-order

TABLE 13-1.1

RELATION BETWEEN DB AND GAIN OR LOSS

DB	Gain	Loss	DB	Gain	Loss	DB	Gain	Loss	DB	Gain	Loss
0.0	1.000	1.000	5.0	1.778	0.562	10.0	3.162	0.316	15.0	5.623	0.178
.1	1.012	.988	.1	1.799	.556	.1	3.199	.313	.1	5.689	.176
.2	1.023	.977	.2	1.820	.549	.2	3.236	.309	.2	5.754	.174
.3	1.035	.966	.3	1.841	.543	.3	3.273	.306	.3	5.821	.172
.4	1.047	.955	.4	1.862	.537	.4	3.311	.302	.4	5.888	.170
.5	1.059	.944	.5	1.884	.531	.5	3.350	.298	.5	5.957	.168
.6	1.072	.933	.6	1.906	.525	.6	3.388	.295	.6	6.026	.166
.7	1.084	.922	.7	1.928	.519	.7	3.428	.292	.7	6.096	.164
.8	1.096	.912	.8	1.950	.513	.8	3.467	.288	.8	6.166	.162
.9	1.109	.902	.9	1.972	.507	.9	3.508	.285	.9	6.237	.160
1.0	1.122	.891	6.0	1.995	.501	11.0	3.548	.282	16.0	6.310	.158
.1	1.135	.881	.1	2.018	.496	.1	3.589	.279	.1	6.383	.157
.2	1.148	.871	.2	2.042	.490	.2	3.631	.275	.2	6.456	.155
.3	1.162	.861	.3	2.065	.484	.3	3.673	.272	.3	6.531	.153
.4	1.175	.851	.4	2.089	.479	.4	3.715	.269	.4	6.607	.151
.5	1.189	.841	.5	2.113	.473	.5	3.758	.266	.5	6.684	.150
.6	1.202	.832	.6	2.138	.468	.6	3.802	.263	.6	6.761	.148
.7	1.216	.822	.7	2.163	.462	.7	3.846	.260	.7	6.839	.146
.8	1.230	.813	.8	2.188	.459	.8	3.890	.257	.8	6.918	.145
9	1 245	.803	9	2 214	452	.9	3.935	.254	.9	6.998	143
2.0	1.259	.794	7.0	2.239	.447	12.0	3.981	.251	17.0	7.079	.141
.1	1.274	.785	.1	2.265	.441	.1	4.027	.248	.1	7.161	.140
.2	1.288	.776	.2	2.291	.436	.2	4.074	.245	.2	7.244	.138
.3	1.303	.767	.3	2.317	.432	.3	4.121	.243	.3	7.328	.136
.4	1.318	.759	.4	2.344	.427	.4	4.169	.240	.4	7.413	.135
.5	1.334	.750	.5	2.371	.422	.5	4.217	.237	.5	7.499	.133
.6	1.349	.741	.6	2.399	.417	.6	4.266	.234	.6	7.586	.132
.7	1.365	.733	.7	2.427	.412	.7	4.315	.232	.7	7.674	.130
.8	1.380	.725	.8	2.455	.407	.8	4.365	.229	.8	7.762	.129
.9	1.396	.716	.9	2.483	.403	.9	4.416	.226	.9	7.852	.127
3.0	1.413	.708	8.0	2.512	.398	13.0	4.467	.224	18.0	7.943	.126
.1	1.429	.700	.1	2.541	.394	.1	4.519	.221	.1	8.035	.124
.2	1.445	.692	.2	2.571	.388	.2	4.571	.219	.2	8.128	.123
.3	1.462	.684	.3	2.601	.384	.3	4.624	.216	.3	8.222	.122
.4	1.476	.676	.4	2.630	.380	.4	4.677	.214	.4	8.318	.120
.5	1.496	.668	.5	2.661	.376	.5	4.732	.211	.5	8.414	.119
.6	1.514	.660	.6	2.692	.371	.6	4.786	.209	.6	8.511	.117
.7	1.531	.653	.7	2.723	.367	.7	4.842	.207	.7	8.610	.116
.8	1.549	.646	.8	2.745	.363	.8	4.898	.204	.8	8.710	.115
.9	1.567	.638	.9	2.786	.359	.9	4.955	.202	.9	8.810	.113
4.0	1.585	.631	9.0	2.818	.355	14.0	5.012	.200	19.0	8.913	.112
.1	1.603	.624	.1	2.851	.351	.1	5.070	.197	.1	9.016	.111
.2	1.622	.617	.2	2.884	.347	.2	5.129	.195	.2	9.120	.110
.3	1.641	.609	.3	2.918	.343	.3	5.188	.193	.3	9.226	.108
.4	1.660	.602	.4	2.951	.339	.4	5.248	.191	.4	9.333	.107
.5	1.679	.596	.5	2.985	.335	.5	5.309	.188	.5	9.441	.106
.6	1.698	.589	.6	3.020	.331	.6	5.370	.186	.6	9.550	.105
.7	1.718	.582	.7	3.055	.327	.7	5.432	.184	.7	9.661	.103
.8	1.738	.575	.8	3.090	.324	.8	5.495	.182	.8	9.772	.102
.9	1.758	.569	.9	3.126	.320	.9	5.559	.180	.9	9.886	.101
									20.0	10.000	.100

factors, i.e.

$$KGH(s) = \frac{K_o(\tau_A s + 1)(\tau_B s + 1)(\tau_C s^2 + \tau_D s + 1) \cdots}{s^n(\tau_1 s + 1)(\tau_2 s^2 + \tau_3 s + 1)(\tau_4 s + 1) \cdots} \tag{13-1.2}$$

From Chapter 5, the frequency response is computing by substituting $j\omega$ for s in Eq. (13-1.2)

$$KGH(j\omega) = \frac{K_o(j\tau_A\omega + 1)(j\tau_B\omega + 1)[(j\omega)^2\tau_C + j\tau_D\omega + 1] \cdots}{(j\omega)^n(j\tau_1\omega + 1)[(j\omega)^2\tau_2 + j\tau_3\omega + 1](j\omega\tau_4 + 1) \cdots} \tag{13-1.3}$$

Each of the preceding numerator and denominator components can also be stated in exponential polar form

$$A_i(\omega)e^{j\theta(\omega)} = j\tau_i\omega + 1 \tag{13-1.4}$$

so that

$$A_T(\omega)e^{j\theta_T(\omega)}$$

$$= \frac{K_o \cdot A_A(\omega)e^{j\theta_A(\omega)} \cdot A_B(\omega)e^{j\theta_B(\omega)} \cdot A_{CD}(\omega)e^{j\theta_{CD}(\omega)} \cdots}{[A_o(\omega)e^{j90°}]^n \cdot A_1(\omega)e^{j\theta_1(\omega)} \cdot A_{23}(\omega)e^{j\theta_{23}(\omega)} \cdots} \tag{13-1.5}$$

Equation (13-1.5) is next linearized by logarithmic techniques. Since, from Chapter 2

$$\log_e Ae^{j\theta} = \text{Log}_e A + j\theta \tag{13-1.6}$$

Eq. (13-1.5) can be decomposed into a set of two relationships, the first representing the real part, and the second corresponding to the imaginary part of Eq. (13-1.3). Since two complex numbers are equal if, and only if, their real parts and imaginary parts are identical

$$\text{Log}_e A_T = \text{Log}_e K_o + \text{Log}_e A_A + \text{Log}_e A_B + \cdots$$

$$- n \text{Log}_e A_o - \text{Log}_e A_1 - \cdots \tag{13-1.7}$$

$$\theta_T = \theta_A + \theta_B + \theta_{CD} + \cdots - n \, 90° - \theta_1 - \theta_{23} - \cdots \tag{13-1.8}$$

where, in Eqs. (13-1.7) and (13-1.8), both amplitude and phase of the total response (A_T and θ_T) and each of the respective component responses are dependent upon the input-frequency parameter. Remembering that $\log_{10} x = \frac{1}{2.303}(\log_e x)$, and combining Eqs. (13-1.1) and (13-1.7)

$$A_{T\text{db}} = K_{o\text{db}} + A_{A\text{db}} + A_{B\text{db}} + \cdots - A_{1\text{db}} - A_{23\text{db}} - \cdots \tag{13-1.9}$$

However, if the quantity $1/(j\tau_i\omega + 1)$ is computed, rather than $j\tau_i\omega + 1$ of Eq. (13-1.5), Eq. (13-1.9) is rewritten in final form

$$A_{T_{db}} = K_{0_{db}} + A_{A_{db}} + A_{B_{db}}$$
$$+ A'_{1_{db}} + A'_{23_{db}} + \cdots$$
$$\text{(13-1.10)}$$

and

$$\theta_T = \theta_A + \theta_B + \cdots + n(-90°)$$
$$+ \theta'_1 + \theta'_2 + \cdots \quad \text{(13-1.11)}$$

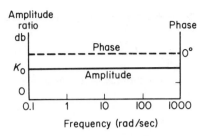

Figure 13-1.1   Bode diagram for gain constant K_0.

where the prime superscripts indicate that the reciprocals of the denominator quantities of Eq. (13-1.9) are actually plotted. Equations (13-1.11) and (13-1.10) comprise the Bode diagram. It now remains to define the amplitude ratio and phase-angle characteristics of the common frequency-variant functions encountered in practically all servo systems, i.e.

Integrator $\dfrac{1}{s}$

Differentiator s

Lag $\dfrac{1}{\tau s + 1}$

Lead $\tau s + 1$

Quadratics $(\tau^2 s^2 + 2\zeta\tau s + 1)$ or $\dfrac{1}{\tau^2 s^2 + 2\zeta\tau s + 1}$

Before beginning the general approach, however, let us consider the frequency-invariant factor K_0. This quantity is frequency invariant in that its value is not affected by frequency, i.e., K_0 is a positive constant with 0-degree phase shift over all frequencies. Thus, the Bode plot for the component K_0 is as illustrated in Fig. 13-1.1.

13-2 INTEGRATOR AND DIFFERENTIATOR CHARACTERISTICS

The first-order (simple) differentiator has the transfer function

$$G(s) = s \qquad\qquad \text{(13-2.1)}$$

or, for a sinusoidally varying input

$$G(j\omega) = j\omega \tag{13-2.2}$$

On the s-plane diagram of Fig. 13-2.1, Eq. (13-2.2) is plotted as a vertical

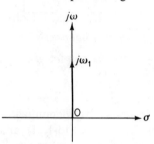

Figure 13-2.1 s-plane diagram of $j\omega_1$.

vector with a phase angle of $+90°$, and an amplitude that varies directly with frequency. Thus, the amplitude ratio $G(j\omega)$ doubles (increases by approximately 6 db) each time the input frequency doubles. Defining a *factor of two* in frequency as one *octave*, we say that the differentiator amplitude ratio increases by 6 db/octave. (Although the true amplitude increase is $20 \log_{10} 2.0 = 6.0206$ db, a value of 6 db/octave is always assumed to facilitate plotting.) One *decade* is defined as a *factor of ten* in frequency; hence, the differentiator amplitude ratio increases at a rate of 20 db/decade. The frequency at which $G(j\omega)$ exhibits a gain of unity (0 db) is evidently one radian/sec, i.e.

$$G(j\omega) = \omega \qquad G(j\omega) = 1 \quad \text{for } \omega_{co} = 1$$

Thus, the amplitude ratio and phase characteristics of the simple differentiator can be plotted as in Fig. 13-2.2.

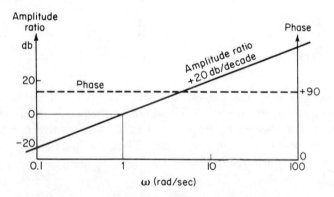

Figure 13-2.2 Bode diagram for simple differentiator.

The nth-order differentiator $G(j\omega) = (j\omega)^n$ is plotted as a linear addition of n first-order differentiator Bode diagrams. As illustrated in Fig. 13-2.3, this quantity exhibits a phase lead of $90n$ degrees, and an amplitude ratio that increases at a rate of $20n$ db/decade.

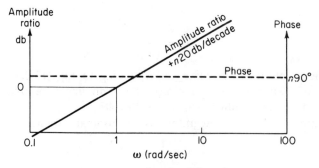

Figure 13-2.3 nth order differentiator.

An nth-order derivative with gain, such as

$$G(j\omega) = K_o(j\omega)^n \qquad (13\text{-}2.3)$$

can be plotted by one of two separate methods, both of which yield identical end results. A linear addition of K_0 (expressed in db) and $(j\omega)^n$ is suggested in Fig. 13-2.4(a). In addition, however, we can plot the function of Eq. (13-2.3) directly by noting that at the unity crossover frequency (i.e., the frequency at which $G(j\omega) = 0$ db)

$$|G(j\omega)| = 1 = |K_o(j\omega)^n| = K_o\omega_{co}^n \qquad (13\text{-}2.4)$$

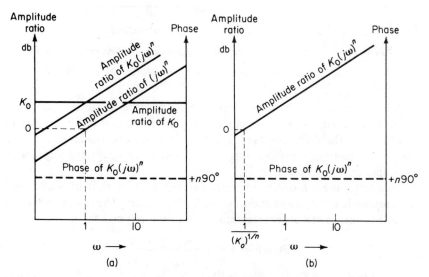

Figure 13-2.4   Bode plot of nth order differentiator with gain K_0 (a) by summing component diagrams; (b) by plotting directly.

such that

$$\omega_{co} = \frac{1}{(K_o)^{1/n}} \qquad \text{(13-2.5)}$$

Hence, the amplitude-ratio curve corresponding to Eq. (13-2.3) increases at a rate of 20 db/decade, and crosses the 0 db line at a frequency of $1/(K_0)^{1/n}$ radians/sec, as illustrated in Fig. 13-2.4(b).

The simple (first-order) integrator has a sinusoidal response

$$G(j\omega) = \frac{1}{j\omega} = -j\frac{1}{\omega} \qquad \text{(13-2.6)}$$

As suggested in Fig. 13-2.5(a), the complex-plane diagram corresponding to Eq. (13-2.6) consists of a negative imaginary-axis vector with an amplitude inversely proportional to the input frequency, i.e., in one decade of frequency,

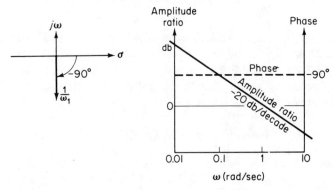

Figure 13-2.5 At an input frequency of ω_1 radians/sec, the first order integrator exhibits an amplitude attenuation of $\dfrac{1}{\omega_1}$ at a phase angle of $-90°$.

$G(j\omega)$ *decreases* by a factor of 10 (20 db). Thus, the first-order integrator exhibits a -20 db/decade amplitude variation and a constant phase lag of $-90°$. Since the 0 db crossover frequency is again one radian/sec, the log frequency diagram corresponding to the first-order integrator appears as indicated in Fig. 13-2.5(b).

Similarly, the nth-order integrator exhibits a phase shift of $-n90°$ and an amplitude-ratio attenuation of $-20n$ db/decade. The unity crossover frequency for an nth-order integrator with gain is defined as

$$|G(j\omega)| = 1 = \left| \frac{K_o}{(j\omega_{co})^n} \right| = \frac{K_o}{\omega_{co}^n}$$

$$\omega_{co} = K_o^{1/n} \qquad \text{(13-2.7)}$$

This final consideration is depicted in Fig. 13-2.6.

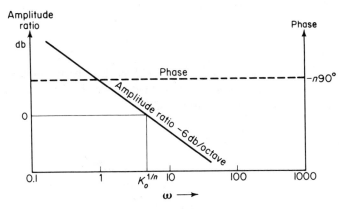

Figure 13-2.6 nth-order integrator with gain.

13-3 LEADS AND LAGS

For first-order lead term

$$G(j\omega) = j\omega\tau + 1 \qquad \text{(13-3.1)}$$

a high and low-frequency analysis is used to study the behavior of the system frequency response at the two extremities in frequency. As suggested in Fig. 13-3.1, the simple lead resembles a positive unity gain (0 db) for very low

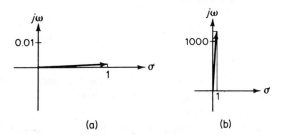

(a)   (b)

Figure 13-3.1   Frequency characteristics of lead term at (a) low frequencies, and (b) high frequencies.

frequency. As $\omega \rightarrow \infty$, however, the amplitude ratio increases at a rate of 20 db/decade and exhibits a $+90°$ phase angle; thus, at high frequencies, the lead term has the characteristics of a first-order differentiator.

For the high-frequency case, i.e., for $\omega\tau \gg 1$, the equivalent differentiator 0 db intercept is computed as

$$G(j\omega) = 1 = \omega_{co}\tau \qquad \text{(13-3.2)}$$

from which

$$\omega_{co} = \frac{1}{\tau}$$
(13-3.3)

Thus, the *asymptotic approximation* of the true lead-term amplitude-ratio frequency-response curve is obtained by extending the high and low-frequency approximations, as illustrated in Fig. 13-3.2.

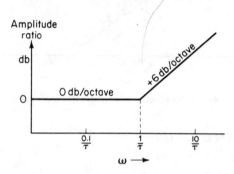

Figure 13-3.2   Asymptotic approximation of first-order lead amplitude ratio.

In many areas of analysis, this approximation is adequate. If a more accurate frequency response is desired, however, the true amplitude ratio can be plotted in a point-by-point manner. To illustrate, at the "corner" frequency $1/\tau$, the amplitude ratio is

$$|G(j\omega)| = \left| j\tau \cdot \frac{1}{\tau} + 1 \right| = 1.414 = +3 \text{ db}$$

Similarly, at one octave above and below the corner frequency, the amplitude ratio is up 1 db from the asymptotic approximation. With respect to phase, the asymptotic approximation is a straight line, originating at $0°$ one decade below the corner frequency and terminating at $+90°$ one decade above the corner frequency, as illustrated in Fig. 13-3.3.

The simple lag term $1/(j\omega\tau + 1)$ can be considered in a manner identical to that of the first-order lead. Since the logarithm of the reciprocal of a quantity is equal to the negative logarithm of the quantity, i.e.

$$20 \log_{10} \frac{1}{j\omega\tau + 1} = -20 \log_{10} (j\omega\tau + 1)$$
(13-3.4)

it follows that the asymptotic approximation of the simple lag is a straight line (0 db) to the corner frequency, followed by a constantly decreasing

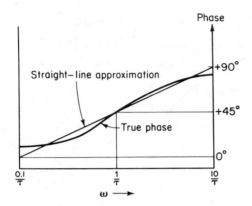

Figure 13-3.3 Approximate and true first-order lead phase.

(-6 db/octave) response for all higher frequencies. Similarly, the system phase varies from $0°$ at low frequencies to $-90°$ at high frequencies. Asymptotic approximations of the first-order lag term are suggested in Fig. 13-3.4.

Templates, suitable for use in the plotting of conventional log frequency diagrams, are shown in Figs. 13-3.5 through 13-3.9. In Fig. 13-3.5, the amplitude ratio and phase characteristics of first-order lead and lag systems are plotted against the logarithm of frequency.

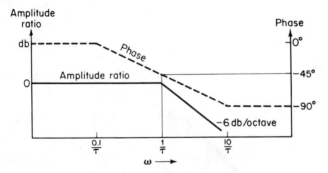

Figure 13-3.4 Asymptotic approximation of first-order lag.

Figures 13-3.6 and 13-3.7 describe the frequency response of a generalized lead-lag system, i.e., a simple lead followed by a first-order lag. The amplitude and phase characteristics illustrated in Figs. 13-3.6 and 13-3.7 respectively are for various values of ratio T_1/T_2 (where T_1 and T_2 are time constants) expressed in db. Thus, the transfer function

$$G(s) = \frac{s+1}{0.1s+1} \qquad (13\text{-}3.5)$$

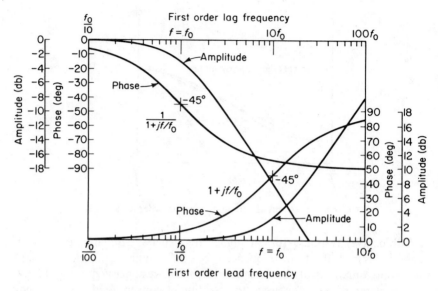

Figure 13-3.5   Characteristics of first-order lead and lag systems.

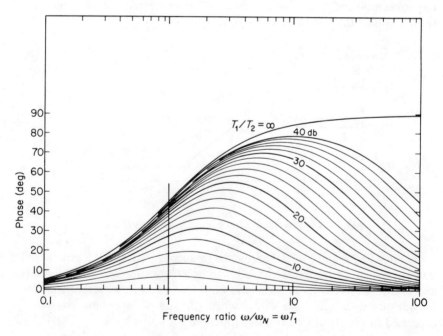

Figure 13-3.6   Phase response of first-order system $(1 + j\omega T_1)/(1 + j\omega T_2)$.

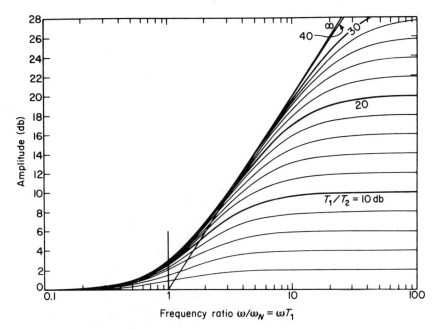

Figure 13-3.7 Amplitude characteristics of first-order system $(1 + j\omega T_1)/(1 + j\omega T_2)$.

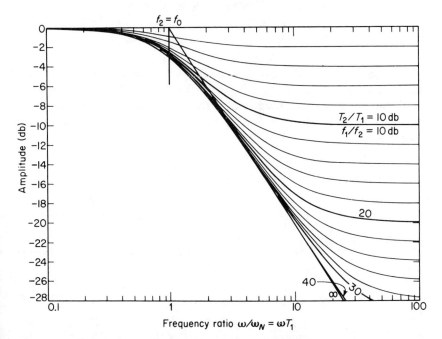

Figure 13-3.8 Amplitude characteristics of first-order system $(1 + j\omega T_1)/(1 + j\omega T_2) = (1 + jf/f_1)/(1 + jf/f_2)$.

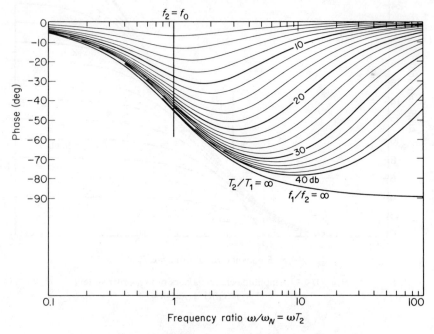

Figure 13-3.9 Phase response of first-order system
$(1 + j\omega T_1)/(1 + j\omega T_2) = (1 + jf/f_1)/(1 + jf/f_2)$.

requires the 20-db lead-lag curve, while the system break frequency is positioned at 1 radian/sec, i.e., the *lead* corner frequency is the one employed.

Figures 13-3.8 and 13-3.9 detail the frequency response of a generalized lag-lead system. In this case, the *lag* corner frequency is employed as the system break.

13-4 QUADRATIC TERMS

The amplitude ratio and phase characteristics corresponding to the quadratics

$$G_1(j\omega) = (j\tau_1\omega)^2 + j2\zeta\tau_1\omega + 1 \qquad \textbf{(13-4.1)}$$

and

$$G_2(j\omega) = \frac{1}{(j\tau_2\omega)^2 + j2\zeta\tau_2\omega + 1} \qquad \textbf{(13-4.2)}$$

are computed in a manner identical to that for the first-order lead and lag terms. For low frequencies, the quadratic terms exhibit unity gain and zero phase shift. For very high frequencies, however, the quadratic lead amplitude ratio increases at a rate of 12 db/octave. Conversely, the quadratic lag amplitude ratio decreases at 12 db/octave. With respect to phase, the high-frequency lead and lag quadratic terms approach $+180°$ and $-180°$ respectively; at the corner frequencies (τ_1 and τ_2), the phase angles are $\pm 90°$. Asymptotic approximations of both quadratic phase and amplitude characteristics are illustrated in Fig. 13-4.1.

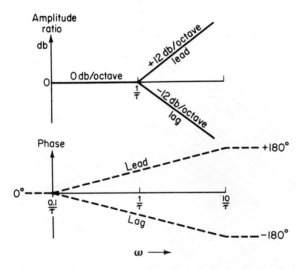

Figure 13-4.1   Asymptotic approximations of quadratic lead and lag components.

In Chapter 8, it was shown that the quadratic (second-order) lag frequency-response characteristics (maximum amplitude resonances, resonant frequency, bandwidth, etc.) were expressed in terms of the system damping ratio (ζ) in addition to the undamped natural frequency [$\omega_n = (1/\tau)$]. Thus, the fact that the generalized quadratic component frequency-response characteristics become a function of damping should not be totally unexpected. The variations of phase and amplitude with both frequency and damping, for second-order lead and lag terms, are detailed in Figs. 13-4.2 and 13-4.3. *In Fig. 13-4.2, the gain curves are plotted in terms of deviations between the true amplitude ratios and the asymptotic approximation.*

13-5   RIGHT HALF-PLANE COMPONENTS

The frequency-response expression for the typical nonminimum phase (right half-plane) zero is

$$G(j\omega) = -j\omega\tau + 1 \qquad (13\text{-}5.1)$$

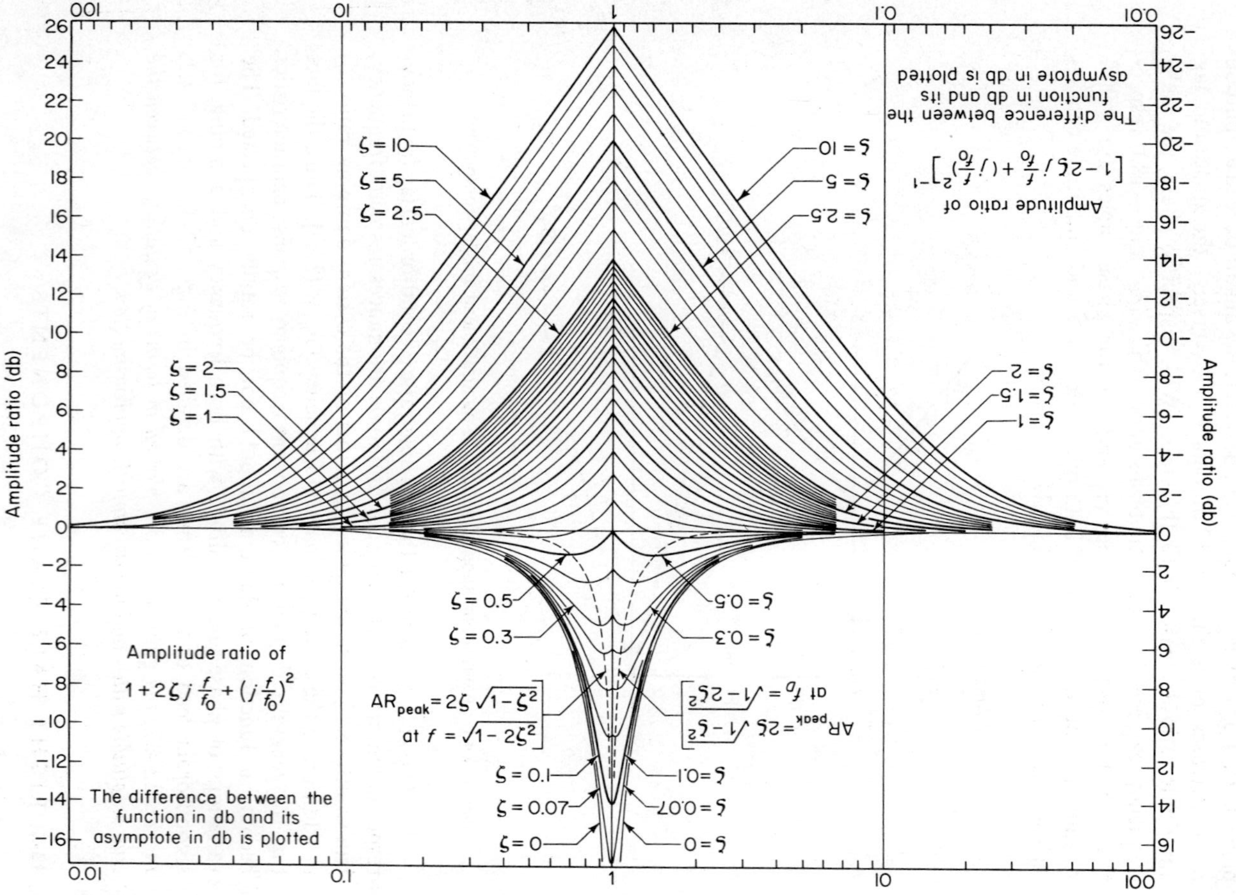

Figure 13-4.2 Amplitude ratio of second-order system lead and lag terms.

Amplitude ratio (db)

Amplitude ratio of
$$\left[1 - 2\zeta j \frac{f}{f_0} + \left(j \frac{f}{f_0}\right)^2\right]^{-1}$$

The difference between the function in db and its asymptote in db is plotted

$\zeta = 1$
$\zeta = 1.5$
$\zeta = 2$

$\zeta = 2.5$
$\zeta = 5$
$\zeta = 10$

$AR_{peak} = 2\zeta\sqrt{1 - \zeta^2}$
at $f_D = \sqrt{1 - 2\zeta^2}$

$\zeta = 0$
$\zeta = 0.07$
$\zeta = 0.1$
$\zeta = 0$
$\zeta = 0.07$
$\zeta = 0.1$

$\zeta = 0.3$
$\zeta = 0.5$

$\zeta = 0.5$
$\zeta = 0.3$

$AR_{peak} = 2\zeta\sqrt{1 - \zeta^2}$
at $f = \sqrt{1 - 2\zeta^2}$

Amplitude ratio of
$$1 + 2\zeta j \frac{f}{f_0} + \left(j \frac{f}{f_0}\right)^2$$

The difference between the function in db and its asymptote in db is plotted

$\zeta = 10$
$\zeta = 5$
$\zeta = 2.5$

$\zeta = 2$
$\zeta = 1.5$
$\zeta = 1$

Amplitude ratio (db)

292

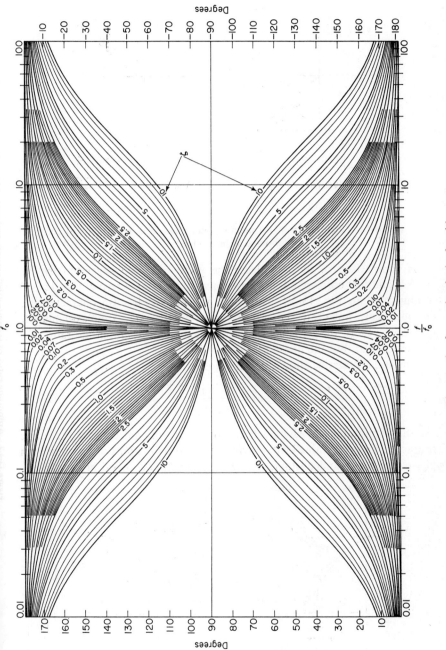

Figure 13-4.3 Phase angle of second-order lead and lag terms.

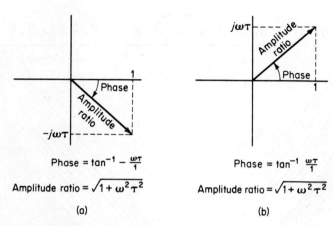

$$\text{Phase} = \tan^{-1} - \frac{\omega\tau}{1}$$

$$\text{Amplitude ratio} = \sqrt{1 + \omega^2\tau^2}$$

(a)

$$\text{Phase} = \tan^{-1} \frac{\omega\tau}{1}$$

$$\text{Amplitude ratio} = \sqrt{1 + \omega^2\tau^2}$$

(b)

Figure 13-5.1 Comparison of (a) nonminimum phase lead term, and (b) conventional stable lead term.

A comparison of the complex-plane vector diagram suggested by Eq. (13-5.1) and that corresponding to the conventional stable zero of Eq. (13-3.1) is illustrated in Fig. 13-5.1. Note that the amplitude-ratio characteristics are identical; however, the phase characteristics are complex-conjugate quantities. Thus, the right half-plane zero exhibits the amplitude ratio of a first-order lead, but the phase of a first-order lag.

Similarly, it can be shown that the unstable lag

$$G(j\omega) = \frac{1}{-j\omega\tau_1 + 1} \tag{13-5.2}$$

has the amplitude-ratio characteristics of a conventional lag, but the phase characteristics of a stable lead. Asymptotic approximations of nonminimum phase zero terms and unstable lag components are described in Fig. 13-5.2.

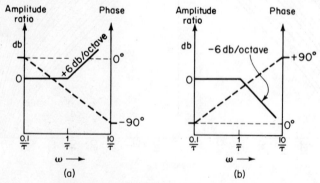

(a)

(b)

Figure 13-5.2 Asymptotic approximations (a) unstable zero, and (b) unstable pole.

13-6 STABILITY MARGINS

Both phase and gain margins are deduced directly from the conventional Bode plot. It should be stressed, however, that *no information regarding systems stability can be obtained from the log frequency diagram*. Only by applying Nyquist's stability criterion to the polar-plot representation of $KGH(j\omega)$ can we determine the stability or instability of the closed loop. If, however, the system is known to be stable, then phase and gain margins

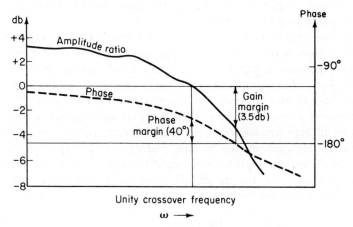

Figure 13-6.1   Calculation of gain and phase margins on the log frequency diagram.

can be derived directly from the log frequency diagram. In Fig. 13-6.1, the phase margin is evidently the variation from the $-180°$ line, corresponding to the frequency at which the amplitude curve intersects the 0-db line. Similarly, the gain margin is the value of gain corresponding to the frequency at which the phase curve intersects the $-180°$ line.

13-7 EXAMPLES OF LOG FREQUENCY PLOT CONSTRUCTION

As an initial example, consider the open-loop transfer function

$$G(s) = \frac{\frac{10}{64}(s + \frac{1}{10})}{s(s^2 + \frac{1}{4}s + \frac{1}{16})} \tag{13-7.1}$$

Rearranging

$$G(s) = \frac{(16/10)(10/64)(s/0.1 + 1)}{s[(s/0.25)^2 + (s/0.25) + 1]} \tag{13-7.2}$$

For a sinusoidal input, one substitutes $j\omega$ for s in Eq. (13-7.2) to yield

$$G(j\omega) = \frac{1/4[(j\omega/0.10) + 1]}{(j\omega)[(j\omega/0.25)^2 + (j\omega/0.25) + 1]} \qquad (13\text{-}7.3)$$

Note that Eqs. (13-7.2) and (13-7.3) are stated in a form of hybrid notation, i.e., rather than writing $\tau s + 1$ (time-constant form) or $s + \omega$ (pole-zero form), one can employ $(s/\omega) + 1$ (hybrid form). This notation tends to bridge the gap between root-locus and log frequency diagram techniques and is widely employed. Comparing the denominator quadratic to Eq. (13-4.2), a damping ratio ζ of 0.5 is indicated.

The first step in plotting Eq. (13-7.3) through the use of asymptotic approximations is to determine the position of the first-order integrator. For this application, use is made of the low-frequency approximation, i.e., the form of the amplitude-ratio curve as $\omega \to 0$. In Eq. (13-7.3), as $\omega \to 0$, the lead and lag terms each approach a limit of unity. Physically, this statement amounts to the evident fact that, as frequency decreases, the effects of all high-frequency components diminish. In the limit, as $\omega \to 0$, all lead and lag elements are of high frequency with respect to the input frequency. Thus, they produce a negligible contribution into the low-frequency section of the amplitude response. Under these conditions, Eq. (13-7.3) can be rewritten as

$$\lim_{\omega \to 0} G(j\omega) = \frac{\frac{1}{4}}{j\omega} \qquad (13\text{-}7.4)$$

To compute the frequency at which the low frequency-approximation exhibits an amplitude ratio of unity

$$\left| \lim_{\omega \to 0} G(j\omega) \right| = 1 = \frac{0.25}{\omega} \qquad (13\text{-}7.5)$$

from which $\omega = 0.25$. The low-frequency approximation is thus plotted as illustrated in Fig. 13-7.1. With Fig. 13-7.1 as a base, the amplitude-ratio curve is generated by summing a $+6$ db/octave component at 0.1 radians/sec together with a -12 db/octave term at 0.25 radians/sec; these breaks correspond to the first-order lead and quadratic lag components respectively. Similarly, we obtain the phase curve by using standard asymptotic approximations. The final log frequency diagram is illustrated in Fig. 13-7.2. For comparative purposes, Eq. (13-7.3) is also plotted by means of the standard template given in Figs. 13-3.5, 13-4.2, and 13-4.3; the results of this more-accurate but time-consuming approach are pictured in Fig. 13-7.3. Note that the amplitude-ratio curves of Figs. 13-7.3 and 13-7.2 compare favorably, particularly at higher frequencies; hence, we see the origin of the term "asymptotic approximation." The phase-shift curves, however, are not in

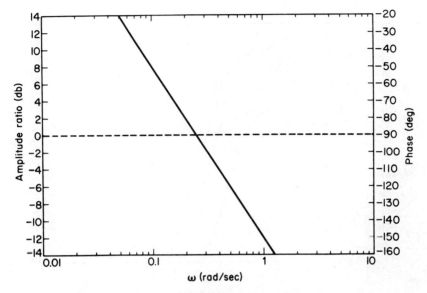

Figure 13-7.1   Low-frequency approximation.

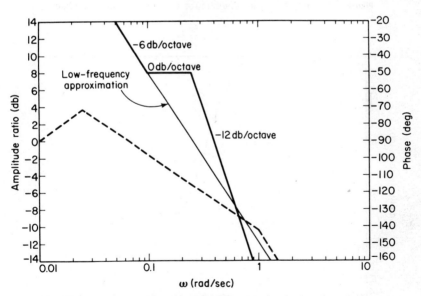

Figure 13-7.2   Log frequency diagram for Eq. (13-7.3) using asymptotic approximations.

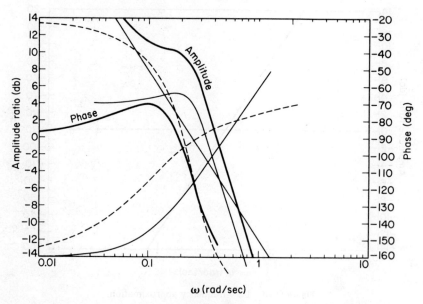

Figure 13-7.3   Log frequency diagram for Eq. (13-7.3) using templates.

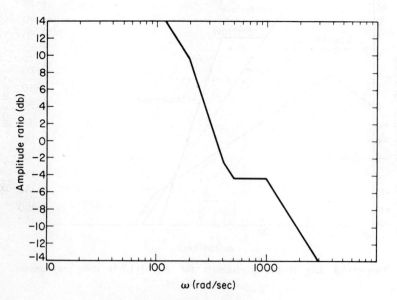

Figure 13-7.4   Asymptotic approximation of Eq. (13-7.6).

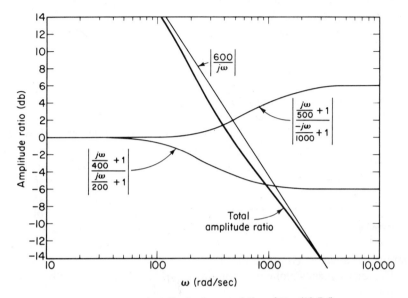

Figure 13-7.5   Amplitude characteristics of Eq. (13-7.6).

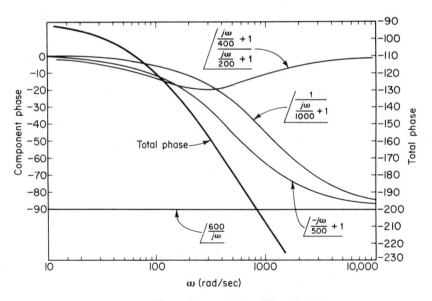

Figure 13-7.6   Phase characteristics of Eq. (13-7.6).

close agreement. Therefore, the templates would normally be employed in the majority of practical applications.

As a second example, consider the open-loop transfer function

$$G(j\omega) = \frac{600[-(j\omega/500) + 1][(j\omega/400 + 1]}{(j\omega)[(j\omega/1000) + 1][(j\omega/200) + 1]} \qquad (13\text{-}7.6)$$

The asymptotic and true amplitude-ratio plots demonstrated in Figs. 13-7.4 and 13-7.5 illustrate the fact that the unstable zero amplitude is identical to that of a stable zero. However, the template-derived phase characteristics of Fig. 13-7.6 reflect the phase reversal exhibited by this component.

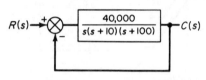

$R(s) \rightarrow \bigotimes \begin{array}{c} \dfrac{40,000}{s(s+10)(s+100)} \end{array} \rightarrow C(s)$

Figure 13-7.7 Closed-loop controller.

For the final example, consider the closed-loop system of Fig. 13-7.7. The problem is one of determining the system gain and phase-margin parameters, assuming that the closed loop is stable.

The log frequency plot corresponding to Fig. 13-7.7 is obtained by plotting the function

$$G(j\omega) = \frac{40}{(j\omega)[(j\omega/10) + 1][(j\omega/100) + 1]} \qquad (13\text{-}7.7)$$

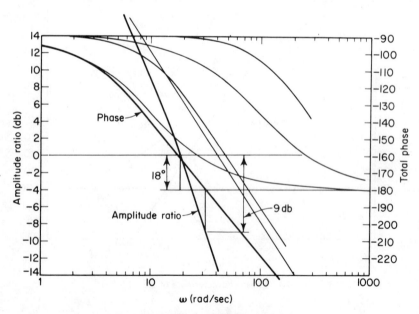

Figure 13-7.8 Bode plot of Eq. (13-7.7).

and appears as illustrated in Fig. 13-7.8. From the log frequency diagram, the phase and gain margins are evidently 18° and 9 db respectively.

PROBLEMS

13.1 Compute log frequency diagrams for the following transfer functions

(a) $KGH(s) = 1/s^3$

(b) $KGH(s) = -1/s$

(c) $KGH(s) = 10/s(s + 10)$

(d) $KGH(s) = \dfrac{1}{s[(s/5) + 1][(s/10) + 1]}$

13.2 An experimentally-derived frequency-response amplitude ratio yields the

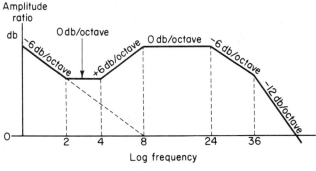

Prob. 13.2

following diagram. What is the associated system-transfer function, assuming no right half-plane poles or zeros?

13.3 For each of the following systems, plot the Bode diagrams and determine phase and gain margins.

(a) $KGH(s) = \dfrac{(s + 1)}{s[(s/4) + 1][(s/15) + 1](5s + 1)}$

(b) $KGH(s) = \dfrac{110(s + 5)}{s^2(s + 25)}$

13.4 Deduce the system type numbers for each of the experimentally derived open-loop system responses.

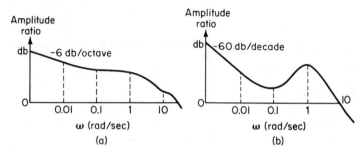

Prob. 13.4

13.5 The hydraulic controller illustrated in the accompanying figure consists of a servoamplifier, servovalve, hydraulic actuator, and dynamic load. Construct the log frequency diagram for this system and deduce the phase and gain margins and unity crossover frequency.

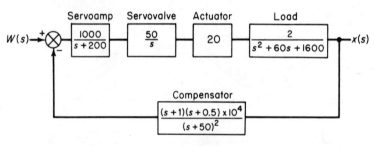

Prob. 13.5

13.6 Determine the value of gain K for which each of the following become marginally stable (180° phase shift at an amplitude ratio of unity).

(a) $KGH(s) = \dfrac{K[-(s/20) + 1][-(s/60) + 1]}{s[(s/20) + 1][(s/50) + 1]}$

(b) $KGH(s) = \dfrac{K(s + 2)}{s^2(s + 10)(s + 25)}$

13.7 The following open-loop systems contain right half-plane poles but can be stabilized through the use of feedback. Compute the value of gain which results in marginal stability.

(a) $KGH(s) = \dfrac{K(s + 5)}{s(s - 10)}$

(b) $KGH(s) = \dfrac{K(s + 5)(s + 15)}{s(s - 10)(s - 20)}$

BIBLIOGRAPHY

1. Bower, J. L. and P. M. Schultheiss, *Introduction to the Design of Servomechanisms*. New York: John Wiley & Sons, Inc., 1958.

2. D'Azzo, J. J. and C. H. Houpis, *Control System Analysis and Synthesis*. New York: McGraw-Hill Book Company, 1960.

APPENDICES

APPENDIX A: TABLE OF LAPLACE TRANSFORMS

	$F(s)$	$f(t)$
1.	1	$u_1(t) \equiv \lim_{\alpha \to 0} \dfrac{u(t) - u(t-a)}{\alpha}$ unit impulse at $t = 0$
2.	s	$u_2(t) \equiv \lim_{a \to 0} \dfrac{u(t) - 2u(t-a) + u(t-2a)}{a^2}$ unit doublet impulse at $t = 0$
3.	$\dfrac{1}{s}$	1 or $u(t)$ unit step at $t = 0$ *CONSTANT*
4.	$\dfrac{1}{s^m}$	$\dfrac{1}{(m-1)!}\, t^{m-1}$
5.	$\dfrac{e^{-as}}{s}$	$u(t-a)$
6.	$\dfrac{1}{s}(e^{-as} - e^{-bs})$	$u(t-a) - u(t-b)$ $a < b$
7.	$\dfrac{1}{s+\alpha}$	$e^{-\alpha t}$
8.	$\dfrac{1}{(s+\alpha)^m}$	$\dfrac{1}{(m-1)!}\, t^{m-1} e^{-\alpha t}$
9.	$\dfrac{1}{s(s+\alpha)}$	$\dfrac{1}{\alpha}[1 - e^{-\alpha t}]$

10.	$\dfrac{s+a_0}{s(s+\alpha)}$	$\dfrac{1}{\alpha}[a_0 - (a_0 - \alpha)e^{-\alpha t}]$
11.	$\dfrac{1}{s^2(s+\alpha)}$	$\dfrac{1}{\alpha^2}[e^{-\alpha t} + \alpha t - 1]$
12.	$\dfrac{s+a_0}{s^2(s+\alpha)}$	$\dfrac{a_0 t}{\alpha} + \left(\dfrac{a_0}{\alpha^2} - \dfrac{1}{\alpha}\right)(e^{-\alpha t} - 1)$
13.	$\dfrac{s^2+a_1 s+a_0}{s^2(s+\alpha)}$	$\dfrac{1}{\alpha^2}[(a_0 - a_1\alpha + \alpha^2)e^{-\alpha t} + a_0\alpha t + a_1\alpha - a_0]$
14.	$\dfrac{1}{(s+\alpha)(s+\gamma)}$	$\dfrac{e^{-\alpha t} - e^{-\gamma t}}{\gamma - \alpha}$
15.	$\dfrac{s+a_0}{(s+\alpha)(s+\gamma)}$	$\dfrac{(a_0 - \alpha)e^{-\alpha t} - (a_0 - \gamma)e^{-\gamma t}}{\gamma - \alpha}$
16.	$\dfrac{1}{s(s+\alpha)(s+\beta)}$	$\dfrac{1}{\alpha\beta} - \dfrac{e^{-\alpha t}}{\alpha(\beta - \alpha)} - \dfrac{e^{-\beta t}}{\beta(\alpha - \beta)}$
17.	$\dfrac{s+a_0}{s(s+\alpha)(s+\beta)}$	$\dfrac{a_0}{\alpha\beta} - \dfrac{(a_0 - \alpha)}{\alpha(\beta - \alpha)}e^{-\alpha t} - \dfrac{(a_0 - \beta)}{\beta(\alpha - \beta)}e^{-\beta t}$
18.	$\dfrac{s^2+a_1 s+a_0}{s(s+\alpha)(s+\beta)}$	$\dfrac{a_0}{\alpha\beta} - \dfrac{\alpha^2 - a_1\alpha + a_0}{\alpha(\beta - \alpha)}e^{-\alpha t} - \dfrac{\beta^2 - a_1\beta + a_0}{\beta(\alpha - \beta)}e^{-\beta t}$
19.	$\dfrac{1}{s^2(s+\alpha)(s+\beta)}$	$\dfrac{1}{\alpha^2\beta^2}\left[\dfrac{1}{\alpha - \beta}(\alpha^2 e^{-\beta t} - \beta^2 e^{-\alpha t}) + \alpha\beta t - \alpha - \beta\right]$

F(s)	f(t)
20. $\dfrac{s + a_0}{s^2(s + \alpha)(s + \beta)}$	$\dfrac{1}{\alpha\beta}[1 + a_0 t] - \dfrac{a_0(\alpha + \beta)}{\alpha^2\beta^2} + \dfrac{1}{\beta - \alpha}\left[\dfrac{a_0 - \alpha}{\alpha^2}e^{-\alpha t} - \dfrac{a_0 - \beta}{\beta^2}e^{-\beta t}\right]$
21. $\dfrac{s^2 + a_1 s + a_0}{s^2(s + \alpha)(s + \beta)}$	$\dfrac{1}{\alpha\beta}[a_1 + a_0 t] - \dfrac{a_0(\alpha + \beta)}{\alpha^2\beta^2} - \dfrac{1}{\alpha - \beta}\left[\left(1 - \dfrac{a_1}{\alpha} + \dfrac{a_0}{\alpha^2}\right)e^{-\alpha t} - \left(1 - \dfrac{a_1}{\beta} + \dfrac{a_0}{\beta^2}\right)e^{-\beta t}\right]$
22. $\dfrac{s^3 + a_2 s^2 + a_1 s + a_0}{s^2(s + \alpha)(s + \beta)}$	$\dfrac{1}{\alpha\beta}[a_1 + a_0 t] - \dfrac{a_0(\alpha + \beta)}{\alpha^2\beta^2} + \dfrac{1}{\alpha - \beta}\left[\left(\alpha - a_2 + \dfrac{a_1}{\alpha} - \dfrac{a_0}{\alpha^2}\right)e^{-\alpha t} - \left(\beta - a_2 + \dfrac{a_1}{\beta} - \dfrac{a_0}{\beta^2}\right)e^{-\beta t}\right]$
23. $\dfrac{1}{(s + \alpha)(s + \gamma)(s + \delta)}$	$\dfrac{e^{-\alpha t}}{(\gamma - \alpha)(\delta - \alpha)} + \dfrac{e^{-\gamma t}}{(\alpha - \gamma)(\delta - \gamma)} + \dfrac{e^{-\delta t}}{(\alpha - \delta)(\gamma - \delta)}$
24. $\dfrac{s + a_0}{(s + \alpha)(s + \gamma)(s + \delta)}$	$\dfrac{(a_0 - \alpha)e^{-\alpha t}}{(\gamma - \alpha)(\delta - \alpha)} + \dfrac{(a_0 - \gamma)e^{-\gamma t}}{(\alpha - \gamma)(\delta - \gamma)} + \dfrac{(a_0 - \delta)e^{-\delta t}}{(\alpha - \delta)(\gamma - \delta)}$
25. $\dfrac{s^2 + a_1 s + a_0}{(s + \alpha)(s + \gamma)(s + \delta)}$	$\dfrac{\alpha^2 - a_1\alpha + a_0}{(\gamma - \alpha)(\delta - \alpha)}e^{-\alpha t} + \dfrac{\gamma^2 - a_1\gamma + a_0}{(\alpha - \gamma)(\delta - \gamma)}e^{-\gamma t} + \dfrac{\delta^2 - a_1\delta + a_0}{(\alpha - \delta)(\gamma - \delta)}e^{-\delta t}$
26. $\dfrac{1}{s(s + \alpha)(s + \beta)(s + \gamma)}$	$\dfrac{1}{\alpha\beta\gamma} - \dfrac{e^{-\alpha t}}{\alpha(\beta - \alpha)(\gamma - \alpha)} - \dfrac{e^{-\beta t}}{\beta(\alpha - \beta)(\gamma - \beta)} - \dfrac{e^{-\gamma t}}{\gamma(\alpha - \gamma)(\beta - \gamma)}$
27. $\dfrac{s + a_0}{s(s + \alpha)(s + \beta)(s + \gamma)}$	$\dfrac{a_0}{\alpha\beta\gamma} - \dfrac{(a_0 - \alpha)e^{-\alpha t}}{\alpha(\beta - \alpha)(\gamma - \alpha)} - \dfrac{(a_0 - \beta)e^{-\beta t}}{\beta(\alpha - \beta)(\gamma - \beta)} - \dfrac{(a_0 - \gamma)e^{-\gamma t}}{\gamma(\alpha - \gamma)(\beta - \gamma)}$
28. $\dfrac{s^2 + a_1 s + a_0}{s(s + \alpha)(s + \beta)(s + \gamma)}$	$\dfrac{a_0}{\alpha\beta\gamma} - \dfrac{\alpha^2 - a_1\alpha + a_0}{\alpha(\beta - \alpha)(\gamma - \alpha)}e^{-\alpha t} - \dfrac{\beta^2 - a_1\beta + a_0}{\beta(\alpha - \beta)(\gamma - \beta)}e^{-\beta t} - \dfrac{\gamma^2 - a_1\gamma + a_0}{\gamma(\alpha - \gamma)(\beta - \gamma)}e^{-\gamma t}$

29.	$\dfrac{s^3 + a_2 s^2 + a_1 s + a_0}{s(s+\alpha)(s+\beta)(s+\gamma)}$	$\dfrac{a_0}{\alpha\beta\gamma} + \dfrac{\alpha^2 - a_2\alpha + a_1 - a_0/\alpha}{(\beta-\alpha)(\gamma-\alpha)}e^{-\alpha t} + \dfrac{\beta^2 - a_2\beta + a_1 - a_0/\beta}{(\alpha-\beta)(\gamma-\beta)}e^{-\beta t} + \dfrac{\gamma^2 + a_2\gamma + a_1 - a_0/\gamma}{(\alpha-\gamma)(\beta-\gamma)}e^{-\gamma t}$
30.	$\dfrac{1}{s^2(s+\alpha)(s+\beta)(s+\gamma)}$	$\dfrac{\alpha\beta(\gamma t - 1) - \gamma(\alpha+\beta)}{\alpha^2\beta^2\gamma^2} + \dfrac{e^{-\alpha t}}{\alpha^2(\beta-\alpha)(\gamma-\alpha)} + \dfrac{e^{-\beta t}}{\beta^2(\alpha-\beta)(\gamma-\beta)} + \dfrac{e^{-\gamma t}}{\gamma^2(\alpha-\gamma)(\beta-\gamma)}$
31.	$\dfrac{s + a_0}{s^2(s+\alpha)(s+\beta)(s+\gamma)}$	$\dfrac{1}{\alpha\beta\gamma}[1 + a_0 t] - \dfrac{a_0(\alpha\beta+\alpha\gamma+\beta\gamma)}{\alpha^2\beta^2\gamma^2} + \dfrac{(a_0-\alpha)e^{-\alpha t}}{\alpha^2(\beta-\alpha)(\gamma-\alpha)} + \dfrac{(a_0-\beta)e^{-\beta t}}{\beta^2(\alpha-\beta)(\gamma-\beta)} + \dfrac{(a_0-\gamma)e^{-\gamma t}}{\gamma^2(\alpha-\gamma)(\beta-\gamma)}$
32.	$\dfrac{s^2 + a_1 s + a_0}{s^2(s+\alpha)(s+\beta)(s+\gamma)}$	$\dfrac{1}{\alpha\beta\gamma}[a_1 + a_0 t] - \dfrac{a_0(\alpha\beta+\alpha\gamma+\beta\gamma)}{\alpha^2\beta^2\gamma^2} + \dfrac{(\alpha^2 - a_1\alpha + a_0)e^{-\alpha t}}{\alpha^2(\beta-\alpha)(\gamma-\alpha)} + \dfrac{(\beta^2 - a_1\beta + a_0)e^{-\beta t}}{\beta^2(\alpha-\beta)(\gamma-\beta)} + \dfrac{(\gamma^2 - a_1\gamma + a_0)e^{-\gamma t}}{\gamma^2(\alpha-\gamma)(\beta-\gamma)}$
33.	$\dfrac{s^3 + a_2 s^2 + a_1 s + a_0}{s^2(s+\alpha)(s+\beta)(s+\gamma)}$	$\dfrac{1}{\alpha\beta\gamma}[a_1 + a_0 t] - \dfrac{a_0(\alpha\beta+\alpha\gamma+\beta\gamma)}{\alpha^2\beta^2\gamma^2} + \dfrac{(-\alpha^3 + a_2\alpha^2 - a_1\alpha + a_0)}{\alpha^2(\beta-\alpha)(\gamma-\alpha)}e^{-\alpha t} + \dfrac{(-\beta^3 + a_2\beta^2 - a_1\beta + a_0)}{\beta^2(\alpha-\beta)(\gamma-\beta)}e^{-\beta t} + \dfrac{(-\gamma^3 + a_2\gamma^2 - a_1\gamma + a_0)}{\gamma^2(\alpha-\gamma)(\beta-\gamma)}e^{-\gamma t}$
34.	$\dfrac{1}{s^2 + \beta^2}$	$\dfrac{1}{\beta}\sin\beta t$
35.	$\dfrac{1}{s^2 - \beta^2}$	$\dfrac{1}{\beta}\sinh\beta t$
36.	$\dfrac{s + a_0}{s^2 + \beta^2}$	$\dfrac{1}{\beta}\sqrt{a_0^2 + \beta^2}\,\sin(\beta t + \psi)$ $\qquad \psi = \tan^{-1}\dfrac{\beta}{a_0}$
37.	$\dfrac{s}{s^2 + \beta^2}$	$\cos\beta t$

(handwritten annotations near row 34: $\dfrac{\beta}{s^2+\beta^2}$, $\dfrac{s}{s^2+\beta^2}$, SIN βt)

309

$F(s)$	$f(t)$
38. $\dfrac{s}{s^3 - \beta^2}$	$\cosh \beta t$
39. $\dfrac{1}{s(s^2 + \beta^2)}$	$\dfrac{1}{\beta^2}[1 - \cos \beta t]$
40. $\dfrac{s + a_0}{s(s^2 + \beta^2)}$	$\dfrac{a_0}{\beta^2} + \dfrac{1}{\beta}\sqrt{1 + \dfrac{a_0^2}{\beta^2}}\sin(\beta t - \psi) \qquad \psi = \tan^{-1}\dfrac{a_0}{\beta}$
41. $\dfrac{s^2 + a_1\delta + a_0}{s(s^2 + \beta^2)}$	$\dfrac{a_0}{\beta^2} + \sqrt{\dfrac{a_1^2}{\beta^2} + \left(1 - \dfrac{a_0}{\beta^2}\right)^2}\cos(\beta t - \psi) \qquad \psi = \tan^{-1}\dfrac{a_1\beta}{\beta^2 - a_0}$
42. $\dfrac{1}{s^2(s^2 + \beta^2)}$	$\dfrac{1}{\beta^2}\left[t - \dfrac{1}{\beta}\sin \beta t\right]$
43. $\dfrac{s + a_0}{s^2(s^2 + \beta^2)}$	$\dfrac{1}{\beta^2}\left[1 + \alpha_0 t - \sqrt{1 + \left(\dfrac{a_0}{\beta}\right)^2}\sin(\beta t + \psi)\right] \qquad \psi = \tan^{-1}\dfrac{\beta}{a_0}$
44. $\dfrac{s^2 + a_1 s + a_0}{s^2(s^2 + \beta^2)}$	$\dfrac{1}{\beta^2}\left[a_1 + a_0 t - \sqrt{a_1^2 + \left(\dfrac{a_0}{\beta} - \beta\right)^2}\sin(\beta t + \psi)\right] \qquad \psi = \tan^{-1}\dfrac{a_1\beta}{\alpha_0 - \beta^2}$
45. $\dfrac{s^3 + a_2 s^2 + a_1 s + a_0}{s^2(s^2 + \beta^2)}$	$\dfrac{1}{\beta^2}\left[a_1 + a_0 t - \sqrt{(a_1 - \beta^2)^2 + \left(\dfrac{a_0}{\beta} - a_2\beta\right)^2}\sin(\beta t + \psi)\right] \qquad \psi = \tan^{-1}\dfrac{\beta(a_1 - \beta^2)}{a_0 - a_2\beta^2}$

46. $\dfrac{1}{(s+\alpha)(s^2+\beta^2)}$

$$\frac{1}{\alpha^2+\beta^2}\left[e^{-\alpha t}+\frac{\alpha}{\beta}\sin\beta t-\cos\beta t\right]$$

47. $\dfrac{s+a_0}{(s+\alpha)(s^2+\beta^2)}$

$$\frac{a_0-\alpha}{\alpha^2+\beta^2}e^{-\alpha t}+\frac{1}{\beta}\sqrt{\frac{a_0^2+\beta^2}{\alpha^2+\beta^2}}\sin(\beta t+\psi)\qquad \psi=\tan^{-1}\frac{\alpha}{\beta}-\tan^{-1}\frac{a_0}{\beta}$$

48. $\dfrac{s^2+a_1s+a_0}{(s+\alpha)(s^2+\beta^2)}$

$$\frac{\alpha^2-a_1\alpha+a_0}{\alpha^2+\beta^2}e^{-\alpha t}+\frac{1}{\beta}\sqrt{\frac{(a_0-\beta^2)^2+a_1^2\beta^2}{\alpha^2+\beta^2}}\sin(\beta t+\psi)$$

$$\psi=\tan^{-1}\frac{\alpha}{\beta}-\tan^{-1}\frac{a_0-\beta^2}{a_1\beta}$$

49. $\dfrac{1}{s(s+\alpha)(s^2+\beta^2)}$

$$\frac{1}{\alpha\beta^2}-\frac{1}{\alpha^2+\beta^2}\left[\frac{e^{-\alpha t}}{\alpha}+\frac{\alpha}{\beta^2}\cos\beta t+\frac{1}{\beta}\sin\beta t\right]$$

50. $\dfrac{s+a_0}{s(s+\alpha)(s^2+\beta^2)}$

$$\frac{a_0}{\alpha\beta^2}+\frac{\alpha-a_0}{\alpha(\alpha^2+\beta^2)}e^{-\alpha t}-\frac{1}{\beta^2}\sqrt{\frac{a_0^2+\beta^2}{\alpha^2+\beta^2}}\cos(\beta t+\psi)\qquad \psi=\tan^{-1}\frac{\alpha}{\beta}-\tan^{-1}\frac{a_0}{\beta}$$

51. $\dfrac{s^2+a_1s+a_0}{s(s+\alpha)(s^2+\beta^2)}$

$$\frac{a_0}{\alpha\beta^2}-\frac{\alpha^2-a_1\alpha+a_0}{\alpha(\alpha^2+\beta^2)}e^{-\alpha t}-\frac{1}{\beta^2}\sqrt{\frac{(a_0-\beta^2)^2+a_1^3\beta^2}{\alpha^2+\beta^2}}\cos(\beta t+\psi)$$

$$\psi=\tan^{-1}\frac{\alpha}{\beta}-\tan^{-1}\frac{a_0-\beta^2}{a_1\beta}$$

52. $\dfrac{s^3+a_2s^2+a_1s+a_0}{s(s+\alpha)(s^2+\beta^2)}$

$$\frac{a_0}{\alpha\beta^2}-\frac{-\alpha^3+a_2\alpha^2-a_1\alpha+a_0}{\alpha(\alpha^2+\beta^2)}e^{-\alpha t}-\frac{1}{\beta^2}\sqrt{\frac{(a_0-a_2\beta^2)^2+\beta^2(a_1-\beta^2)^2}{\alpha^2+\beta^2}}\cos(\beta t+\psi)$$

$$\psi=\tan^{-1}\frac{a_1-\beta^2}{a_0/\beta-a_2\beta}-\tan^{-1}\frac{\beta}{\alpha}$$

$F(s)$	$f(t)$
53. $\dfrac{1}{s^2(s+\alpha)(s^2+\beta^2)}$	$\dfrac{1}{\alpha\beta^2}\left[t - \dfrac{1}{\alpha}\right] + \dfrac{e^{-\alpha t}}{\alpha^2(\alpha^2+\beta^2)} + \dfrac{\cos(\beta t + \psi)}{\beta^3\sqrt{\alpha^2+\beta^2}} \qquad \psi = \tan^{-1}\dfrac{\alpha}{\beta}$
54. $\dfrac{s+a_0}{s^2(s+\alpha)(s^2+\beta^2)}$	$\dfrac{1}{\alpha\beta^2}\left[1 - a_0\left(\dfrac{1}{\alpha} - t\right)\right] + \dfrac{(a_0-\alpha)e^{-\alpha t}}{\alpha^2(\alpha^2+\beta^2)} + \dfrac{1}{\beta^3}\sqrt{\dfrac{a_0^2+\beta^2}{\alpha^2+\beta^2}}\cos(\beta t + \psi)$ $\psi = \tan^{-1}\dfrac{\alpha}{\beta} + \tan^{-1}\dfrac{\beta}{a_0}$
55. $\dfrac{s^2+a_1 s+a_0}{s^2(s+\alpha)(s^2+\beta^2)}$	$\dfrac{1}{\alpha\beta^2}[a_1 + a_0 t] - \dfrac{a_0}{\alpha^2\beta^2} + \dfrac{\alpha^2 - a_1\alpha + a_0}{\alpha^2(\alpha^2+\beta^2)}e^{-\alpha t} + \dfrac{1}{\beta^3}\sqrt{\dfrac{(a_0-\beta^2)^2 + a_1^2\beta^2}{\alpha^2+\beta^2}}\cos(\beta t + \psi)$ $\psi = \tan^{-1}\dfrac{\alpha}{\beta} + \tan^{-1}\dfrac{a_1\beta}{a_0-\beta^2}$
56. $\dfrac{s^3+a_2 s^2+a_1 s+a_0}{s^2(s+\alpha)(s^2+\beta^2)}$	$\dfrac{1}{\alpha\beta^2}[a_1 + a_0 t] - \dfrac{a_0}{\alpha^2\beta^2} - \dfrac{\alpha^2(\alpha - a_2) + a_1\alpha - a_0}{\alpha^2(\alpha^2+\beta^2)}e^{-\alpha t}$ $\quad + \dfrac{1}{\beta^2}\sqrt{\dfrac{(a_1 - \beta^2)^2 + (a_0/\beta - a_2\beta)^2}{\alpha^2+\beta^2}}\cos(\beta t + \psi)$ $\psi = \tan^{-1}\dfrac{\alpha}{\beta} + \tan^{-1}\dfrac{\beta(a_1 - \beta^2)}{a_0 - a_2\beta^2}$
57. $\dfrac{1}{(s+\alpha)(s+\gamma)(s^2+\beta^2)}$	$\dfrac{e^{-\alpha t}}{(\gamma - \alpha)(\alpha^2+\beta^2)} + \dfrac{e^{-\gamma t}}{(\alpha - \gamma)(\gamma^2+\beta^2)} + \dfrac{\sin(\beta t - \psi)}{\beta\sqrt{\beta^2(\alpha+\gamma)^2 + (\alpha\gamma - \beta^2)^2}}$ $\psi = \tan^{-1}\dfrac{\beta}{\alpha} + \tan^{-1}\dfrac{\beta}{\gamma}$

58. $\dfrac{s + a_0}{(s + \alpha)(s + \gamma)(s^2 + \beta^2)}$

$$\frac{(a_0 - \alpha)e^{-\alpha t}}{(\gamma - \alpha)(\alpha^2 + \beta^2)} + \frac{(a_0 - \gamma)e^{-\gamma t}}{(\alpha - \gamma)(\gamma^2 + \beta^2)} + \frac{1}{\beta}\sqrt{\frac{a_0^2 + \beta^2}{(\alpha^2 + \beta^2)(\gamma^2 + \beta^2)}}\sin(\beta t + \psi)$$

$$\psi = \tan^{-1}\frac{\gamma}{\beta} - \tan^{-1}\frac{\beta}{\alpha} - \tan^{-1}\frac{a_0}{\beta}$$

59. $\dfrac{s^2 + a_1 s + a_0}{(s + \alpha)(s + \gamma)(s^2 + \beta^2)}$

$$\frac{\alpha^2 - a_1\alpha + a_0}{(\gamma - \alpha)(\alpha^2 + \beta^2)}e^{-\alpha t} + \frac{\gamma^2 - a_1\gamma + a_0}{(\alpha - \gamma)(\gamma^2 + \beta^2)}e^{-\gamma t} + \frac{1}{\beta}\sqrt{\frac{a_1^2\beta^2 + (a_0 - \beta^2)^2}{(\alpha^2 + \beta^2)(\gamma^2 + \beta^2)}}\sin(\beta t + \psi)$$

$$\psi = \tan^{-1}\frac{a_1\beta}{a_0 - \beta^2} - \tan^{-1}\frac{\beta}{\alpha} - \tan^{-1}\frac{\beta}{\gamma}$$

60. $\dfrac{s^3 + a_2 s^2 + a_1 s + a_0}{(s + \alpha)(s + \gamma)(s^2 + \beta^2)}$

$$\frac{-\alpha^3 + a_2\alpha^2 - a_1\alpha + a_0}{(\gamma - \alpha)(\alpha^2 + \beta^2)}e^{-\alpha t} + \frac{-\gamma^3 + a_2\gamma^2 - a_1\gamma + a_0}{(\alpha - \gamma)(\gamma^2 + \beta^2)}e^{-\gamma t}$$

$$+ \frac{1}{\beta}\sqrt{\frac{(a_0 - a_2\beta^2)^2 + \beta^2(a_1 - \beta^2)^2}{(\alpha^2 + \beta^2)(\gamma^2 + \beta^2)}}\sin(\beta t + \psi)$$

$$\psi = \tan^{-1}\frac{\beta(a_1 - \beta^2)}{a_0 - a_2\beta^2} - \tan^{-1}\frac{\beta}{\alpha} - \tan^{-1}\frac{\beta}{\gamma}$$

61. $\dfrac{1}{s(s + \alpha)(s + \gamma)(s^2 + \beta^2)}$

$$\frac{1}{\alpha\gamma\beta^2} + \frac{e^{-\alpha t}}{\alpha(\alpha - \gamma)(\alpha^2 + \beta^2)} + \frac{e^{-\gamma t}}{\gamma(\gamma - \alpha)(\gamma^2 + \beta^2)} + \frac{\cos(\beta t + \psi)}{\beta^2\sqrt{(\alpha\gamma - \beta^2)^2 + \beta^2(\alpha + \gamma)^2}}$$

$$\psi = \tan^{-1}\frac{\gamma}{\beta} + \tan^{-1}\frac{\alpha}{\beta}$$

62. $\dfrac{s + a_0}{s(s + \alpha)(s + \gamma)(s^2 + \beta^2)}$

$$\frac{a_0}{\alpha\gamma\beta^2} + \frac{(\alpha - a_0)e^{-\alpha t}}{\alpha(\gamma - \alpha)(\alpha^2 + \beta^2)} + \frac{(\gamma - a_0)e^{-\gamma t}}{\gamma(\alpha - \gamma)(\gamma^2 + \beta^2)} + \frac{1}{\beta^2}\sqrt{\frac{\alpha_0^2 + \beta^2}{(\alpha\gamma - \beta^2)^2 + \beta^2(\alpha + \gamma)^2}}\sin(\beta t - \psi)$$

$$\psi = \tan^{-1}\frac{a_0}{\beta} + \tan^{-1}\frac{\beta}{\alpha} + \tan^{-1}\frac{\beta}{\gamma}$$

	$F(s)$	$f(t)$
63.	$\dfrac{s^2 + a_1 s + a_0}{s(s+\alpha)(s+\gamma)(s^2+\beta^2)}$	$\dfrac{a_0}{\alpha\gamma\beta^2} + \dfrac{\alpha - a_1 + a_0/\alpha}{(\alpha-\gamma)(\alpha^2+\beta^2)} e^{-\alpha t} + \dfrac{\gamma - a_1 + a_0/\gamma}{(\gamma-\alpha)(\gamma^2+\beta^2)} e^{-\gamma t} +$ $\dfrac{1}{\beta^2}\sqrt{\dfrac{(a_0-\beta^2)^2 + a_1^2\beta^2}{(\alpha\gamma - \beta^2)^2 + \beta^2(\alpha+\gamma)^2}}\, \sin(\beta t - \psi)$ $\psi = \tan^{-1}\dfrac{a_0 - \beta^2}{a_1\beta} + \tan^{-1}\dfrac{\beta}{\alpha} + \tan^{-1}\dfrac{\beta}{\gamma}$
64.	$\dfrac{s^3 + a_2 s^2 + a_1 s + a_0}{s(s+\alpha)(s+\gamma)(s^2+\beta^2)}$	$\dfrac{a_0}{\alpha\gamma\beta^2} + \dfrac{\alpha^2 - a_2\alpha + a_1 - a_0/\alpha}{(\gamma-\alpha)(\alpha^2+\beta^2)} e^{-\alpha t} + \dfrac{\gamma^2 - a_2\gamma + a_1 - a_0/\gamma}{(\alpha-\gamma)(\gamma^2+\beta^2)} e^{-\gamma t} +$ $\dfrac{1}{\beta^2}\sqrt{\dfrac{(a_0 - a_2\beta^2)^2 + \beta^2(a_1 - \beta^2)^2}{(\alpha\gamma - \beta^2)^2 + \beta^2(\alpha+\gamma)^2}}\, \sin(\beta t - \psi)$ $\psi = \tan^{-1}\dfrac{a_0 - a_2\beta^2}{\beta(a_1 - \beta^2)} + \tan^{-1}\dfrac{\beta}{\alpha} + \tan^{-1}\dfrac{\beta}{\gamma}$
65.	$\dfrac{1}{s^2(s+\alpha)(s+\gamma)(s^2+\beta^2)}$	$\dfrac{1}{\alpha\gamma\beta^2}\left[t - \dfrac{1}{\alpha} - \dfrac{1}{\gamma}\right] + \dfrac{e^{-\alpha t}}{\alpha^2(\gamma-\alpha)(\alpha^2+\beta^2)} + \dfrac{e^{-\gamma t}}{\gamma^2(\alpha-\gamma)(\gamma^2+\beta^2)} + \dfrac{\cos(\beta t + \psi)}{\beta^3\sqrt{(\alpha\gamma - \beta^2)^2 + (\alpha+\gamma)^2\beta^2}}$ $\psi = \tan^{-1}\dfrac{\gamma}{\beta} - \tan^{-1}\dfrac{\beta}{\alpha}$
66.	$\dfrac{s + a_0}{s^2(s+\alpha)(s+\gamma)(s^2+\beta^2)}$	$\dfrac{1}{\alpha\gamma\beta^2}\left[1 + a_0\left(t - \dfrac{1}{\gamma} - \dfrac{1}{\alpha}\right)\right] + \dfrac{(a_0 - \alpha)e^{-\alpha t}}{\alpha^2(\gamma - \alpha)(\alpha^2+\beta^2)} + \dfrac{(a_0 - \gamma)e^{-\gamma t}}{\gamma^2(\alpha - \gamma)(\gamma^2+\beta^2)} +$ $\dfrac{1}{\beta^3}\sqrt{\dfrac{a_0^2 + \beta^2}{(\alpha\gamma - \beta^2)^2 + \beta^2(\alpha + \gamma)^2}}\, \cos(\beta t + \psi)$ $\psi = \tan^{-1}\dfrac{\gamma}{\beta} - \tan^{-1}\dfrac{\beta}{\alpha} + \tan^{-1}\dfrac{\beta}{a_0}$

67. $\dfrac{s^2 + a_1 s + a_0}{s^2(s+\alpha)(s+\gamma)(s^2+\beta^2)}$

$$\frac{1}{\alpha\gamma\beta^2}\left[a_1 + a_0\left(t - \frac{1}{\gamma} - \frac{1}{\alpha}\right)\right] + \frac{(\alpha^2 - a_1\alpha + a_0)e^{-\alpha t}}{\alpha^2(\gamma-\alpha)(\alpha^2+\beta^2)} + \frac{(\gamma^2 - a_1\gamma + a_0)e^{-\gamma}}{\gamma^2(\alpha-\gamma)(\gamma^2+\beta^2)}$$

$$+ \frac{1}{\beta^3}\sqrt{\frac{a_1^2\beta^2 + (a_0-\beta^2)^2}{(\alpha\gamma-\beta^2)^2 + \beta^2(\alpha+\gamma)^2}}\,\cos(\beta t + \psi)$$

$$\psi = \tan^{-1}\frac{\gamma}{\beta} - \tan^{-1}\frac{\beta}{\alpha} + \tan^{-1}\frac{a_1\beta}{a_0 - \beta^2}$$

68. $\dfrac{s^3 + a_2 s^2 + a_1 s + a_0}{s^2(s+\alpha)(s+\gamma)(s^2+\beta^2)}$

$$\frac{1}{\alpha\gamma\beta^2}\left[a_1 + a_0\left(t - \frac{1}{\gamma} - \frac{1}{\alpha}\right)\right] + \frac{-\alpha^3 + a_2\alpha^2 - a_1\alpha + a_0}{\alpha^2(\gamma-\alpha)(\alpha^2+\beta^2)}\,e^{-\alpha t} + \frac{-\gamma^3 + a_1\gamma^2 - a_1\gamma + a_0}{\gamma^2(\alpha-\gamma)(\gamma^2+\beta^2)}\,e^{-\gamma t}$$

$$+ \frac{1}{\beta^3}\sqrt{\frac{(a_0 - a_1\beta^2)^2 + \beta^2(\beta^2 - a_1)^2}{(\alpha\gamma - \beta^2)^2 + \beta^2(\alpha+\gamma)^2}}\,\cos(\beta t + \psi)$$

$$\psi = \tan^{-1}\frac{\gamma}{\beta} - \tan^{-1}\frac{\beta}{\alpha} - \tan^{-1}\frac{\beta(\beta^2 - a_1)}{a_0 - a_2\beta^2}$$

69. $\dfrac{1}{(s^2+\beta^2)(s^2+\lambda^2)}$

$$\frac{1}{\lambda^2 - \beta^2}\left[\frac{1}{\beta}\sin\beta t - \frac{1}{\lambda}\sin\lambda t\right]$$

70. $\dfrac{s + a_0}{(s^2+\beta^2)(s^2+\lambda^2)}$

$$\frac{1}{\lambda^2 - \beta^2}\left[\sqrt{1 + \frac{a_0^2}{\beta^2}}\cos(\beta t - \psi_1) - \sqrt{1 + \frac{a_0^2}{\lambda^2}}\cos(\lambda t - \psi_2)\right]$$

$$\psi_1 = \tan^{-1}\frac{a_0}{\beta} \qquad \psi_2 = \tan^{-1}\frac{a_0}{\lambda}$$

71. $\dfrac{s^2 + a_1 s + a_0}{(s^2+\beta^2)(s^2+\lambda^2)}$

$$\frac{1}{\lambda^2 - \beta^2}\left[\sqrt{a_1^2 + \left(\frac{\beta^2 - a_0}{\beta}\right)^2}\cos(\beta t + \psi_1) - \sqrt{a_1^2 + \left(\frac{\lambda^2 - a_0}{\lambda}\right)^2}\cos(\lambda t + \psi_2)\right]$$

$$\psi_1 = \tan^{-1}\frac{\beta^2 - a_0}{a_1\beta} \qquad \psi_2 = \tan^{-1}\frac{\lambda^2 - a_0}{a_1\lambda}$$

APPENDIX A: TABLE OF LAPLACE TRANSFORMS (cont.)

	$F(s)$	$f(t)$
72.	$\dfrac{s^3 + a_2 s^2 + a_1 s + a_0}{(s^2 + \beta^2)(s^2 + \lambda^2)}$	$\dfrac{1}{\lambda^2 - \beta^2}\left[\sqrt{(a_1 - \beta^2)^2 + \left(\dfrac{a_2\beta^2 - a_0}{\beta}\right)^2}\cos(\beta t + \psi_1) - \sqrt{(a_1 - \lambda^2)^2 + \left(\dfrac{a_2\lambda^2 - a_0}{\lambda}\right)^2}\cos(\lambda t + \psi_2)\right]$ $\psi_1 = \tan^{-1}\dfrac{a_2\beta^2 - a_0}{\beta(a_1 - \beta^2)} \qquad \psi_2 = \tan^{-1}\dfrac{a_2\lambda^2 - a_0}{\lambda(a_1 - \lambda^2)}$
73.	$\dfrac{1}{(s+\alpha)^2 + \beta^2}$	$\dfrac{1}{\beta}e^{-\alpha t}\sin\beta t$
74.	$\dfrac{s + a_0}{(s+\alpha)^2 + \beta^2}$	$\dfrac{1}{\beta}\sqrt{\beta^2 + (a_0 - \alpha)^2}\,e^{-\alpha t}\sin(\beta t + \psi) \qquad \psi = \dfrac{\tan^{-1}\beta}{a_0 - \alpha}$
75.	$\dfrac{1}{s[(s+\alpha)^2 + \beta^2]}$	$\dfrac{1}{\alpha^2 + \beta^2} - \dfrac{e^{-\alpha t}\sin(\beta t + \psi)}{\beta\sqrt{\alpha^2 + \beta^2}} \qquad \psi = \tan^{-1}\dfrac{\beta}{\alpha}$
76.	$\dfrac{s + a_0}{s[(s+\alpha)^2 + \beta^2]}$	$\dfrac{a_0}{\alpha^2 + \beta^2} - \dfrac{1}{\beta}\sqrt{\dfrac{\beta^2 + (a_0 - \alpha)^2}{\alpha^2 + \beta^2}}\,e^{-\alpha t}\sin(\beta t + \psi) \qquad \psi = \tan^{-1}\dfrac{\beta}{\alpha} + \dfrac{\tan^{-1}\beta}{a_0 - \alpha}$
77.	$\dfrac{s^2 + a_1 s + a_0}{s[(s+\alpha)^2 + \beta^2]}$	$\dfrac{a_0}{\alpha^2 + \beta^2} - \dfrac{1}{\beta}\sqrt{\dfrac{(\alpha^2 - \beta^2 - a_1\alpha + a_0)^2 + \beta^2(a_1 - 2\alpha)^2}{\alpha^2 + \beta^2}}\,e^{-\alpha t}\sin(\beta t + \psi)$ $\psi = \tan^{-1}\dfrac{\beta}{\alpha} + \tan^{-1}\dfrac{\beta(a_1 - 2\alpha)}{\alpha^2 - \beta^2 + a_0 - a_1\alpha}$
78.	$\dfrac{1}{s^2[(s+\alpha)^2 + \beta^2]}$	$\dfrac{1}{\alpha^2 + \beta^2}\left[t - \dfrac{2\alpha}{\alpha^2 + \beta^2} + \dfrac{e^{-\alpha t}\sin(\beta t + \psi)}{\beta(\alpha^2 + \beta^2)}\right] \qquad \psi = 2\tan^{-1}\dfrac{\beta}{\alpha}$

79. $\dfrac{s + a_0}{s^2[(s + \alpha)^2 + \beta^2]}$

$$\frac{1}{\alpha^2 + \beta^2}\left[a_0 t + 1 - \frac{2a_0\alpha}{\alpha^2 + \beta^2}\right] + \frac{\sqrt{\beta^2 + (a_0 - \alpha)^2}}{\beta(\alpha^2 + \beta^2)}\,e^{-\alpha t}\sin(\beta t + \psi)$$

$$\psi = 2\tan^{-1}\frac{\beta}{\alpha} + \tan^{-1}\frac{\beta}{a_0 - \alpha}$$

80. $\dfrac{s^2 + a_1 s + a_0}{s^2[(s + \alpha)^2 + \beta^2]}$

$$\frac{1}{\alpha^2 + \beta^2}\left[a_0 t + a_1 - \frac{2a_0\alpha}{\alpha^2 + \beta^2}\right] + \frac{\sqrt{\beta^2(2\alpha - a_1)^2 + (\alpha^2 - \beta^2 - a_1\alpha + a_0)^2}}{\beta(\alpha^2 + \beta^2)}\,e^{-\alpha t}\sin(\beta t + \psi)$$

$$\psi = 2\tan^{-1}\frac{\beta}{\alpha} - \tan^{-1}\frac{\beta(2\alpha - a_1)}{\alpha^2 - \beta^2 - a_1\alpha + a_0}$$

81. $\dfrac{s^3 + a_2 s^2 + a_1 s + a_0}{s^2[(s + \alpha)^2 + \beta^2]}$

$$\frac{1}{\alpha^2 + \beta^2}\left[a_0 t + a_1 - \frac{2a_0\alpha}{\alpha^2 + \beta^2}\right]$$
$$+ \frac{\sqrt{[(3\alpha^2 - \beta^2) - (2\alpha a_2 - a_1)]^2\beta^2 + [\alpha(3\beta^2 - \alpha^2) + a_2(\alpha^2 - \beta^2) + (a_0 - a_1\alpha)]^2}}{\beta(\alpha^2 + \beta^2)}\,e^{-\alpha t}\sin(\beta t + \psi)$$

$$\psi = 2\tan^{-1}\frac{\beta}{\alpha} + \tan^{-1}\frac{\beta[(3\alpha^2 - \beta^2) - (2\alpha a_2 - a_1)]}{\alpha(3\beta^2 - \alpha^2) + a_2(\alpha^2 - \beta^2) + (a_0 - a_1\alpha)}$$

82. $\dfrac{1}{(s + \gamma)[(s + \alpha)^2 + \beta^2]}$

$$\frac{e^{-\gamma t}}{(\gamma - \alpha)^2 + \beta^2} + \frac{e^{-\alpha t}\sin(\beta t - \psi)}{\beta\sqrt{(\gamma - \alpha)^2 + \beta^2}} \qquad \psi = \tan^{-1}\frac{\beta}{\gamma - \alpha}$$

83. $\dfrac{s + a_0}{(s + \gamma)[(s + \alpha)^2 + \beta^2]}$

$$\frac{(a_0 - \gamma)e^{-\gamma t}}{(\gamma - \alpha)^2 + \beta^2} + \frac{1}{\beta}\sqrt{\frac{(a_0 - \alpha)^2 + \beta^2}{(\gamma - \alpha)^2 + \beta^2}}\,e^{-\alpha t}\sin(\beta t + \psi)$$

$$\psi = \tan^{-1}\frac{\beta}{a_0 - \alpha} - \tan^{-1}\frac{\beta}{\gamma - \alpha}$$

$F(s)$	$f(t)$
84. $\dfrac{s^2 + a_1 s + a_0}{(s + \gamma)[(s + \alpha)^2 + \beta^2]}$	$\dfrac{\gamma^2 - a_1\gamma + a_0}{(\gamma - \alpha)^2 + \beta^2} e^{-\gamma t} + \dfrac{1}{\beta}\sqrt{\dfrac{(\alpha^2 - \beta^2 - a_1\alpha + a_0)^2 + \beta^2(a_1 - 2\alpha)^2}{(\gamma - \alpha)^2 + \beta^2}}\, e^{-\alpha t}\sin(\beta t + \psi)$ $\psi = \tan^{-1}\dfrac{\beta(a_1 - 2\alpha)}{a^2 - \beta^2 - a_1\alpha + a_0} - \tan^{-1}\dfrac{\beta}{\gamma - \alpha}$
85. $\dfrac{1}{s(s + \gamma)[(s + \alpha)^2 + \beta^2]}$	$\dfrac{1}{\gamma(\alpha^2 + \beta^2)} - \dfrac{e^{-\gamma t}}{\gamma[(\alpha - \gamma)^2 + \beta^2]} + \dfrac{e^{-\alpha t}\sin(\beta t + \psi)}{\beta\sqrt{(\alpha^2 + \beta^2)[(\alpha - \gamma)^2 + \beta^2]}}$ $\psi = \tan^{-1}\dfrac{\beta}{\alpha} + \tan^{-1}\dfrac{\beta}{\alpha - \gamma}$
86. $\dfrac{s + a_0}{s(s + \gamma)[(s + \alpha)^2 + \beta^2]}$	$\dfrac{a_0}{\gamma(\alpha^2 + \beta^2)} + \dfrac{(\gamma - a_0)\,e^{-\gamma t}}{\gamma[(\alpha - \gamma)^2 + \beta^2]} + \dfrac{1}{\beta\sqrt{\alpha^2 + \beta^2}}\sqrt{\dfrac{(a_0 - \alpha)^2 + \beta^2}{(\alpha - \gamma)^2 + \beta^2}}\, e^{-\alpha t}\sin(\beta t + \psi)$ $\psi = \tan^{-1}\dfrac{\beta}{\alpha - \gamma} + \tan^{-1}\dfrac{\beta}{\alpha} + \tan^{-1}\dfrac{\beta}{a_0 - \alpha}$
87. $\dfrac{s^2 + a_1 s + a_0}{s(s + \gamma)[(s + \alpha)^2 + \beta^2]}$	$\dfrac{a_0}{\gamma(\alpha^2 + \beta^2)} - \dfrac{(\gamma^2 - a_1\gamma + a_0)}{\gamma[(\alpha - \gamma)^2 + \beta^2]}\, e^{-\gamma t} + \dfrac{1}{\beta}\sqrt{\dfrac{\beta^2(a_1 - 2\alpha)^2 + (a_0 - a_1\alpha + \alpha^2 - \beta^2)^2}{(\alpha^2 + \beta^2)[(\alpha - \gamma)^2 + \beta^2]}}\, e^{-\alpha t}\sin(\beta t + \psi)$ $\psi = \tan^{-1}\dfrac{\beta}{\alpha - \gamma} + \tan^{-1}\dfrac{\beta}{\alpha} - \tan^{-1}\dfrac{\beta(2\alpha - a_1)}{\alpha^2 - \beta^2 - a_1\alpha + a_0}$

88. $\dfrac{s^3 + a_2 s^2 + a_1 s + a_0}{s(s+\gamma)[(s+\alpha)^2 + \beta^2]}$

$$\frac{a_0}{\gamma(\alpha^2+\beta^2)} + \frac{\gamma^3 - a_2\gamma^2 + a_1\gamma - a_0}{\gamma[(\alpha-\gamma)^2+\beta^2]}e^{-\gamma t}$$

$$+ \frac{1}{\beta}\sqrt{\frac{\beta^2(3\alpha^2-\beta^2-2\alpha a_2+a_1)^2 + [\alpha^2(3\beta^2-\alpha^2)+a_2(\alpha^2-\beta^2)-a_1\alpha+a_0]^2}{(\alpha^2+\beta^2)[\beta^2+(\alpha-\gamma)^2]}}\, e^{-\alpha t}\cos(\beta t + \psi)$$

$$\psi = \tan^{-1}\frac{\gamma-\alpha}{\beta} + \tan^{-1}\frac{\beta}{\alpha} + \tan^{-1}\frac{\beta(3\alpha^2-\beta^2-2\alpha a_2+a_1)}{\alpha(3\beta^2-\alpha^2)+a_2(\alpha^2-\beta^2)-a_1\alpha+a_0}$$

---

89. $\dfrac{1}{s^2(s+\gamma)[(s+\alpha)^2 + \beta^2]}$

$$\frac{1}{\gamma(\alpha^2+\beta^2)}\left[\, t - \frac{1}{\gamma} - \frac{2\alpha}{\alpha^2+\beta^2} \right] + \frac{e^{-\gamma t}}{\gamma^2[(\gamma-\alpha)^2+\beta^2]} + \frac{e^{-\alpha t}\sin(\beta t+\psi)}{\beta(\alpha^2+\beta^2)\sqrt{(\gamma-\alpha)^2+\beta^2}}$$

$$\psi = 2\tan^{-1}\frac{\beta}{\alpha} - \tan^{-1}\frac{\beta}{\gamma-\alpha}$$

---

90. $\dfrac{s + a_0}{s^2(s+\gamma)[(s+\alpha)^2 + \beta^2]}$

$$\frac{a_0}{\gamma(\alpha^2+\beta^2)}\left[\, t + \frac{1}{a_0} - \frac{1}{\gamma} - \frac{2\alpha}{\alpha^2+\beta^2} \right] + \frac{(a_0-\gamma)e^{-\gamma t}}{\gamma^2[(\gamma-\alpha)^2+\beta^2]} + \frac{e^{-\alpha t}\sin(\beta t+\psi)}{\beta(\alpha^2+\beta^2)}\sqrt{\frac{(a_0-\alpha)^2+\beta^2}{(\gamma-\alpha)^2+\beta^2}}$$

$$\psi = 2\tan^{-1}\frac{\beta}{\alpha} - \tan^{-1}\frac{\beta}{\gamma-\alpha} + \tan^{-1}\frac{\beta}{a_0-\alpha}$$

---

91. $\dfrac{s^2 + a_1 s + a_0}{s^2(s+\gamma)[(s+\alpha)^2 + \beta^2]}$

$$\frac{a_0}{\gamma(\alpha^2+\beta^2)}\left[\, t + \frac{a_1}{a_0} - \frac{1}{\gamma} - \frac{2\alpha}{\alpha^2+\beta^2} \right] + \frac{(\gamma^2 - a_1\gamma + a_0)e^{-\gamma t}}{\gamma^2[(\gamma-\alpha)^2+\beta^2]}$$

$$+ \frac{e^{-\alpha t}\sin(\beta t+\psi)}{\beta(\alpha^2+\beta^2)}\sqrt{\frac{(\alpha^2-\beta^2-a_1\alpha+a_0)^2+\beta^2(a_1-2\alpha)^2}{(\gamma-\alpha)^2+\beta^2}}$$

$$\psi = 2\tan^{-1}\frac{\beta}{\alpha} - \tan^{-1}\frac{\beta}{\gamma-\alpha} + \tan^{-1}\frac{\beta(a_1-2\alpha)}{\alpha^2-\beta^2-a_1\alpha+a_0}$$

$F(s)$	$f(t)$
92. $\dfrac{s^3 + a_2 s^2 + a_1 s + a_0}{s^2(s+\gamma)[(s+\alpha)^2 + \beta^2]}$	$a_0\left[t + \dfrac{a_1}{a_0} - \dfrac{1}{\gamma} - \dfrac{2\alpha}{\alpha^2+\beta^2}\right] + \dfrac{-\gamma^3 + a_2\gamma^2 - a_1\gamma + a_0}{\gamma^2[(\gamma-\alpha)^2+\beta^2]}e^{-\gamma t} + \dfrac{e^{-\alpha t}\sin(\beta t + \psi)}{\beta(\alpha^2+\beta^2)}$ $\times \dfrac{\sqrt{[\alpha(3\beta^2 - \alpha^2) + a_2(\alpha^2 - \beta^2) - a_1\alpha + a_0]^2 + \beta^2[a_1 + 3\alpha^2 - \beta^2 - 2a_2\alpha]^2}}{(\gamma-\alpha)^2 + \beta^2}$ $\psi = 2\tan^{-1}\dfrac{\beta}{\alpha} - \tan^{-1}\dfrac{\beta}{\gamma - \alpha} + \tan^{-1}\dfrac{\beta(3\alpha^2 - \beta^2 - 2a_2\alpha + a_1)}{\alpha(3\beta^2 - \alpha^2) + a_2(\alpha^2 - \beta^2) a_1\alpha + a_0)}$
93. $\dfrac{1}{(s+\gamma)(s+\delta)[(s+\alpha)^2 + \beta^2]}$	$\dfrac{e^{-\gamma t}}{(\delta - \gamma)[(\alpha - \gamma)^2 + \beta^2]} + \dfrac{e^{-\delta t}}{(\gamma - \delta)[(\alpha - \delta)^2 + \beta^2]} + \dfrac{e^{-\alpha t}\cos(\beta t + \psi)}{\beta\sqrt{[\quad - \delta)^2 + \beta^2][(\alpha - \gamma)^2 + \beta^2]}}$ $\psi = \tan^{-1}\dfrac{\beta}{\alpha - \delta} - \tan^{-1}\dfrac{\alpha - \gamma}{\beta}$
94. $\dfrac{s + a_0}{(s+\gamma)(s+\delta)[(s+\alpha)^2 + \beta^2]}$	$\dfrac{(a_0 - \gamma)e^{-\gamma t}}{(\delta - \gamma)[(\alpha - \gamma)^2 + \beta^2]} + \dfrac{(a_0 - \delta)e^{-\delta t}}{(\gamma - \delta)[(\alpha - \delta)^2 + \beta^2]}$ $+ \dfrac{1}{\beta}\sqrt{\dfrac{(a_0 - \alpha)^2 + \beta^2}{[(\alpha - \delta)^2 + \beta^2][(\alpha - \gamma)^2 + \beta^2]}}\; e^{-\alpha t}\cos(\beta t + \psi)$ $\psi = \tan^{-1}\dfrac{\beta}{\alpha - \delta} - \tan^{-1}\dfrac{\alpha - \gamma}{\beta} + \tan^{-1}\dfrac{\beta}{a_0 - \alpha}$

95. $\dfrac{s^2 + a_1 s + a_0}{(s+\gamma)(s+\delta)[(s+\alpha)^2 + \beta^2]}$

$$\frac{(\gamma^2 - a_1\gamma + a_0)e^{-\gamma t}}{(\delta - \gamma)[(\alpha - \gamma)^2 + \beta^2]} + \frac{(\delta^2 - a_1\delta + a_0)e^{-\delta t}}{(\gamma - \delta)[(\alpha - \delta)^2 + \beta^2]}$$

$$+ \frac{1}{\bar\beta}\sqrt{\frac{(\alpha^2 - \beta^2 - a_1\alpha + a_0)^2 + \beta^2(a_1 - 2\alpha)^2}{[(\alpha - \delta)^2][(\alpha - \gamma)^2 + \beta^2]}}\; e^{-\alpha t}\cos(\beta t + \psi)$$

$$\psi = \tan^{-1}\frac{\beta}{\alpha - \delta} - \tan^{-1}\frac{\alpha - \gamma}{\beta} + \tan^{-1}\frac{\beta(a_1 - 2\alpha)}{\alpha^2 - \beta^2 - a_1\alpha + a_0}$$

---

96. $\dfrac{s^3 + a_2 s^2 + a_1 s + a_0}{(s+\gamma)(s+\delta)[(s+\alpha)^2 + \beta^2]}$

$$\frac{-\gamma^3 + a_2\gamma^2 - a_1\gamma + a_0}{(\delta - \gamma)[(\alpha - \gamma)^2 + \beta^2]}e^{-\gamma t} + \frac{-\delta^3 + a_2\delta^2 - a_1\delta + a_0}{(\gamma - \delta)[(\alpha - \delta)^2 + \beta^2]}e^{-\delta t}$$

$$+ \frac{1}{\bar\beta}\sqrt{\frac{[(\alpha^2 - \beta^2)(a_2 - \alpha) + a(2\beta^2 - a_1) + a_0]^2 + \beta^2[(3\alpha^2 - \beta^2) - 2a_0\alpha + a_1]^2}{[(\alpha - \delta)^2 + \beta^2][(\alpha - \gamma)^2 + \beta^2]}}\; e^{-\alpha t}\cos(\beta t + \psi)$$

$$\psi = \tan^{-1}\frac{\beta}{\alpha - \delta} - \tan^{-1}\frac{\alpha - \gamma}{\beta} + \tan^{-1}\frac{\beta[(3\alpha^2 - \beta^2) - 2a_2\alpha + a_1]}{(\alpha^2 - \beta^2)(a_2 - \alpha) + \alpha(2\beta^2 - a_1) + a_0}$$

---

97. $\dfrac{1}{(s^2 + \lambda^2)[(s+\alpha)^2 + \beta^2]}$

$$\frac{1}{\lambda}\sin(\lambda t + \psi_1) + \frac{1}{\bar\beta}e^{-\alpha t}\sin(\beta t + \psi_2)$$

$$\sqrt{4\alpha^2\lambda^2 + (\alpha^2 + \beta^2 - \lambda^2)^2}$$

$$\psi_1 = \tan^{-1}\frac{-2\alpha\lambda}{\alpha^2 + \beta^2 - \lambda^2} \qquad \psi_2 = \tan^{-1}\frac{2\alpha\beta}{\alpha^2 - \beta^2 - \lambda^2}$$

---

98. $\dfrac{s + a_0}{(s^2 + \lambda^2)[(s+\alpha)^2 + \beta^2]}$

$$\frac{1}{\lambda}\sqrt{\frac{a_0^2 + \lambda^2}{4\alpha^2\lambda^2 + (\alpha^2 + \beta^2 - \lambda^2)^2}}\sin(\lambda t + \psi_1) + \frac{1}{\bar\beta}\sqrt{\frac{(a_0 - \alpha)^2 + \beta^2}{4\alpha^2\lambda^2 + (\alpha^2 + \beta^2 - \lambda^2)^2}}\; e^{-\alpha t}\sin(\beta t + \psi_2)$$

$$\psi_1 = \tan^{-1}\frac{\lambda}{a_0} - \tan^{-1}\frac{-2\alpha\lambda}{\alpha^2 + \beta^2 - \lambda^2} \qquad \psi_2 = \tan^{-1}\frac{\beta}{a_0 - \alpha} + \tan^{-1}\frac{2\alpha\beta}{\alpha^2 - \beta^2 - \lambda^2}$$

APPENDIX A: TABLE OF LAPLACE TRANSFORMS (cont.)

$F(s)$	$f(t)$

99.

$$\frac{s^2 + a_1 s + a_0}{(s^2 + \lambda^2)[(s+\alpha)^2 + \beta^2]}$$

$$\frac{1}{\lambda}\sqrt{\frac{a_1^2\lambda^2 + (a_0 - \lambda^2)^2}{4\alpha^2\lambda^2 + (\alpha^2 + \beta^2 - \lambda^2)^2}}\,\sin(\lambda t + \psi_1)$$
$$+\frac{1}{\beta}\sqrt{\frac{\beta^2(a_1 - 2\alpha)^2 + (\alpha^2 - \beta^2 - a_1\alpha + a_0)^2}{4\alpha^2\lambda^2 + (\alpha^2 + \beta^2 - \lambda^2)^2}}\,e^{-\alpha t}\sin(\beta t + \psi_2)$$

$$\psi_1 = \tan^{-1}\frac{a_1\lambda}{a_0 - \lambda^2} - \tan^{-1}\frac{2\alpha\lambda}{\alpha^2 + \beta^2 - \lambda^2}$$

$$\psi_2 = \tan^{-1}\frac{\beta(a_1 - 2\alpha)}{\alpha^2 - \beta^2 - a_1\alpha + a_0} + \tan^{-1}\frac{2\alpha\beta}{\alpha^2 - \beta^2 + \lambda^2}$$

100.

$$\frac{s^2 + a_2 s^2 + a_1 s + a_0}{(s^2 + \lambda^2)[(s+\alpha)^2 + \beta^2]}$$

$$\frac{1}{\lambda}\sqrt{\frac{(a_2\lambda^2 - a_0)^2 + \lambda^2(a_1 - \lambda^2)^2}{4\alpha^2\lambda^2 + (\alpha^2 + \beta^2 - \lambda^2)^2}}\,\sin(\lambda t + \psi_1)$$
$$+\frac{1}{\beta}\sqrt{\frac{(\alpha^2 - \beta^2)(a_2 - \alpha) + \alpha(2\beta^2 - a_1) + a_0]^2 + \beta^2[3\alpha^2 - \beta^2 - 2\alpha a_2 + a_1]^2}{4\alpha^2\lambda^2 + (\alpha^2 + \beta^2 - \lambda^2)^2}}\,e^{-\alpha t}\sin(\beta t + \psi_2)$$

$$\psi_1 = \tan^{-1}\frac{a_2\lambda^2 - a_0}{\lambda(a_1 - \lambda^2)} + \tan^{-1}\frac{\alpha^2 + \beta^2 - \lambda^2}{2\alpha\lambda}$$

$$\psi_2 = \tan^{-1}\frac{2\alpha\beta}{\alpha^2 - \beta^2 + \lambda^2} + \tan^{-1}\frac{\beta(3\alpha^2 - \beta^2 - 2\alpha a_2 + a_1)}{(\alpha^2 - \beta^2)(a_2 - \alpha) + \alpha(2\beta^2 - a_1) + a_0}$$

101.

$$\frac{1}{s(\delta^2 + \lambda^2)[(s+\alpha)^2 + \beta^2]}$$

$$\frac{1}{\lambda^2(\alpha^2 + \beta^2)} - \frac{\sin(\lambda t + \psi_1)}{\lambda^2\sqrt{4\alpha^2\lambda^2 + (\alpha^2 + \beta^2 - \lambda^2)^2}} + \frac{e^{-\alpha t}\sin(\beta t - \psi_2)}{\beta\sqrt{(\alpha^2 + \beta^2)[4\alpha^2\lambda^2 + (\alpha^2 + \beta^2 - \lambda^2)^2]}}$$

$$\psi_1 = \tan^{-1}\frac{\alpha^2 + \beta^2 - \lambda^2}{2\alpha\lambda} \qquad \psi_2 = \tan^{-1}\frac{\alpha}{\beta} + \tan^{-1}\frac{\alpha^2 + \beta^2 - \lambda^2}{2\alpha\beta}$$

102.

$$\frac{s + a_0}{s(\delta^2 + \lambda^2)[(s + \alpha)^2 + \beta^2]}$$

$$\frac{a_0}{\lambda^2(\alpha^2 + \beta^2)} - \frac{1}{\lambda^2}\sqrt{\frac{a_0^2 + \lambda^2}{4\alpha^2\lambda^2 + (\alpha^2 + \beta^2 - \lambda^2)^2}}\sin(\lambda t + \psi_1)$$
$$+ \frac{1}{\beta}\sqrt{\frac{(\alpha - a_0)^2 + \beta^2}{(\alpha^2 + \beta^2)[4\alpha^2\lambda^2 + (\alpha^2 + \beta^2 - \lambda^2)^2]}}\,e^{-\alpha t}\sin(\beta t + \psi_2)$$

$$\psi_1 = \tan^{-1}\frac{\alpha^2 + \beta^2 - \lambda^2}{2\alpha\lambda} + \tan^{-1}\frac{\lambda}{a_0}$$

$$\psi_2 = \tan^{-1}\frac{\alpha - a_0}{\beta} + \tan^{-1}\frac{\beta}{\alpha} - \tan^{-1}\frac{\alpha^2 - \beta^2 + \lambda^2}{2\alpha\beta}$$

103.

$$\frac{s^2 + a_1 s + a_0}{s(s^2 + \lambda^2)[(s + \alpha)^2 + \beta^2]}$$

$$\frac{a_0}{\lambda^2(\alpha^2 + \beta^2)} - \frac{1}{\lambda^2}\sqrt{\frac{(a_0 - \lambda^2)^2 + a_1^2\lambda^2}{4\alpha^2\lambda^2 + (\alpha^2 + \beta^2 - \lambda^2)^2}}\sin(\lambda t + \psi_1)$$
$$- \frac{1}{\beta}\sqrt{\frac{\beta^2(a_1 - 2\alpha)^2 + (\alpha^2 - \beta^2 - a_1\alpha + a_0)^2}{(\alpha^2 + \beta^2)[4\alpha^2\lambda^2 + (\alpha^2 + \beta^2 - \lambda^2)^2]}}\,e^{-\alpha t}\sin(\beta t + \psi_2)$$

$$\psi_1 = \tan^{-1}\frac{a_1\lambda}{a_0 - \lambda^2} + \tan^{-1}\frac{\alpha^2 + \beta^2 - \lambda^2}{2\alpha\lambda}$$

$$\psi_2 = \tan^{-1}\frac{\alpha^2 - \beta^2 - a_1\alpha + a_0}{\beta(2\alpha - a_1)} + \tan^{-1}\frac{\beta}{\alpha} - \tan^{-1}\frac{\alpha^2 - \beta^2 + \lambda^2}{2\alpha\beta}$$

104.

$$\frac{s^3 + a_2 s^2 + a_1 s + a_0}{s(s^2 + \lambda^2)[(s + \alpha)^2 + \beta^2]}$$

$$\frac{a_0}{\lambda^2(\alpha^2 + \beta^2)} + \frac{1}{\lambda^2}\sqrt{\frac{(a_2\lambda^2 - a_0)^2 + \lambda^2(a_1 - \lambda^2)^2}{4\alpha^2\lambda^2 + (\alpha^2 + \beta^2 - \lambda^2)^2}}\sin(\lambda t + \psi_1)$$
$$+ \frac{1}{\beta}\sqrt{\frac{[\alpha^2 - \beta^2](a_2 - \alpha) + \alpha(2\beta^2 - a_1) + a_0]^2 + \beta^2(3\alpha^2 - \beta^2 - 2a_2\alpha + a_0)^2}{(\alpha^2 + \beta^2)[4\alpha^2\lambda^2 + (\alpha^2 + \beta^2 - \lambda^2)^2]}}\,e^{-\alpha t}\sin(\beta t + \psi_2)$$

$$\psi_1 = \tan^{-1}\frac{a_2\lambda^2 - a_0}{\lambda(a_1 - \lambda^2)} - \tan^{-1}\frac{2\alpha\lambda}{\alpha^2 + \beta^2 - \lambda^2}$$

$$\psi_2 = \tan^{-1}\frac{\beta(3\alpha^2 - \beta^2 - 2a_2\alpha + a_1)}{(\alpha^2 - \beta^2)(a_2 - \alpha) + \alpha(2\beta^2 - a_1) + a_0} - \tan^{-1}\frac{\alpha}{\beta} - \tan^{-1}\frac{\alpha^2 - \beta^2 + \lambda^2}{2\alpha\beta}$$

$F(s)$	$f(t)$
105. $\dfrac{1}{(s+\gamma)(s^2+\lambda^2)[(s+\alpha)^2+\beta^2]}$	$\dfrac{1}{(\gamma^2+\lambda^2)[(\alpha-\gamma)^2+\beta^2]}e^{-\gamma t} - \dfrac{1}{\lambda}\sqrt{\dfrac{1}{(\gamma^2+\lambda^2)[4\alpha^2\lambda^2+(\alpha^2+\beta^2-\lambda^2)^2]}}\sin(\lambda t+\psi_1)$ $+\dfrac{e^{-\alpha t}\sin(\beta t+\psi_2)}{\beta\sqrt{[(\gamma-\alpha)^2+\beta^2][4\alpha^2\lambda^2+(\alpha^2+\beta^2-\lambda^2)^2]}}$ $\psi_1=\tan^{-1}\dfrac{\gamma}{\lambda}+\tan^{-1}\dfrac{\alpha^2+\beta^2-\lambda^2}{2\alpha\lambda}$ $\psi_2=\tan^{-1}\dfrac{\gamma-\alpha}{\beta}-\tan^{-1}\dfrac{\alpha^2-\beta^2+\lambda^2}{2\alpha\beta}$
106. $\dfrac{s+a_0}{(s+\gamma)(s^2+\lambda^2)[(s+\alpha)^2+\beta^2]}$	$\dfrac{(a_0-\gamma)e^{-\gamma t}}{(\gamma^2+\lambda^2)[(\alpha-\gamma)^2+\beta^2]} - \dfrac{1}{\lambda}\sqrt{\dfrac{a_0^2+\lambda^2}{(\gamma^2+\lambda^2)[4\alpha^2\lambda^2+(\alpha^2+\beta^2-\lambda^2)^2]}}\sin(\lambda t+\psi_1)$ $+\dfrac{1}{\beta}\sqrt{\dfrac{\beta^2+(a_0-\alpha)^2}{[(\gamma-\alpha)^2+\beta^2][4\alpha^2\lambda^2+(\alpha^2+\beta^2-\lambda^2)^2]}}\,e^{-\alpha t}\sin(\beta t+\psi_2)$ $\psi_1=\tan^{-1}\dfrac{\lambda}{a_0}+\tan^{-1}\dfrac{\gamma}{\lambda}+\tan^{-1}\dfrac{\alpha^2+\beta^2-\lambda^2}{2\alpha\lambda}$ $\psi_2=\tan^{-1}\dfrac{\beta}{a_0-\alpha}+\tan^{-1}\dfrac{\gamma-\alpha}{\beta}-\tan^{-1}\dfrac{\alpha^2-\beta^2+\lambda^2}{2\alpha\beta}$
107. $\dfrac{s^2+a_1 s+a_0}{(s+\gamma)(s^2+\lambda^2)[(s+\alpha)^2+\beta^2]}$	$\dfrac{(\gamma^2-a_1\gamma+a_0)e^{-\gamma t}}{(\gamma^2+\lambda^2)[(\alpha-\gamma)^2+\beta^2]} + \dfrac{1}{\lambda}\sqrt{\dfrac{a_1^2\lambda^2+(a_0-\lambda^2)^2}{(\gamma^2+\lambda^2)[4\alpha^2\lambda^2+(\alpha^2+\beta^2-\lambda^2)^2]}}\sin(\lambda t+\psi_1)$ $+\dfrac{1}{\beta}\sqrt{\dfrac{\beta^2(a_1-2\alpha)^2+(\alpha^2-\beta^2-a_1\alpha+a_0)^2}{[(\gamma-\alpha)^2+\beta^2][4\alpha^2\lambda^2+(\alpha^2+\beta^2-\lambda^2)^2]}}\,e^{-\alpha t}\sin(\beta t+\psi_2)$ $\psi_1=\tan^{-1}\dfrac{\gamma}{\lambda}-\tan^{-1}\dfrac{2\alpha\lambda}{\alpha^2+\beta^2-\lambda^2}-\tan^{-1}\dfrac{a_0-\lambda^2}{a_1\lambda}$ $\psi_2=\tan^{-1}\dfrac{\beta(a_1-2\alpha)}{\alpha^2-\beta^2-a_1\alpha+a_0}+\tan^{-1}\dfrac{\gamma-\alpha}{\beta}-\tan^{-1}\dfrac{\alpha^2-\beta^2+\lambda^2}{2\alpha\beta}$

108. $\dfrac{s^3 + a_2 s^2 + a_1 s + a_0}{(s+\gamma)[(s+\alpha)^2 + \beta^2]}$

$$\frac{-\gamma^3 + a_2\gamma^2 - a_1\gamma + a_0}{(\gamma^2 + \lambda^2)[(\alpha - \gamma)^2 + \beta^2]}\, e^{-\gamma t} + \frac{1}{\lambda}\sqrt{\frac{\lambda^2(a_1 - \lambda^2)^2 + (a_0 - a_2\lambda^2)^2}{(\gamma^2 + \lambda^2)[4\alpha^2\lambda^2 + (\alpha^2 + \beta^2 - \lambda^2)^2]}}\, \sin(\lambda t + \psi_1)$$

$$+ \frac{1}{\beta}\sqrt{\frac{[(3\beta^2 - \alpha^2)\alpha + a_2(\alpha^2 - \beta^2) - a_1\alpha + a_0]^2 + \beta^2[(3\alpha^2 - \beta^2) - 2a_2\alpha + a_1]^2}{[(\gamma - \alpha)^2 + \beta^2][4\alpha^2\lambda^2 + (\alpha^2 + \beta^2 - \lambda^2)^2]}}\, e^{-\alpha t}\sin(\beta t + \psi_2)$$

$$\psi_1 = \tan^{-1}\frac{\lambda(a_1 - \lambda^2)}{a_0 - a_2\lambda^2} - \tan^{-1}\frac{2\alpha\lambda}{\alpha^2 + \beta^2 - \lambda^2} - \tan^{-1}\frac{\lambda}{\gamma}$$

$$\psi_2 = \tan^{-1}\frac{\gamma - \alpha}{\beta} - \tan^{-1}\frac{\alpha^2 - \beta^2 + \lambda^2}{2\alpha\beta} + \tan^{-1}\frac{\beta[3\alpha^2 - \beta^2 - 2a_2\alpha + a_1]}{(3\beta^2 - \alpha^2)\alpha + a_2(\alpha^2 - \beta^2) - a_1\alpha + a_0}$$

109. $\dfrac{s + a_0}{(s+\alpha)^2}$

$$[(a_0 - \alpha)t + 1]e^{-\alpha t}$$

110. $\dfrac{1}{s(s+\alpha)^2}$

$$\frac{1}{\alpha^2}[1 - (1 + \alpha t)e^{-\alpha t}]$$

111. $\dfrac{s + a_0}{s(s+\alpha)^2}$

$$\frac{a_0}{\alpha^2} + \frac{1}{\alpha}\left[(\alpha - a_0)t - \frac{a_0}{\alpha}\right]e^{-\alpha t}$$

112. $\dfrac{s^2 + a_1 s + a_0}{s(s+\alpha)^2}$

$$\frac{a_0}{\alpha^2} + \frac{1}{\alpha}\left[(a_1\alpha - a_0 - \alpha^2)t + \frac{\alpha^2 a_0}{\alpha}\right]e^{-\alpha t}$$

113. $\dfrac{1}{s^2(s+\alpha)^2}$

$$\frac{1}{\alpha^2}\left[t - \frac{2}{\alpha}\right] + \frac{1}{\alpha^2}\left[\frac{t}{\alpha} + \frac{2}{\alpha}\right]e^{-\alpha t}$$

114. $\dfrac{s + a_0}{s^2(s+\alpha)^2}$

$$\frac{1}{\alpha^2}\left[a_0 t + 1 - \frac{2a_0}{\alpha}\right] + \frac{1}{\alpha^2}\left[(a_0 - \alpha)t - 1 + \frac{2a_0}{\alpha}\right]e^{-\alpha t}$$

APPENDIX A: TABLE OF LAPLACE TRANSFORMS (cont.)

	$F(s)$	$f(t)$
115.	$\dfrac{s^2 + a_1 s + a_0}{s^2(s+\alpha)^2}$	$\dfrac{1}{\alpha^2}\left[a_0 t + a_1 - \dfrac{2a_0}{\alpha}\right] + \dfrac{1}{\alpha^2}\left[(\alpha^2 - a_1\alpha + a_0)t - a_1 + \dfrac{2a_0}{\alpha}\right]e^{-\alpha t}$
116.	$\dfrac{s^3 + a_2 s^2 + a_1 s + a_0}{s^2(s+\alpha)^2}$	$\dfrac{1}{\alpha^2}\left[a_0 t + a_1 - \dfrac{2a_0}{\alpha}\right] + \dfrac{1}{\alpha^2}\left[(a_0 - a_1\alpha + a_2\alpha^2 - \alpha^3)t + \alpha^2 - a_1 + \dfrac{2a_0}{\alpha}\right]e^{-\alpha t}$
117.	$\dfrac{1}{(s+\gamma)(s+\alpha)^2}$	$\dfrac{1}{(\gamma-\alpha)^2}e^{-\gamma t} + \dfrac{(\gamma-\alpha)t - 1}{(\gamma-\alpha)^2}e^{-\alpha t}$
118.	$\dfrac{s + a_0}{(s+\gamma)(s+\alpha)^2}$	$\dfrac{a_0 - \gamma}{(\gamma-\alpha)^2}e^{-\gamma t} + \left[\dfrac{a_0 - \alpha}{\gamma-\alpha}\,t + \dfrac{\gamma - a_0}{(\gamma-\alpha)^2}\right]e^{-\alpha t}$
119.	$\dfrac{s^2 + a_1 s + a_0}{(s+\gamma)(s+\alpha)^2}$	$\dfrac{\gamma^2 - a_1\gamma + a_0}{(\gamma-\alpha)^2}e^{-\gamma t} + \left[\dfrac{\alpha^2 - a_1\alpha + a_0}{\gamma-\alpha}\,t + \dfrac{\alpha^2 - 2\alpha\gamma + a_1\gamma - a_0}{(\gamma-\alpha)^2}\right]e^{-\alpha t}$
120.	$\dfrac{1}{s(s+\gamma)(s+\alpha)^2}$	$\dfrac{1}{\gamma\alpha^2} - \dfrac{1}{\gamma^2(\gamma-\alpha)^2}e^{-\gamma t} - \left[\dfrac{t}{\alpha(\gamma-\alpha)} + \dfrac{\gamma - 2\alpha}{\alpha^2(\gamma-\alpha)^2}\right]e^{-\alpha t}$
121.	$\dfrac{s + a_0}{s(s+\gamma)(s+\alpha)^2}$	$\dfrac{a_0}{\gamma\alpha^2} + \dfrac{\gamma - a_0}{\gamma^2(\alpha-\gamma)^2}e^{-\gamma t} + \left[\dfrac{a_0 - \alpha}{\alpha(\alpha-\gamma)}\,t + \dfrac{a_0(2\alpha-\gamma) - \alpha^2}{\alpha^2(\alpha-\gamma)^2}\right]e^{-\alpha t}$
122.	$\dfrac{s^2 + a_1 s + a_0}{s(s+\gamma)(s+\alpha)^2}$	$\dfrac{a_0}{\gamma\alpha^2} - \dfrac{\gamma^2 - a_1\gamma + a_0}{\gamma(\alpha-\gamma)^2}e^{-\gamma t} + \left[\dfrac{\alpha^2 - a_1\alpha + a_0}{\alpha(\alpha-\gamma)}\,t + \dfrac{a_0(2\alpha-\gamma) + \alpha^2(\gamma - a_1)}{\alpha^2(\alpha-\gamma)^2}\right]e^{-\alpha t}$

123. $\dfrac{s^3 + a_2 s^2 + a_1 s + a_0}{s(s+\gamma)(s+\alpha)^2}$

$$\frac{a_0}{\gamma\alpha^2} + \frac{\gamma^3 - a_2\gamma^2 + a_1\gamma - a_0}{\gamma(\alpha-\gamma)^2}e^{-\gamma t} + \left[\frac{\alpha^3 - a_2\alpha^2 + a_1\alpha - a_0}{\alpha(\gamma-\alpha)}t + \frac{\alpha^4 - 2\gamma\alpha^3 + \alpha^2(a_2\gamma - a_1) + a_0(2\alpha - \gamma)}{\alpha^2(\alpha-\gamma)^2}\right]e^{-\alpha t}$$

---

124. $\dfrac{1}{s^2(s+\gamma)(s+\alpha)^2}$

$$\frac{1}{\gamma\alpha^2}\left[t - \frac{2}{\alpha} - \frac{1}{\gamma}\right] + \frac{1}{\gamma^2(\alpha-\gamma)^2}e^{-\gamma t} + \left[\frac{1}{\alpha^2(\gamma-\alpha)}t + \frac{2(\gamma-\alpha)-\alpha}{\alpha^3(\alpha-\gamma)^2}\right]e^{-\alpha t}$$

---

125. $\dfrac{s+a_0}{s^2(s+\gamma)(s+\alpha)^2}$

$$\frac{a_0}{\gamma\alpha^2}\left[t + \frac{1}{a_0} - \frac{1}{\gamma} - \frac{2}{\alpha}\right] + \frac{a_0-\gamma}{\gamma^2(\alpha-\gamma)^2}e^{-\gamma t} + \left[\frac{a_0-\alpha}{\alpha^2(\gamma-\alpha)}t + \frac{(2\alpha-\gamma)(\alpha-2a_0) + a_0\alpha}{\alpha^3(\alpha-\gamma)^2}\right]e^{-\alpha t}$$

---

126. $\dfrac{s^2+a_1 s+a_0}{s^2(s+\gamma)(s+\alpha)^2}$

$$\frac{a_0}{\gamma\alpha^2}\left[t + \frac{a_1}{a_0} - \frac{1}{\gamma} - \frac{2}{\alpha}\right] + \frac{\gamma^2 - a_1\gamma + a_0}{\gamma^2(\alpha-\gamma)^2}e^{-\gamma t}$$
$$+ \left[\frac{\alpha^2 - a_1\alpha + a_0}{\alpha^2(\gamma-\alpha)}t + \frac{\alpha^2(2a_1 - \alpha) - \alpha(3a_0 + a_1\gamma) + 2a_0\gamma}{\alpha^3(\alpha-\gamma)^2}\right]e^{-\alpha t}$$

---

127. $\dfrac{s^3+a_2 s^2+a_1 s+a_0}{s^2(s+\gamma)(s+\alpha)^2}$

$$\frac{a_0}{\gamma\alpha^2}\left[t + \frac{a_1}{a_0} - \frac{1}{\gamma} - \frac{2}{\alpha}\right] + \frac{-\gamma^3 + a_2\gamma^2 - a_1\gamma + a_0}{\gamma^2(\alpha-\gamma)^2}e^{-\gamma t}$$
$$+ \left[\frac{-\alpha^3 + a_2\alpha^2 - a_1\alpha + a_0}{\alpha^2(\gamma-\alpha)}t + \frac{\alpha^3(\gamma-a_2) + a_0(\gamma-\alpha) - (a_1\alpha - a_0)(\gamma - 2\alpha)}{\alpha^3(\alpha-\gamma)^2}\right]e^{-\alpha t}$$

---

128. $\dfrac{1}{(s+\gamma)(s+\delta)(s+\alpha)^2}$

$$\frac{1}{(\delta-\gamma)(\alpha-\gamma)^2}e^{-\gamma t} + \frac{1}{(\gamma-\delta)(\alpha-\delta)^2}e^{-\delta t} + \left[\frac{1}{(\alpha-\gamma)(\alpha-\delta)}t + \frac{2\alpha-\gamma-\delta}{(\alpha-\gamma)^2(\alpha-\delta)^2}\right]e^{-\alpha t}$$

$F(s)$	$f(t)$
129. $\dfrac{s + a_0}{(s + \gamma)(s + \delta)(s + \alpha)^2}$	$\dfrac{a_0 - \gamma}{(\delta - \gamma)(\alpha - \gamma)^2} e^{-\gamma t} + \dfrac{a_0 - \delta}{(\gamma - \delta)(\alpha - \delta)^2} e^{-\delta t}$ $+ \left[\dfrac{a_0 - \alpha}{(\alpha - \gamma)(\alpha - \delta)}\, t + \dfrac{a_0(2\alpha - \gamma - \delta) + \gamma\delta - \alpha^2}{(\alpha - \gamma)^2(\alpha - \delta)^2} \right] e^{-\alpha t}$
130. $\dfrac{s^2 + a_1 s + a_0}{(s + \gamma)(s + \delta)(s + \alpha)^2}$	$\dfrac{\gamma^2 - a_1\gamma + a_0}{(\delta - \gamma)(\alpha - \gamma)^2} e^{-\gamma t} + \dfrac{\delta^2 - a_1\delta + a_0}{(\gamma - \delta)(\alpha - \delta)^2} e^{-\delta t}$ $+ \left[\dfrac{\alpha^2 - a_1\alpha + a_0}{(\alpha - \gamma)(\alpha - \delta)}\, t + \dfrac{(\gamma + \delta)(\alpha^2 - a_0) + \gamma\delta(a_1 - 2\alpha) - \alpha(a_1\alpha - 2a_0)}{(\alpha - \gamma)^2(\alpha - \delta)^2} \right] e^{-\alpha t}$
131. $\dfrac{s^3 + a_2 s^2 + a_1 s + a_0}{(s + \gamma)(s + \delta)(s + \alpha)^2}$	$\dfrac{-\gamma^3 + a_2\gamma^2 - a_1\gamma + a_0}{(\delta - \gamma)(\alpha - \gamma)^2} e^{-\gamma t} + \dfrac{-\delta^3 + a_2\delta^2 - a_1\delta + a_0}{(\gamma - \delta)(\alpha - \delta)^2} e^{-\delta t} + \left[\dfrac{-\alpha^3 + a_2\alpha^2 - a_1\alpha + a_0}{(\alpha - \gamma)(\alpha - \delta)}\, t + \right.$ $\left. \dfrac{\alpha^2\{\alpha^2 - 2\alpha(\gamma + \delta) + 3\gamma\delta\} + (\gamma + \delta)(a_2\alpha^2 - a_0) + a_1(\gamma\delta - \alpha^2) - 2\alpha(a_2\gamma\delta - a_0)}{(\alpha - \gamma)^2(\alpha - \delta)^2} \right] e^{-\alpha t}$
132. $\dfrac{1}{s(s + \gamma)(s + \delta)(s + \alpha)^2}$	$\dfrac{1}{\gamma\delta\alpha^2} + \dfrac{e^{-\gamma t}}{\gamma(\gamma - \delta)(\alpha - \gamma)^2} + \dfrac{e^{-\delta t}}{\delta(\delta - \gamma)(\alpha - \delta)^2}$ $+ \left[\dfrac{t}{\alpha(\alpha - \gamma)(\delta - \alpha)} - \dfrac{(\alpha - \gamma)(\alpha - \delta) + \alpha(2\alpha - \gamma - \delta)}{\alpha^2(\alpha - \gamma)^2(\alpha - \delta)^2} \right] e^{-\alpha t}$
133. $\dfrac{s + a_0}{s(s + \gamma)(s + \delta)(s + \alpha)^2}$	$\dfrac{a_0}{\gamma\delta\alpha^2} + \dfrac{(\gamma - a_0)e^{-\gamma t}}{\gamma(\delta - \gamma)(\alpha - \gamma)^2} + \dfrac{(\delta - a_0)e^{-\delta t}}{\delta(\gamma - \delta)(\alpha - \delta)^2}$ $+ \left[\dfrac{(\alpha - a_0)t}{\alpha(\alpha - \gamma)(\alpha - \delta)} - \dfrac{a_0(\alpha - \gamma)(\alpha - \delta) + \alpha(a_0 - \alpha)(2\alpha - \gamma - \delta)}{\alpha^2(\alpha - \gamma)^2(\alpha - \delta)^2} \right] e^{-\alpha t}$

134.

$$\frac{s^2 + a_1 s + a_0}{s(s+\gamma)(s+\delta)(s+\alpha)^2}$$

$$\frac{a_0}{\gamma\delta\alpha^2} + \frac{\gamma^2 - a_1\gamma + a_0}{\gamma(\gamma-\delta)(\alpha-\gamma)^2}e^{-\gamma t} + \frac{\delta^2 - a_1\delta + a_0}{\delta(\delta-\gamma)(\alpha-\delta)^2}e^{-\delta t}$$
$$+ \left[\frac{\alpha^2 - a_1\alpha + a_0}{\alpha(\alpha-\gamma)(\delta-\alpha)}t - \frac{a_0(\alpha-\gamma)(\alpha-\delta) + \alpha(a_0 - a_1\alpha)(2\alpha - \gamma - \delta) - \alpha^2(\gamma\delta - \alpha^2)}{\alpha^2(\alpha-\gamma)^2(\alpha-\delta)^2}\right]e^{-\alpha t}$$

135.

$$\frac{s^3 + a_2 s^2 + a_1 s + a_0}{s(s+\gamma)(s+\delta)(s+\alpha)^2}$$

$$\frac{a_0}{\gamma\delta\alpha^2} + \frac{\gamma^3 - a_2\gamma^2 + a_1\gamma - a_0}{\gamma(\delta-\gamma)(\alpha-\gamma)^2}e^{-\gamma t} + \frac{\delta^3 - a_2\delta^2 + a_1\delta - a_0}{\delta(\gamma-\delta)(\alpha-\delta)^2}e^{-\delta t}$$
$$+ \left[\frac{\alpha^3 - a_2\alpha^2 + a_1\alpha - a_0}{\alpha(\alpha-\gamma)(\alpha-\delta)}t \right.$$
$$\left. - \frac{(\alpha-\gamma)(\alpha-\delta)\{a_0 - \alpha^2(a_3 - 2\alpha)\} + \alpha(2\alpha - \gamma - \delta)\{a_0 - \alpha a_1 + \alpha^2(a_2 - \alpha)\}}{\alpha^2(\alpha-\gamma)^2(\alpha-\delta)^2}\right]e^{-\alpha t}$$

136.

$$\frac{1}{s^2(s+\gamma)(s+\delta)(s+\alpha)^2}$$

$$\frac{1}{\gamma\delta\alpha^2}\left[t - \frac{2}{\alpha} - \frac{1}{\gamma} - \frac{1}{\delta}\right] + \frac{e^{-\gamma t}}{\gamma^2(\delta-\gamma)(\alpha-\gamma)^2} + \frac{e^{-\delta t}}{\delta^2(\gamma-\delta)(\alpha-\delta)^2}$$
$$+ \left[\frac{t}{\alpha^2(\alpha-\gamma)(\alpha-\delta)} + \frac{2\alpha(\alpha-\gamma)(\alpha-\delta) + \alpha(2\alpha - \gamma - \delta)}{\alpha^3(\alpha-\gamma)^2(\alpha-\delta)^2}\right]e^{-\alpha t}$$

137.

$$\frac{s + a_0}{s^2(s+\gamma)(s+\delta)(s+\alpha)^2}$$

$$\frac{1}{\gamma\delta\alpha^2}\left[a_0 t + 1 - a_0\left(\frac{1}{\gamma} + \frac{1}{\delta} + \frac{2}{\alpha}\right)\right] + \frac{(a_0 - \gamma)e^{-\gamma t}}{\gamma^2(\delta - \gamma)(\alpha - \gamma)^2} + \frac{(a_0 - \delta)e^{-\delta t}}{\delta^2(\gamma - \delta)(\alpha - \delta)^2}$$
$$+ \frac{(a_0 - \alpha)t}{\alpha^2(\alpha - \gamma)(\alpha - \delta)} - \frac{(\alpha - \gamma)(\alpha - \delta)(\alpha - 2a_0) + \alpha(\alpha - a_0)(2\alpha - \gamma - \delta)}{\alpha^3(\alpha - \gamma)^2(\alpha - \delta)^2}e^{-\alpha t}$$

138.

$$\frac{s^2 + a_1 s + a_0}{s^2(s+\gamma)(s+\delta)(s+\alpha)^2}$$

$$\frac{1}{\gamma\delta\alpha^2}\left[a_0 t + a_1 - a_0\left(\frac{1}{\gamma} + \frac{1}{\delta} + \frac{2}{\alpha}\right)\right] + \frac{\gamma^2 - a_1\gamma + a_0}{\gamma^2(\delta - \gamma)(\alpha - \gamma)^2}e^{-\gamma t} + \frac{\delta^2 - a_1\delta + a_0}{\delta^2(\gamma - \delta)(\alpha - \delta)^2}e^{\delta t}$$
$$+ \frac{(\alpha^2 - a_1\alpha + a_0)t}{\alpha^2(\alpha - \gamma)(\alpha - \delta)} + \frac{(\alpha - \gamma)(\alpha - \delta)(2a_0 - a_1\alpha) + \alpha(\alpha^2 - a_1\alpha + a_0)(2\alpha - \gamma - \delta)}{\alpha^3(\alpha - \gamma)^2(\alpha - \delta)^2}e^{-\alpha t}$$

$F(s)$	$f(t)$
139. $\dfrac{s^3 + a_2 s^2 + a_1 s + a_0}{s^2(s+\gamma)(s+\delta)(s+\alpha)^2}$	$\dfrac{1}{\gamma\delta\alpha^2}\left[a_0 t + a_1 - a_0\left(\dfrac{1}{\gamma} + \dfrac{1}{\delta} + \dfrac{2}{\alpha}\right)\right] + \dfrac{-\gamma^3 + a_2\gamma^2 - a_1\gamma + a_0}{\gamma^2(\delta-\gamma)(\alpha-\gamma)^2}e^{-\gamma t}$ $+\ \dfrac{-\delta^3 + a_2\delta^2 - a_1\delta + a_0}{\delta^2(\gamma-\delta)(\alpha-\delta)^2}e^{-\delta t} + \left[\dfrac{-\alpha^3 + a_2\alpha^2 - a_1\alpha + a_0}{\alpha^2(\alpha-\gamma)(\alpha-\delta)}\,t\right.$ $+\ \dfrac{2(\alpha-\gamma)(\alpha-\delta)(a_0 - a_1\alpha) + \alpha(a_0 + a_2\alpha^2)(2\alpha - \gamma - \delta) - \alpha(a_1 + \alpha^2)(\alpha^2 - \gamma\delta)}{\alpha^3(\alpha-\gamma)^2(\alpha-\delta)^2}\left.\vphantom{\dfrac{}{}}\right]e^{-\alpha t}$
140. $\dfrac{1}{(s^2+\beta^2)(s+\alpha)^2}$	$\dfrac{1}{\beta(\alpha^2+\beta^2)}\sin(\beta t - \psi) + \left[\dfrac{t}{\alpha^2+\beta^2} + \dfrac{2\alpha}{(\alpha^2+\beta^2)^2}\right]e^{-\alpha t}$ $\psi = 2\tan^{-1}\dfrac{\beta}{\alpha}$
141. $\dfrac{s + a_0}{(s^2+\beta^2)(s+\alpha)^2}$	$\dfrac{\sqrt{a_0^2+\beta^2}}{\beta(\alpha^2+\beta^2)}\sin(\beta t + \psi) + \left[\dfrac{a_0-\alpha}{\alpha^2+\beta^2}\,t + \dfrac{2a_0\alpha + \beta^2 - \alpha^2}{(\alpha^2+\beta^2)^2}\right]e^{-\alpha t}$ $\psi = \tan^{-1}\dfrac{\beta}{a_0} - 2\tan^{-1}\dfrac{\beta}{\alpha}$
142. $\dfrac{s^2 + a_1 s + a_0}{(s^2+\beta^2)(s+\alpha)^2}$	$\dfrac{\sqrt{(a_0-\beta^2)^2 + a_1^2\beta^2}}{\beta(\alpha^2+\beta^2)}\sin(\beta t + \psi) + \left[\dfrac{\alpha^2 - a_1\alpha + a_0}{\alpha^2+\beta^2}\,t + \dfrac{a_1(\beta^2 - \alpha^2) + 2\alpha(a_0 - \beta^2)}{(\alpha^2 + \beta^2)^2}\right]e^{-\alpha t}$ $\psi = \tan^{-1}\dfrac{a_1\beta}{a_0 - \beta^2} - 2\tan^{-1}\dfrac{\beta}{\alpha}$

143. $\dfrac{s^3 + a_2 s^2 + a_1 s + a_0}{(s^2 + \beta^2)(s + \alpha)^2}$

$$\frac{\sqrt{(a_0 - a_2\beta^2)^2 + \beta^2(a_1 - \beta^2)^2}}{\beta(\alpha^2 + \beta^2)} \sin(\beta t + \psi)$$

$$+ \left[\frac{-\alpha^3 + a_2\alpha^2 - a_1\alpha + a_0}{\alpha^2 + \beta^2}\, t - \frac{a_2\beta^2 - a_0}{\beta(a_1 - \beta^2)} + \frac{\alpha^4 + \alpha^2(3\beta^2 - a_1) + 2\alpha(a_0 - a_2\beta^2) + a_1\beta^2}{(\alpha^2 + \beta^2)^2}\right] e^{-\alpha t}$$

$$\psi = \tan^{-1}\frac{\alpha}{\beta} - \tan^{-1}\frac{\beta}{\alpha} + \tan^{-1}\frac{a_2\beta^2 - a_0}{\beta(a_1 - \beta^2)}$$

144. $\dfrac{1}{s(s^2 + \beta^2)(s + \alpha)^2}$

$$\frac{1}{\alpha^2\beta^2} - \left[\frac{t}{\alpha(\alpha^2 + \beta^2)} + \frac{3\alpha^2 + \beta^2}{\alpha^2(\alpha^2 + \beta^2)^2}\right] e^{-\alpha t} - \frac{1}{\beta^2(\alpha^2 + \beta^2)} \sin(\beta t + \psi)$$

$$\psi = \tan^{-1}\frac{\alpha}{\beta} - \tan^{-1}\frac{\beta}{\alpha}$$

145. $\dfrac{s + a_0}{s(s^2 + \beta^2)(s + \alpha)^2}$

$$\frac{a_0}{\alpha^2\beta^2} + \left[\frac{\alpha - a_0}{\alpha(\alpha^2 + \beta^2)}\, t + \frac{2\alpha^2(\alpha - a_0) - a_0(\alpha^2 + \beta^2)}{\alpha^2(\alpha^2 + \beta^2)^2}\right] e^{-\alpha t} - \frac{\sqrt{a_0^2 + \beta^2}}{\beta^2(\alpha^2 + \beta^2)} \cos(\beta t + \psi)$$

$$\psi = \tan^{-1}\frac{\beta}{a_0} - 2\tan^{-1}\frac{\beta}{\alpha}$$

146. $\dfrac{s^2 + a_1 s + a_0}{s(s^2 + \beta^2)(s + \alpha)^2}$

$$\frac{a_0}{\alpha^2\beta^2} - \left[\frac{\alpha^2 - a_1\alpha + a_0}{\alpha(\alpha^2 + \beta^2)}\, t + \frac{\alpha^2\{(\alpha^2 - \beta^2) + 2(a_0 - a_1\alpha)\} + a_0(\alpha^2 + \beta^2)}{\alpha^2(\alpha^2 + \beta^2)^2}\right] e^{-\alpha t}$$

$$- \frac{\sqrt{a_1^2\beta^2 + (a_0 - \beta^2)^2}}{\beta^2(\alpha^2 + \beta^2)} \sin(\beta t + \psi)$$

$$\psi = \tan^{-1}\frac{\alpha}{\beta} - \tan^{-1}\frac{\beta}{\alpha} + \tan^{-1}\frac{a_1\beta}{a_0 - \beta^2}$$

APPENDIX A: TABLE OF LAPLACE TRANSFORMS (cont.)

$F(s)$	$f(t)$
147. $\dfrac{s^3 + a_2 s^2 + a_1 s + a_0}{s(s^2 + \beta^2)(s + \alpha)^2}$	$\dfrac{a_0}{\alpha^2\beta^2} + \left[\dfrac{\alpha^3 - a_2\alpha^2 + a_1\alpha - a_0}{\alpha(\alpha^2+\beta^2)}\,t + \dfrac{2\alpha^3(a_1-\beta^2) - \alpha^2\{2a_0 + a_2(\alpha^2-\beta^2)\} - a_0(\alpha^2+\beta^2)}{\alpha^2(\alpha^2+\beta^2)^2}\right]e^{-\alpha t}$ $+ \dfrac{\sqrt{(a_2\beta^2 - a_0)^2 + \beta^2(a_1 - \beta^2)^2}}{\beta^2(\alpha^2+\beta^2)}\sin(\beta t + \psi)$ $\psi = \tan^{-1}\dfrac{\alpha}{\beta} - \tan^{-1}\dfrac{\beta}{\alpha} + \tan^{-1}\dfrac{\beta(\beta^2 - a_1)}{a_2\beta^2 - a_0}$
148. $\dfrac{1}{s^2(s^2 + \beta^2)(s + \alpha)^2}$	$\dfrac{1}{\alpha^2\beta^2}\left[t - \dfrac{2}{\alpha}\right] + \left[\dfrac{t}{\alpha^2(\alpha^2+\beta^2)} + \dfrac{2(2\alpha^2 + \beta^2)}{\alpha^3(\alpha^2+\beta^2)^2}\right]e^{-\alpha t} + \dfrac{1}{\beta^3(\alpha^2+\beta^2)}\sin(\beta t + \psi)$ $\psi = 2\tan^{-1}\dfrac{\alpha}{\beta}$
149. $\dfrac{s + a_0}{s^2(s^2 + \beta^2)(s + \alpha)^2}$	$\dfrac{1}{\alpha^2\beta^2}\left[a_0 t + 1 - \dfrac{2a_0}{\alpha}\right] + \left[\dfrac{(\alpha_0 - \alpha)t}{\alpha^2(\alpha^2+\beta^2)} + \dfrac{(\alpha^2 + \beta^2)(2a_0 - \alpha) + 2\alpha^2(a_0 - \alpha)}{\alpha^3(\alpha^2+\beta^2)^2}\right]e^{-\alpha t}$ $+ \dfrac{\sqrt{a_0^2 + \beta^2}}{\beta^3(\alpha^2+\beta^2)}\sin(\beta t + \psi)$ $\psi = 2\tan^{-1}\dfrac{\alpha}{\beta} + \tan^{-1}\dfrac{\beta}{a_0}$
150. $\dfrac{s^2 + a_1 s + a_0}{s^2(s^2 + \beta^2)(s + \alpha)^2}$	$\dfrac{1}{\alpha^2\beta^2}\left[a_0 t + a_1 - \dfrac{2a_0}{\alpha}\right] + \left[\dfrac{\alpha^2 - a_1\alpha + a_0}{\alpha^2(\alpha^2+\beta^2)}\,t + \dfrac{(2a_0 - a_1\alpha)(\alpha^2+\beta^2) + 2\alpha^2(a_0 - a_1\alpha + \alpha^2)}{\alpha^3(\alpha^2+\beta^2)^2}\right]e^{-\alpha t}$ $+ \dfrac{\sqrt{(a_0 - \beta^2)^2 + a_1^2\beta^2}}{\beta^3(\alpha^2+\beta^2)}\sin(\beta t + \psi)$ $\psi = 2\tan^{-1}\dfrac{\alpha}{\beta} + \tan^{-1}\dfrac{a_1\beta}{a_0 - \beta^2}$

151. $\dfrac{s^3 + a_2 s^2 + a_1 s + a_0}{s^2(s^2 + \beta^2)(s + \alpha)^2}$

$$\frac{1}{\alpha^2\beta^2}\left[a_0 t + a_1 - \frac{2a_0}{\alpha}\right] + \left[\frac{-\alpha^3 + a_1\alpha^2 - a_1\alpha + a_0}{\alpha^2(\alpha^2 + \beta^2)}t + \frac{(2a_0 - a_1\alpha)(\alpha^2 + \beta^2) - \alpha^3(\alpha^2 - \beta^2) + 2\alpha^2[\alpha(a_2\alpha - a_1) + a_0]}{\alpha^3(\alpha^2 + \beta^2)^2}\right]e^{-\alpha t}$$

$$+ \frac{\sqrt{(a_0 - a_2\beta^2)^2 + (\beta^2 - a_1)^2\beta^2}}{\beta^3(\alpha^2 + \beta^2)}\sin(\beta t + \psi)$$

$$\psi = \tan^{-1}\frac{\alpha}{\beta} - \tan^{-1}\frac{\beta}{\alpha} + \tan^{-1}\frac{a_0 - a_2\beta^2}{\beta(\beta^2 - a_1)}$$

152. $\dfrac{1}{(s + \gamma)(s^2 + \beta^2)(s + \alpha)^2}$

$$\frac{e^{-\gamma t}}{(\gamma^2 + \beta^2)(\alpha - \gamma)^2} + \left[\frac{t}{(\gamma - \alpha)(\alpha^2 + \beta^2)} + \frac{2\alpha(\gamma - \alpha) - (\alpha^2 + \beta^2)}{(\gamma - \alpha)^2(\alpha^2 + \beta^2)^2}\right]e^{-\alpha t} + \frac{\sin(\beta t - \psi)}{\beta(\alpha^2 + \beta^2)\sqrt{\gamma^2 + \beta^2}}$$

$$\psi = \tan^{-1}\frac{\beta}{\gamma} + 2\tan^{-1}\frac{\beta}{\alpha}$$

153. $\dfrac{s + a_0}{(s + \gamma)(s^2 + \beta^2)(s + \alpha)^2}$

$$\frac{(a_0 - \gamma)e^{-\gamma t}}{(\gamma^2 + \beta^2)(\alpha - \gamma)^2} + \left[\frac{(a_0 - \alpha)t}{(\gamma - \alpha)(\alpha^2 + \beta^2)} + \frac{\alpha(\gamma - \alpha)(2a_0 - \alpha) + \beta^2(\gamma - a_0) + \alpha^2(\alpha - a_0)}{(\gamma - \alpha)^2(\alpha^2 + \beta^2)^2}\right]e^{-\alpha t}$$

$$+ \frac{\sin(\beta t + \psi)}{\beta(\alpha^2 + \beta^2)}\sqrt{\frac{a_0^2 + \beta^2}{\gamma^2 + \beta^2}}$$

$$\psi = \tan^{-1}\frac{\gamma}{\beta} - 2\tan^{-1}\frac{\beta}{\alpha} - \tan^{-1}\frac{a_0}{\beta}$$

154. $\dfrac{s^2 + a_1 s + a_0}{(s + \gamma)(s^2 + \beta^2)(s + \alpha)^2}$

$$\frac{\gamma^2 - a_1\gamma + a_0}{(\gamma^2 + \beta^2)(\alpha - \gamma)^2}e^{-\gamma t} + \left[\frac{\alpha^2 - a_1\alpha + a_0}{(\gamma - \alpha)(\alpha^2 + \beta^2)}t + \frac{(\gamma - \alpha)(\alpha^2 + \beta^2)(a_1 - 2\alpha) - (\alpha^2 - a_1\alpha + a_0)(3\alpha^2 + \beta^2 - 2\alpha\gamma)}{(\gamma - \alpha)^2(\alpha^2 + \beta^2)^2}\right]e^{-\alpha t}$$

$$+ \frac{\sin(\beta t + \psi)}{\beta(\alpha^2 + \beta^2)}\sqrt{\frac{a_1^2\beta^2 + (a_0 - \beta^2)^2}{\gamma^2 + \beta^2}}$$

$$\psi = \tan^{-1}\frac{a_1\beta}{a_0 - \beta^2} - \tan^{-1}\frac{\beta}{\gamma} - 2\tan^{-1}\frac{\beta}{\alpha}$$

APPENDIX A: TABLE OF LAPLACE TRANSFORMS (cont.)

$F(s)$	$f(t)$
155. $\dfrac{s^3 + a_2 s^2 + a_1 s + a_0}{(\delta + \gamma)(\delta^2 + \beta^2)(s + \alpha)^2}$	$\dfrac{-\gamma^3 + a_2\gamma^2 - a_1\gamma + a_0}{(\alpha - \gamma)^2(\gamma^2 + \beta^2)}e^{-\gamma t} + \dfrac{\sin(\beta t + \psi)}{\beta(\alpha^2 + \beta^2)}\sqrt{\dfrac{(a_0 - a_2\beta^2)^2 + \beta^2(a_1 - \beta^2)^2}{\gamma^2 + \beta^2}}$ $+\left[\dfrac{-a^3 + a_2\alpha^2 - a_1\alpha + a_0}{(\gamma - \alpha)(\alpha^2 + \beta^2)}t + \dfrac{\begin{array}{c}(\alpha^2 + \beta^2)(\gamma\alpha^2 - a_0) - (\alpha^2 - \beta^2)(a_2\alpha^2 + a_1\gamma)\\[2pt] + 2\alpha[(\gamma - \alpha)(a_0 - \alpha\beta^2) - a_2\gamma\beta^2 + a_1\alpha^2]\end{array}}{(\gamma - \alpha)^2(\alpha^2 + \beta^2)^2}\right]e^{-\alpha t}$ $\psi = \tan^{-1}\dfrac{\beta(a_1 - \beta^2)}{a_0 - a_2\beta^2} - 2\tan^{-1}\dfrac{\beta}{\alpha} - \tan^{-1}\dfrac{\beta}{\gamma}$
156. $\dfrac{1}{(s+\gamma)^2[(s+\alpha)^2 + \beta^2]}$	$\dfrac{1}{\beta^2 + (\alpha - \gamma)^2}\left[te^{-\gamma t} + \dfrac{2(\gamma - \alpha)}{\beta^2 + (\alpha - \gamma)^2}e^{-\gamma t} + \dfrac{1}{\beta}e^{-\alpha t}\sin(\beta t - \psi)\right]$ $\psi = 2\tan^{-1}\dfrac{\beta}{\gamma - \alpha}$
157. $\dfrac{s + a_0}{(s+\gamma)^2[(s+\alpha)^2 + \beta^2]}$	$\left[\dfrac{(a_0 - \gamma)t}{(\alpha - \gamma)^2 + \beta^2} - \dfrac{\gamma^2 - 2a_0(\gamma - \alpha) - (\alpha^2 + \beta^2)}{[(\alpha - \gamma)^2 + \beta^2]^2}\right]e^{-\gamma t} + \dfrac{\sqrt{\beta^2 + (a_0 - \alpha)^2}}{\beta[\beta^2 + (\alpha - \gamma)^2]}e^{-\alpha t}\sin(\beta t + \psi)$ $\psi = \tan^{-1}\dfrac{\beta}{a_0 - \alpha} - 2\tan^{-1}\dfrac{\beta}{\gamma - \alpha}$
158. $\dfrac{s^2 + a_1 s + a_0}{(\delta + \gamma)^2[(s+\alpha)^2 + \beta^2]}$	$\left[\dfrac{-\gamma^2 - a_1\gamma + a_0}{\beta^2 + (\alpha - \gamma)^2}t + \dfrac{[\beta^2 + (\alpha - \gamma)^2](a_1 - 2\gamma) - 2(\alpha - \gamma)(\gamma^2 - a_1\gamma + a_0)}{[\beta^2 + (\alpha - \gamma)^2]^2}\right]e^{-\gamma t}$ $+ \dfrac{\sqrt{(\alpha^2 - \beta^2 - a_1\alpha + a_0)^2 + \beta^2(a_1 - 2\alpha)^2}}{\beta[\beta^2 + (\alpha - \gamma)^2]}e^{-\alpha t}\sin(\beta t + \psi)$ $\psi = \tan^{-1}\dfrac{\beta(a_1 - 2\alpha)}{\alpha^2 - \beta^2 - a_1\alpha + a_0} - 2\tan^{-1}\dfrac{\beta}{\gamma - \alpha}$

159. $\dfrac{s^3 + a_2 s^2 + a_1 s + a_0}{(s+\gamma)^2[(s+\alpha)^2+\beta^2]}$

$$\left[\frac{-\gamma^3 + a_2\gamma^2 - a_1\gamma + a_0}{\beta^2+(\alpha-\gamma)^2}\,t + \frac{(3\gamma^2 - 2a_2\gamma + a_1)[\beta^2+\alpha(\alpha-\gamma)] - (\alpha-\gamma)(2a_0 - a_1\gamma + \gamma^3)}{[\beta^2+(\alpha-\gamma)^2]^2}\right]e^{-\gamma t}$$

$$+\;\frac{\sqrt{[(\beta^2-\alpha^2)(\alpha-a_2)+\alpha(2\beta^2-a_1)+a_0]^2+\beta^2[3\alpha^2-\beta^2-2a_2\alpha+a_1]^2}}{\beta[\beta^2+(\alpha-\gamma)^2]}\,e^{-\alpha t}\sin(\beta t+\psi)$$

$$\psi = \tan^{-1}\frac{\beta[3\alpha^2-\beta^2-2a_2\alpha+a_1]}{(\beta^2-\alpha^2)(\alpha-a_2)+\alpha(2\beta^2-a_1)+a_0} - 2\tan^{-1}\frac{\beta}{\gamma-\alpha}$$

---

160. $\dfrac{1}{s(s+\gamma)^2[(s+\alpha)^2+\beta^2]}$

$$\frac{1}{\gamma^2(\alpha^2+\beta^2)} - \left[\frac{t}{\gamma[(\alpha-\gamma)^2+\beta^2]} + \frac{[(\alpha-\gamma)^2+\beta^2]-2\gamma(\alpha-\gamma)}{\gamma^2[(\alpha-\gamma)^2+\beta^2]^2}\right]e^{-\gamma t}$$

$$+\;\frac{e^{-\alpha t}\sin(\beta t+\psi)}{\beta[\beta^2+(\alpha-\gamma)^2]\sqrt{\alpha^2+\beta^2}}$$

$$\psi = \tan^{-1}\frac{\beta}{\alpha} + 2\tan^{-1}\frac{\gamma-\alpha}{\beta}$$

---

161. $\dfrac{s+a_0}{s(s+\gamma)^2[(s+\alpha)^2+\beta^2]}$

$$\frac{a_0}{\gamma^2(\alpha^2+\beta^2)} + \left[\frac{(\gamma-a_0)t}{\gamma[(\alpha-\gamma)^2+\beta^2]} + \frac{2\gamma(\alpha-\gamma)(a_0-\gamma) - a_0[(\alpha-\gamma)^2+\beta^2]}{\gamma^2[(\alpha-\gamma)^2+\beta^2]^2}\right]e^{-\gamma t}$$

$$+\;\frac{e^{-\alpha t}}{\beta[(\gamma-\alpha)^2+\beta^2]}\sqrt{\frac{(a_0-\alpha)^2+\beta^2}{\alpha^2+\beta^2}}\,\sin(\beta t+\psi)$$

$$\psi = \tan^{-1}\frac{\beta}{\alpha} - 2\tan^{-1}\frac{\beta}{\gamma-\alpha} - \tan^{-1}\frac{\beta}{\alpha-a_0}$$

---

162. $\dfrac{s^2+a_1 s + a_0}{s(s+\gamma)^2[(s+\alpha)^2+\beta^2]}$

$$\frac{a_0}{\gamma^2(\alpha^2+\beta^2)} + \left[\frac{-\gamma^2+a_1\gamma-a_0}{\gamma[(\alpha-\gamma)^2+\beta^2]}\,t + \frac{[(\alpha-\gamma)^2+\beta^2](\gamma^2-a_0) + 2\gamma(\alpha-\gamma)(\gamma^2-a_1\gamma+a_0)}{\gamma^2[(\alpha-\gamma)^2+\beta^2]^2}\right]e^{-\gamma t}$$

$$+\;\frac{e^{-\alpha t}}{\beta[(\gamma-\alpha)^2+\beta^2]}\sqrt{\frac{(\alpha^2-\beta^2-a_1\alpha+a_0)^2+(2\alpha-a_1)^2\beta^2}{\alpha^2+\beta^2}}\,\sin(\beta t+\psi)$$

$$\psi = \tan^{-1}\frac{\alpha^2-\beta^2-a_1\alpha+a_0}{\beta(2\alpha-a_1)} + \tan^{-1}\frac{\beta}{\alpha} + \tan^{-1}\frac{\gamma-\alpha}{\beta} - \tan^{-1}\frac{\beta}{\gamma-\alpha}$$

335

	$F(s)$	$f(t)$

163.

$$F(s) = \frac{s^3 + a_2 s^2 + a_1 s + a_0}{s(s+\gamma)^2[(s+\alpha)^2 + \beta^2]}$$

$$f(t) = \frac{a_0}{\gamma^2(\alpha^2+\beta^2)} + \left[\frac{\gamma^3 - a_2\gamma^2 + a_1\gamma - a_0}{\gamma[(\alpha-\gamma)^2+\beta^2]}\,t + \frac{[(\alpha-\gamma)^2+\beta^2][\gamma^2(a_2-2\gamma)-a_0] + 2\gamma(\alpha-\gamma)[\gamma^2(a_2-\gamma)+(a_0-a_1\gamma)]}{\gamma^2[(\alpha-\gamma)^2+\beta^2]^2}\right]e^{-\gamma t}$$

$$+ \frac{e^{-\alpha t}}{\beta[(\gamma-\alpha)^2+\beta^2]}\sqrt{\frac{[(\alpha^2-\beta^2)(a_2-\alpha)+\alpha(2\beta^2-a_1)+a_0]^2 + \beta^2[3\alpha^2-\beta^2-2\alpha a_2+a_1]^2}{\alpha^2+\beta^2}}\,\sin(\beta t + \psi)$$

$$\psi = \tan^{-1}\frac{\beta(3\alpha^2-\beta^2-2\alpha a_2+a_1)}{\alpha(3\beta^2-\alpha^2)+a_2(\alpha^2-\beta^2)-a_1\alpha+a_0} + \tan^{-1}\frac{\alpha}{\beta} + 2\tan^{-1}\frac{\gamma-\alpha}{\beta}$$

164.

$$F(s) = \frac{1}{s^2(s+\gamma)^2[(s+\alpha)^2 + \beta^2]}$$

$$f(t) = \frac{t}{\gamma^2(\alpha^2+\beta^2)} - \frac{2(\alpha^2+\beta^2+\alpha\gamma)}{\gamma^3(\alpha^2+\beta^2)^2} + \left[\frac{t}{\gamma^2[(\alpha-\gamma)^2+\beta^2]} + \frac{2[(\alpha-\gamma)^2+\beta^2]-2\gamma(\alpha-\gamma)}{\gamma^3[(\alpha-\gamma)^2+\beta^2]^2}\right]e^{-\gamma t} + \frac{e^{-\alpha t}\sin(\beta t + \psi)}{\beta(\alpha^2+\beta^2)[(\gamma-\alpha)^2+\beta^2]}$$

$$\psi = \tan^{-1}\frac{\gamma-\alpha}{\beta} - \tan^{-1}\frac{\beta}{\gamma-\alpha} - \tan^{-1}\frac{\alpha}{\beta} + \tan^{-1}\frac{\beta}{\alpha}$$

165.

$$F(s) = \frac{s+a_0}{s^2(s+\gamma)^2[(s+\alpha)^2 + \beta^2]}$$

$$f(t) = \frac{a_0 t}{\gamma^2(\alpha^2+\beta^2)} + \frac{(\alpha^2+\beta^2)(\gamma-2a_0)-2\alpha a_0\gamma}{\gamma^3(\alpha^2+\beta^2)^2} + \left[\frac{(a_0-\gamma)t}{\gamma^2[(\alpha-\gamma)^2+\beta^2]} + \frac{(2a_0-\gamma)[(\alpha-\gamma)^2+\beta^2]-2\gamma(\alpha-\gamma)(a_0-\gamma)}{\gamma^3[(\alpha-\gamma)^2+\beta^2]^2}\right]e^{-\gamma t}$$

$$+ \frac{\sqrt{(a_0-\alpha)^2+\beta^2}}{\beta(\alpha^2+\beta^2)[(\gamma-\alpha)^2+\beta^2]}\,e^{-\alpha t}\sin(\beta t + \psi)$$

$$\psi = \tan^{-1}\frac{\beta}{a_0-\alpha} + \tan^{-1}\frac{\gamma-\alpha}{\beta} - \tan^{-1}\frac{\beta}{\gamma-\alpha} - \tan^{-1}\frac{\alpha}{\beta} + \tan^{-1}\frac{\beta}{\alpha}$$

166. $\dfrac{s^2 + a_1 s + a_0}{s^2(s+\gamma)^2[(s+\alpha)^2+\beta^2]}$

$$\frac{a_0 t}{\gamma^2(\alpha^2+\beta^2)} + \frac{(\alpha^2+\beta^2)(\gamma a_1 - 2a_0) - 2\alpha a_0\gamma}{\gamma^3(\alpha^2+\beta^2)^2}$$

$$+\ \frac{(\gamma^2 - a_1\gamma + a_0)t}{\gamma^2[(\alpha-\gamma)^2+\beta^2]} + \left[\frac{(2a_0 - a_1\gamma)[(\alpha-\gamma)^2+\beta^2] + 2\gamma(\gamma-\alpha)(\gamma^2 - a_1\gamma + a_0)}{\gamma^3[(\alpha-\gamma)^2+\beta^2]^2}\right]e^{-\gamma t}$$

$$+\ \frac{\sqrt{(\alpha^2-\beta^2 - a_1\alpha + a_0)^2 + (a_1 - 2\alpha)^2\beta^2}}{\beta(\alpha^2+\beta^2)[(\gamma-\alpha)^2+\beta^2]}\, e^{-\alpha t}\sin(\beta t + \psi)$$

$$\psi = \tan^{-1}\frac{\beta(a_1-2\alpha)}{\alpha^2-\beta^2 - a_1\alpha + a_0} + \tan^{-1}\frac{\gamma-\alpha}{\beta} - \tan^{-1}\frac{\beta}{\gamma-\alpha} - \tan^{-1}\frac{\alpha}{\beta} + \tan^{-1}\frac{\beta}{\alpha}$$

---

167. $\dfrac{s^3 + a_2 s^2 + a_1 s + a_0}{s^2(s+\gamma)^2[(s+\alpha)^2+\beta^2]}$

$$\frac{a_0 t}{\gamma^2(\alpha^2+\beta^2)} + \frac{(\alpha^2+\beta^2)(\gamma a_1 - 2a_0) - 2\alpha a_0\gamma}{\gamma^3(\alpha^2+\beta^2)^2} + \left[\frac{-\gamma^3 + a_2\gamma^2 - a_1\gamma + a_0}{\gamma^2[(\alpha-\gamma)^2+\beta^2]}\right]t$$

$$+\ \frac{[(\alpha-\gamma)^2+\beta^2](\gamma^3 - a_1\gamma + 2a_0) + 2\gamma(\gamma-\alpha)(-\gamma^3 + a_2\gamma^2 - a_1\gamma + a_0)}{\gamma^3[(\alpha-\gamma)^2+\beta^2]^2}\, e^{-\gamma t}$$

$$+\ \frac{\sqrt{[(\alpha^2-\beta^2)(a_2-\alpha) + \alpha(2\beta^2 - a_1) + a_0]^2 + [3\alpha^2 - \beta^2 - 2a_2\alpha + a_1]^2\beta^2}}{\beta(\alpha^2+\beta^2)[(\gamma-\alpha)^2+\beta^2]}\, e^{-\alpha t}\sin(\beta t + \psi)$$

$$\psi = \tan^{-1}\frac{\beta[3\alpha^2 - \beta^2 - 2a_2\alpha + a_1]}{(\alpha^2-\beta^2)(a_2-\alpha) + \alpha(2\beta^2 - a_1) + a_0} + \tan^{-1}\frac{\gamma-\alpha}{\beta} - \tan^{-1}\frac{\beta}{\gamma-\alpha} - \tan^{-1}\frac{\alpha}{\beta} + \tan^{-1}\frac{\beta}{\alpha}$$

---

168. $\dfrac{1}{(s+\lambda)(s+\gamma)^2[(s+\alpha)^2+\beta^2]}$

$$\frac{e^{-\lambda t}}{(\gamma-\lambda)^2[(\alpha-\lambda)^2+\beta^2]} + \left[\frac{t}{(\lambda-\gamma)[(\alpha-\gamma)^2+\beta^2]} + \frac{(\alpha-\gamma)^2+\beta^2 + 2(\lambda-\gamma)(\alpha-\gamma)}{(\lambda-\gamma)^2[(\alpha-\gamma)^2+\beta^2]^2}\right]e^{-\gamma t} + \frac{e^{-\alpha t}\sin(\beta t - \psi)}{\beta[\beta^2 + (\gamma-\alpha)^2]\sqrt{\beta^2 + (\lambda-\alpha)^2}}$$

$$\psi = \tan^{-1}\frac{\beta}{\lambda - \alpha} + 2\tan^{-1}\frac{\beta}{\gamma-\alpha}$$

$F(s)$	$f(t)$
169. $\dfrac{s + a_0}{(s + \lambda)(s + \gamma)^2[(s + \alpha)^2 + \beta^2]}$	$\dfrac{(a_0 - \lambda)e^{-\lambda t}}{(\gamma - \lambda)^2[(\alpha - \lambda)^2 + \beta^2]} + \left[\dfrac{(a_0 - \gamma)t}{(\lambda - \gamma)[(\alpha - \gamma)^2 + \beta^2]}\right.$ $\left. + \dfrac{(\lambda - a_0)[(\alpha - \gamma)^2 + \beta^2] - 2(a_0 - \gamma)(\alpha - \gamma)(\lambda - \gamma)}{(\lambda - \gamma)^2[(\alpha - \gamma)^2 + \beta^2]^2}\right]e^{-\gamma t}$ $+ \sqrt{\dfrac{\beta^2 + (a_0 - \alpha)^2}{\beta^2 + (\lambda - \alpha)^2}}\,\dfrac{e^{-\alpha t}\sin(\beta t + \psi)}{\beta[\beta^2 + (\gamma - \alpha)^2]}$ $\psi = \tan^{-1}\dfrac{\beta}{a_0 - \alpha} - \tan^{-1}\dfrac{\beta}{\lambda - \alpha} - 2\tan^{-1}\dfrac{\beta}{\gamma - \alpha}$
170. $\dfrac{s^2 + a_1 s + a_0}{(s + \lambda)(s + \gamma)^2[(s + \alpha)^2 + \beta^2]}$	$\dfrac{(\lambda^2 - a_1\lambda + a_0)e^{-\lambda t}}{(\gamma - \lambda)^2[(\alpha - \lambda)^2 + \beta^2]} + \left[\dfrac{(\gamma^2 - a_1\gamma + a_0)t}{(\lambda - \gamma)[(\alpha - \gamma)^2 + \beta^2]}\right.$ $\left. + \dfrac{[\gamma^2 + \lambda(a_1 - 2\gamma) - a_0][(\alpha - \gamma)^2 + \beta^2] - 2(\gamma^2 - a_1\gamma + a_0)(\alpha - \gamma)(\lambda - \gamma)}{(\lambda - \gamma)^2[(\alpha - \gamma)^2 + \beta^2]^2}\right]e^{-\gamma t}$ $+ \sqrt{\dfrac{(\alpha^2 - \beta^2 - a_1\alpha + a_0)^2 + \beta^2(a_1 - 2\alpha)^2}{\beta^2 + (\lambda - \alpha)^2}}\,\dfrac{e^{-\alpha t}\sin(\beta t + \psi)}{\beta[\beta^2 + (\gamma - \alpha)^2]}$ $\psi = \tan^{-1}\dfrac{\beta(a_1 - 2\alpha)}{\alpha^2 - \beta^2 - a_1\alpha + a_0} - \tan^{-1}\dfrac{\beta}{\lambda - \alpha} - 2\tan^{-1}\dfrac{\beta}{\gamma - \alpha}$

171. $\dfrac{s^3 + a_2 s^2 + a_1 s + a_0}{(s+\lambda)(s+\alpha)^2[(s+\alpha)^2 + \beta^2]}$

$$\frac{-\lambda^3 + a_2\lambda^2 - a_1\lambda + a_0}{(\gamma-\lambda)^2(\alpha-\lambda)^2 + \beta^2}e^{-\lambda t} + \left[\frac{-\gamma^3 + a_2\gamma^2 - a_1\gamma + a_0}{(\lambda-\gamma)[(\alpha-\gamma)^2+\beta^2]} + \frac{3\gamma^2 - 2a_2\gamma + a_1}{(\lambda-\gamma)[(\alpha-\gamma)^2+\beta^2]}\,t\right.$$

$$\left. - \frac{-\gamma^3 + a_2\gamma^2 - a_1\gamma + a_0}{(\lambda-\gamma)^2[(\alpha-\gamma)^2+\beta^2]} - \frac{2(-\gamma^3 + a_2\gamma^2 - a_1\gamma + a_0)(\alpha-\gamma)}{(\lambda-\gamma)[(\alpha-\gamma)^2+\beta^2]^2}\right]e^{-\gamma t}$$

$$+ \sqrt{\frac{[(\alpha^2-\beta^2)(a_2-\alpha) + \alpha(2\beta^2 - a_1) + a_0]^2 + \beta^2[3\alpha^2 - \beta^2 - 2\alpha a_2 + a_1]^2}{\beta^2 + (\lambda - \alpha)^2}}\cdot\frac{e^{-\alpha t}\sin(\beta t + \psi)}{\beta[\beta^2 + (\gamma-\alpha)^2]}$$

$$\psi = \tan^{-1}\frac{\beta[3\alpha^2 - \beta^2 - 2\alpha a_2 + a_1]}{\alpha(3\beta^2 - \alpha^2) + a_2(\alpha^2 - \beta^2) - a_1\alpha + a_0} - \tan^{-1}\frac{\beta}{\lambda - \alpha} - 2\tan^{-1}\frac{\beta}{\gamma - \alpha}$$

172. $\dfrac{1}{(s+\alpha)^2(s+\gamma)^2}$

$$\left[\frac{t}{(\alpha-\gamma)^2} - \frac{2}{(\alpha-\gamma)^3}\right]e^{-\gamma t} + \left[\frac{t}{(\gamma-\alpha)^2} - \frac{2}{(\gamma-\alpha)^3}\right]e^{-\alpha t}$$

173. $\dfrac{s+a_0}{(s+\alpha)^2(s+\gamma)^2}$

$$\left[\frac{a_0-\gamma}{(\alpha-\gamma)^2}\,t + \frac{\alpha+\gamma-2a_0}{(\alpha-\gamma)^3}\right]e^{-\gamma t} + \left[\frac{a_0-\alpha}{(\gamma-\alpha)^2}\,t + \frac{\alpha+\gamma-2a_0}{(\gamma-\alpha)^3}\right]e^{-\alpha t}$$

174. $\dfrac{s^2 + a_1 s + a_0}{(s+\alpha)^2(s+\gamma)^2}$

$$\left[\frac{\gamma^2 - a_1\gamma + a_0}{(\alpha-\gamma)^2}\,t - \frac{a_1(\alpha+\gamma) - 2(\alpha\gamma + a_0)}{(\gamma-\alpha)^3}\right]e^{-\gamma t}$$
$$+ \left[\frac{\alpha^2 - a_1\alpha + a_0}{(\gamma-\alpha)^2}\,t + \frac{a_1(\alpha+\gamma) - 2(\alpha\gamma + a_0)}{(\gamma-\alpha)^3}\right]e^{-\alpha t}$$

175. $\dfrac{s^3 + a_2 s^2 + a_1 s + a_0}{(s+\alpha)^2(s+\gamma)^2}$

$$\left[\frac{-\gamma^3 + a_2\gamma^2 - a_1\gamma + a_0}{(\alpha-\gamma)^2}\,t + \frac{\gamma^2(3\alpha-\gamma) - 2a_2\alpha\gamma + a_1(\alpha+\gamma) - 2a_0}{(\alpha-\gamma)^3}\right]e^{-\gamma t}$$
$$+ \left[\frac{-\alpha^3 + a_2\alpha^2 - a_1\alpha + a_0}{(\gamma-\alpha)^2}\,t + \frac{\alpha^2(3\gamma-\alpha) - 2a_2\gamma\alpha + a_1(\gamma+\alpha) - 2a_0}{(\gamma-\alpha)^3}\right]e^{-\alpha t}$$

$F(s)$	$f(t)$
176. $\dfrac{1}{s(s+\alpha)^2(s+\gamma)^2}$	$\dfrac{1}{\alpha^2\gamma^2} + \left[-\dfrac{t}{\alpha(\gamma-\alpha)^2} + \dfrac{3\alpha-\gamma}{\alpha^2(\gamma-\alpha)^3} \right]e^{-\alpha t} + \left[-\dfrac{t}{\gamma(\alpha-\gamma)^2} + \dfrac{3\gamma-\alpha}{\gamma^2(\alpha-\gamma)^3} \right]e^{-\gamma t}$
177. $\dfrac{s+a_0}{s(s+\alpha)^2(s+\gamma)^2}$	$\dfrac{a_0}{\alpha^2\gamma^2} + \left[\dfrac{\alpha-a_0}{\alpha(\gamma-\alpha)^2}\,t - \dfrac{2\alpha^2+a_0\gamma-3a_0\alpha}{\alpha^2(\gamma-\alpha)^3} \right]e^{-\alpha t} + \left[\dfrac{\gamma-a_0}{\gamma(\alpha-\gamma)^2}\,t - \dfrac{2\gamma^2-3a_0\gamma+a_0\alpha}{\gamma^2(\alpha-\gamma)^3} \right]e^{-\gamma t}$
178. $\dfrac{s^2+a_1 s+a_0}{s(s+\alpha)^2(s+\gamma)^2}$	$\dfrac{a_0}{\alpha^2\gamma^2} + \left[\dfrac{\alpha^2-a_1\alpha+a_0}{-\alpha(\gamma-\alpha)^2}\,t + \dfrac{(\gamma-\alpha)(\alpha^2-a_0)+2\alpha(\alpha^2-a_1\alpha+a_0)}{-\alpha^2(\gamma-\alpha)^3} \right]e^{-\alpha t}$ $+ \left[\dfrac{\gamma^2-a_1\gamma+a_0}{-\gamma(\alpha-\gamma)^2}\,t + \dfrac{(\alpha-\gamma)(\gamma^2-a_0)+2\gamma(\gamma^2-a_1\gamma+a_0)}{-\gamma^2(\alpha-\gamma)^3} \right]e^{-\gamma t}$
179. $\dfrac{s^3+a_2 s^2+a_1 s+a_0}{s(s+\alpha)^2(s+\gamma)^2}$	$\dfrac{a_0}{\alpha^2\gamma^2} + \left[\dfrac{\alpha^3-a_2\alpha^2+a_1\alpha-a_0}{\alpha(\gamma-\alpha)^2}\,t + \dfrac{\alpha^2[a_2(\alpha+\gamma)-2(a_1+\alpha\gamma)]+a_0(3\alpha-\gamma)}{\alpha^2(\gamma-\alpha)^3} \right]e^{-\alpha t}$ $+ \left[\dfrac{\gamma^3-a_2\gamma^2+a_1\gamma-a_0}{\gamma(\alpha-\gamma)^2}\,t + \dfrac{\gamma^2[a_2(\alpha+\gamma)-2(a_1+\alpha\gamma)]+a_0(3\gamma-\alpha)}{\gamma^2(\alpha-\gamma)^3} \right]e^{-\gamma t}$
180. $\dfrac{1}{s^2(s+\alpha)^2(s+\gamma)^2}$	$\dfrac{1}{\alpha^2\gamma^2}\left[t - \dfrac{2(\alpha+\gamma)}{\alpha\gamma} \right] + \left[\dfrac{t}{\alpha^2(\gamma-\alpha)^2} + \dfrac{2(\gamma-2\alpha)}{\alpha^3(\gamma-\alpha)^3} \right]e^{-\alpha t} + \left[\dfrac{t}{\gamma^2(\alpha-\gamma)^2} + \dfrac{2(\alpha-2\gamma)}{\gamma^3(\alpha-\gamma)^3} \right]e^{-\gamma t}$
181. $\dfrac{s+a_0}{s^2(s+\alpha)^2(s+\gamma)^2}$	$\dfrac{1}{\alpha^2\gamma^2}\left[a_0 t + 1 - \dfrac{2a_0(\alpha+\gamma)}{\alpha\gamma} \right] + \left[\dfrac{(a_0-\alpha)t}{\alpha^2(\gamma-\alpha)^2} + \dfrac{\alpha(3\alpha-\gamma)+2a_0(\gamma-2\alpha)}{\alpha^3(\gamma-\alpha)^3} \right]e^{-\alpha t}$ $+ \left[\dfrac{(a_0-\gamma)t}{\gamma^2(\alpha-\gamma)^2} + \dfrac{\gamma(3\gamma-\alpha)+2a_0(\alpha-2\gamma)}{\gamma^3(\alpha-\gamma)^3} \right]e^{-\gamma t}$

182.

$$\frac{s^2 + a_1 s + a_0}{s^2(s+\alpha)^2(s+\gamma)^2}$$

$$\frac{1}{\alpha^2\gamma^2}\left[a_0 t + a_1 - \frac{2a_0(\alpha+\gamma)}{\alpha\gamma}\right] + \left[\frac{\alpha^2 - a_1\alpha + a_0}{\alpha^2(\gamma-\alpha)^2}\,t + \frac{(\gamma-\alpha)(2a_0 - a_1\alpha) - 2\alpha(\alpha^2 + a_0 - a_1\alpha)}{\alpha^3(\gamma-\alpha)^3}\right]e^{-\alpha t}$$

$$+ \left[\frac{\gamma^2 - a_1\gamma + a_0}{\gamma^2(\alpha-\gamma)^2}\,t + \frac{(\alpha-\gamma)(2a_0 - a_1\gamma) - 2\gamma(\gamma^2 + a_0 - a_1\gamma)}{\gamma^3(\alpha-\gamma)^3}\right]e^{-\gamma t}$$

183.

$$\frac{s^3 + a_2 s^2 + a_1 s + a_0}{s^2(s+\alpha)^2(s+\gamma)^2}$$

$$\frac{1}{\alpha^2\gamma^2}\left[a_0 t + a_1 - \frac{2a_0(\alpha+\gamma)}{\alpha\gamma}\right]$$

$$+\left[\frac{-\alpha^3 + a_2\alpha^2 - a_1\alpha + a_0}{\alpha^2(\gamma-\alpha)^2}\,t + \frac{(\gamma-\alpha)(\alpha^3 - a_1\alpha + 2a_0) - 2\alpha\{(a_0 - a_1\alpha) + \alpha^2(a_2 - \alpha)\}}{\alpha^3(\gamma-\alpha)^3}\right]e^{-\alpha t}$$

$$+\left[\frac{-\gamma^3 + a_2\gamma^2 - a_1\gamma + a_0}{\gamma^2(\alpha-\gamma)^2}\,t + \frac{(\alpha-\gamma)(\gamma^3 - a_1\gamma + 2a_0) - 2\gamma\{(a_0 - a_1\gamma) + \gamma^2(a_2 - \gamma)\}}{\gamma^3(\alpha-\gamma)^3}\right]e^{-\gamma t}$$

184.

$$\frac{1}{(s+\delta)(s+\alpha)^2(s+\gamma)^2}$$

$$\frac{e^{-\delta t}}{(\alpha-\delta)^2(\gamma-\delta)^2} + \left[\frac{t}{(\delta-\alpha)(\gamma-\alpha)^2} + \frac{3\alpha - (\gamma + 2\delta)}{(\delta-\alpha)^2(\gamma-\alpha)^3}\right]e^{-\alpha t}$$

$$+ \left[\frac{t}{(\delta-\gamma)(\alpha-\gamma)^2} + \frac{3\gamma - (\alpha + 2\delta)}{(\delta-\gamma)^2(\alpha-\gamma)^3}\right]e^{-\gamma t}$$

185.

$$\frac{s + a_0}{(s+\delta)(s+\alpha)^2(s+\gamma)^2}$$

$$\frac{a_0 - \delta}{(\alpha-\delta)^2(\gamma-\delta)^2}\,e^{-\delta t} + \left[\frac{a_0 - \alpha}{(\delta-\alpha)(\gamma-\alpha)^2}\,t + \frac{(\alpha - 2a_0)(\delta-\alpha) - a_0(\gamma-\alpha) + (\gamma\delta - \alpha^2)}{(\delta-\alpha)^2(\gamma-\alpha)^3}\right]e^{-\alpha t}$$

$$+ \left[\frac{a_0 - \gamma}{(\delta-\gamma)(\alpha-\gamma)^2}\,t + \frac{(\gamma - 2a_0)(\delta-\gamma) - a_0(\alpha-\gamma) + (\alpha\delta - \gamma^2)}{(\delta-\gamma)^2(\alpha-\gamma)^3}\right]e^{-\gamma t}$$

186.

$$\frac{s^2 + a_1 s + a_0}{(s+\delta)(s+\alpha)^2(s+\gamma)^2}$$

$$\frac{\delta^2 - a_1\delta + a_0}{(\alpha-\delta)^2(\gamma-\delta)^2}\,e^{-\delta t} + \left[\frac{(\alpha^2 - a_1\alpha + a_0)t}{(\delta-\alpha)(\gamma-\alpha)^2} + \frac{2\alpha\gamma - a_1(\alpha+\gamma) + 2a_0}{(\alpha-\delta)(\gamma-\alpha)^2} \cdot \frac{\alpha^2 - a_1\alpha + a_0}{(\delta-\alpha)^2(\gamma-\alpha)^2}\right]e^{-\alpha t}$$

$$+ \left[\frac{(\gamma^2 - a_1\gamma + a_0)t}{(\delta-\gamma)(\alpha-\gamma)^2} + \frac{2\alpha\gamma - a_1(\alpha+\gamma) + 2a_0}{(\delta-\gamma)^2(\alpha-\gamma)^2} \cdot \frac{\gamma^2 - a_1\gamma + a_0}{(\delta-\gamma)^2(\alpha-\gamma)^3}\right]e^{-\gamma t}$$

	$F(s)$	$f(t)$
187.	$\dfrac{s^3 + a_2 s^2 + a_1 s + a_0}{(s+\delta)(s+\alpha)^2(s+\gamma)^2}$	$\dfrac{-\delta^3 + a_2\delta^2 - a_1\delta + a_0}{(\alpha-\delta)^2(\gamma-\delta)^2}\,e^{-\delta t}$

$$+ \left[\frac{\alpha^3 + a_2\alpha^2 - a_1\alpha - a_0}{(\alpha-\delta)(\gamma-\alpha)^2}\,t + \frac{3\alpha^2 - 2a_2\alpha + a_1}{(\delta-\alpha)(\gamma-\alpha)^2} + \frac{(\alpha^3 - a_2\alpha^2 + a_1\alpha - a_0)(2\delta + \gamma - 3\alpha)}{(\delta-\alpha)^2(\gamma-\alpha)^3}\right]e^{-\alpha t}$$

$$+ \left[\frac{\gamma^3 + a_2\gamma^2 - a_1\gamma - a_0}{(\gamma-\delta)(\alpha-\gamma)^2}\,t + \frac{3\gamma^2 - 2a_2\gamma + a_1}{(\delta-\gamma)(\alpha-\gamma)^2} + \frac{(\gamma^3 - a_2\gamma^2 + a_1\gamma - a_0)(2\delta + \alpha - 3\gamma)}{(\delta-\gamma)^2(\alpha-\gamma)^3}\right]e^{-\gamma t}$$

	$F(s)$	$f(t)$
188.	$\dfrac{1}{(s^2+\beta^2)(s+\alpha)^2(s+\gamma)^2}$	$\left[\dfrac{t}{(\alpha^2+\beta^2)(\gamma-\alpha)^2} - \dfrac{2\{(\alpha^2+\beta^2)-\alpha(\gamma-\alpha)\}}{(\alpha^2+\beta^2)^2(\gamma-\alpha)^3}\right]e^{-\alpha t}$

$$+ \left[\frac{t}{(\gamma^2+\beta^2)(\alpha-\gamma)^2} - \frac{2\{(\gamma^2+\beta^2)-\gamma(\alpha-\gamma)\}}{(\gamma^2+\beta^2)^2(\alpha-\gamma)^3}\right]e^{-\gamma t}$$

$$+ \frac{\sin(\beta t + \psi)}{\beta(\alpha^2+\beta^2)(\gamma^2+\beta^2)} \qquad \psi = 2\tan^{-1}\frac{\alpha}{\beta} + 2\tan^{-1}\frac{\gamma}{\beta}$$

	$F(s)$	$f(t)$
189.	$\dfrac{s+a_0}{(s^2+\beta^2)(s+\alpha)^2(s+\gamma)^2}$	$\left[\dfrac{(a_0-\alpha)t}{(\alpha^2+\beta^2)(\gamma-\alpha)^2} + \dfrac{\alpha+\gamma-2a_0}{(\alpha^2+\beta^2)(\gamma-\alpha)^3} + \dfrac{2\alpha(a_0-\alpha)}{(\alpha^2+\beta^2)^2(\gamma-\alpha)^2}\right]e^{-\alpha t}$

$$+ \left[\frac{(a_0-\gamma)t}{(\gamma^2+\beta^2)(\alpha-\gamma)^2} + \frac{\gamma+\alpha-2a_0}{(\gamma^2+\beta^2)(\alpha-\gamma)^3} + \frac{2\gamma(a_0-\gamma)}{(\gamma^2+\beta^2)^2(\alpha-\gamma)^2}\right]e^{-\gamma t} + \frac{\sqrt{a_0^2+\beta^2}}{\beta(\beta^2+\alpha^2)(\beta^2+\gamma^2)}$$

$$\times \sin(\beta t + \psi) + $$

$$\psi = \tan^{-1}\frac{\beta}{a_0} + 2\tan^{-1}\frac{\alpha}{\beta} + 2\tan^{-1}\frac{\gamma}{\beta}$$

190. $\dfrac{s^2 + a_1 s + a_0}{(s^2 + \beta^2)(s + \alpha)^2(s + \gamma)^2}$

$$\left[\frac{(\alpha^2 - a_1\alpha + a_0)t}{(\alpha^2 + \beta^2)(\gamma - \alpha)^2} + \frac{\alpha(a_1 - 2\gamma) + a_1\gamma - 2a_0}{(\alpha^2 + \beta^2)^2(\gamma - \alpha)^3} + \frac{2\alpha(\alpha^2 - a_1\alpha + a_0)}{(\alpha^2 + \beta^2)^2(\gamma - \alpha)^2} \right] e^{-\alpha t}$$

$$+ \left[\frac{(\gamma^2 - a_1\gamma + a_0)t}{(\gamma^2 + \beta^2)(\alpha - \gamma)^2} + \frac{\gamma(a_1 - 2\alpha) + a_1\alpha - 2a_0}{(\gamma^2 + \beta^2)^2(\alpha - \gamma)^2} + \frac{2\gamma(\gamma^2 - a_1\gamma + a_0)}{(\gamma^2 + \beta^2)^2(\alpha - \gamma)^3} \right] e^{-\gamma t}$$

$$+ \frac{\sqrt{a_1^2\beta^2 + (a_0 - \beta^2)^2}}{\beta(\beta^2 + \alpha^2)(\beta^2 + \gamma^2)} \times \sin(\beta t + \psi)$$

$$\psi = \tan^{-1}\frac{a_1\beta}{a_0 - \beta^2} + 2\tan^{-1}\frac{\alpha}{\beta} + 2\tan^{-1}\frac{\gamma}{\beta}$$

191. $\dfrac{s^3 + a_2 s^2 + a_1 s + a_0}{(s^2 + \beta^2)(s + \alpha)^2(s + \gamma)^2}$

$$\left[\frac{(-\alpha^3 + a_2\alpha^2 - a_1\alpha + a_0)t}{(\alpha^2 + \beta^2)(\gamma - \alpha)^2} - \frac{\alpha^3 + \gamma\alpha(2a_2 - 3\alpha) - a_1(\gamma + \alpha) + 2a_0}{(\alpha^2 + \beta^2)(\gamma - \alpha)^3} + \frac{2\alpha(-\alpha^3 + a_2\alpha^2 - a_1\alpha + a_0)}{(\alpha^2 + \beta^2)^2(\gamma - \alpha)^2} \right] e^{-\alpha t}$$

$$+ \left[\frac{(\gamma^3 + a_2\gamma^2 - a_1\gamma + a_0)t}{(\gamma^2 + \beta^2)(\alpha - \gamma)^2} - \frac{\gamma^3 + \gamma\alpha(2a_2 - 3\gamma) - a_1(\gamma + \alpha) + 2a_0}{(\gamma^2 + \beta^2)^2(\alpha - \gamma)^3} + \frac{2\gamma(-\gamma^3 + a_2\gamma^2 - a_1\gamma + a_0)}{(\gamma^2 + \beta^2)^2(\alpha - \gamma)^2} \right] e^{-\gamma t}$$

$$+ \frac{\sqrt{(a_0 - a_2\beta^2)^2 + \beta^2(a_1 - \beta^2)^2}}{\beta(\beta^2 + \alpha^2)(\beta^2 + \gamma^2)} \sin(\beta t + \psi)$$

$$\psi = \tan^{-1}\frac{\beta(a_1 - \beta^2)}{a_0 - a_2\beta^2} + 2\tan^{-1}\frac{\alpha}{\beta} + 2\tan^{-1}\frac{\gamma}{\beta}$$

192. $\dfrac{1}{[(s+\alpha)^2 + \beta^2](s+\lambda)^2(s+\gamma)^2}$

$$\left[\frac{t}{[(\alpha - \lambda)^2 + \beta^2](\gamma - \lambda)^2} - \frac{2}{[(\alpha - \lambda)^2 + \beta^2][(\gamma - \lambda)]^3} - \frac{2(\alpha - \lambda)}{[(\alpha - \lambda)^2 + \beta^2]^2(\gamma - \lambda)^2} \right] e^{-\lambda t}$$

$$+ \frac{e^{-\alpha t}\sin(\beta t + \psi)}{\beta[(\lambda - \alpha)^2 + \beta^2][(\gamma - \alpha)^2 + \beta^2]}$$

$$\left[\frac{t}{[(\alpha - \gamma)^2 + \beta^2](\lambda - \gamma)^2} - \frac{2}{[(\alpha - \gamma)^2 + \beta^2](\lambda - \gamma)} - \frac{2(\alpha - \gamma)}{[(\alpha - \gamma)^2 + \beta^2]^2(\lambda - \gamma)^3} \frac{\beta}{\alpha - \gamma} \right] e^{-\gamma t}$$

$$\psi = 2\tan^{-1}\frac{\beta}{\alpha - \lambda} + 2\tan^{-1}\frac{\beta}{\alpha - \gamma}$$

$F(s)$	$f(t)$
193. $\dfrac{s + a_0}{[(s+\alpha)^2 + \beta^2](s+\lambda)^2(s+\gamma)^2}$	$\left[\dfrac{(a_0 - \lambda)t}{[(\alpha - \lambda)^2 + \beta^2](\gamma - \lambda)^2} + \dfrac{1}{[(\alpha - \lambda)^2 + \beta^2](\gamma - \lambda)^2} - \dfrac{2(a_0 - \lambda)}{[(\alpha - \lambda)^2 + \beta^2](\gamma - \lambda)^3}\right.$ $\left. - \dfrac{2(a_0 - \lambda)(\alpha - \lambda)}{[(\alpha - \lambda)^2 + \beta^2]^2(\gamma - \lambda)^2}\right] e^{-\lambda t} + \left[\dfrac{(a_0 - \gamma)t}{[(\alpha - \gamma)^2 + \beta^2](\lambda - \gamma)^2} + \dfrac{1}{[(\alpha - \gamma)^2 + \beta^2](\lambda - \gamma)^2}\right.$ $\left. - \dfrac{2(a_0 - \gamma)}{[(\alpha - \gamma)^2 + \beta^2](\lambda - \gamma)^3} - \dfrac{2(a_0 - \gamma)(\alpha - \gamma)}{[(\alpha - \gamma)^2 + \beta^2]^2(\lambda - \gamma)^2}\right] e^{-\gamma t}$ $+ \dfrac{\sqrt{\beta^2 + (a_0 - \alpha)^2}}{\beta[(\lambda - \alpha)^2 + \beta^2][(\gamma - \alpha)^2 + \beta^2]} e^{-\alpha t}\sin(\beta t + \psi)$ $\psi = \tan^{-1}\dfrac{\beta}{a_0 - \alpha} + 2\tan^{-1}\dfrac{\beta}{\alpha - \lambda} + 2\tan^{-1}\dfrac{\beta}{\alpha - \gamma}$
194. $\dfrac{s^2 + a_1 s + a_0}{[(s+\alpha)^2 + \beta^2](s+\lambda)^2(s+\gamma)^2}$	$\left[\dfrac{(\lambda^2 - a_1\lambda + a_0)t}{[(\alpha - \lambda)^2 + \beta^2](\gamma - \lambda)^2} + \dfrac{a_1 - 2\lambda}{[(\alpha - \lambda)^2 + \beta^2](\gamma - \lambda)^2} - \dfrac{2(\lambda^2 - a_1\lambda + a_0)}{[(\alpha - \lambda)^2 + \beta^2](\gamma - \lambda)^3}\right.$ $\left. - \dfrac{2(\alpha - \lambda)(\lambda^2 - a_1\lambda + a_0)}{[(\alpha - \lambda)^2 + \beta^2]^2(\gamma - \lambda)^2}\right] e^{-\lambda t} + \left[\dfrac{(\gamma^2 - a_1\gamma + a_0)t}{[(\alpha - \gamma)^2 + \beta^2](\lambda - \gamma)^2} + \dfrac{a_1 - 2\gamma}{[(\alpha - \gamma)^2 + \beta^2](\lambda - \gamma)^2}\right.$ $\left. - \dfrac{2(\gamma^2 - a_1\gamma + a_0)}{[(\alpha - \gamma)^2 + \beta^2](\lambda - \gamma)^3} - \dfrac{2(\alpha - \gamma)(\gamma^2 - a_1\gamma + a_0)}{[(\alpha - \gamma)^2 + \beta^2]^2(\lambda - \gamma)^2}\right] e^{-\gamma t}$ $+ \dfrac{\sqrt{[\alpha(\alpha - a_1) - \beta^2 + a_0]^2 + \beta^2[a_1 - 2\alpha]^2}}{\beta[(\lambda - \alpha)^2 + \beta^2][(\gamma - \alpha)^2 + \beta^2]} e^{-\alpha t}\sin(\beta t + \psi)$ $\psi = \tan^{-1}\dfrac{\beta(a_1 - 2\alpha)}{\alpha(\alpha - a_1) - \beta^2 + a_0} + 2\tan^{-1}\dfrac{\beta}{\alpha - \lambda} + 2\tan^{-1}\dfrac{\beta}{\alpha - \gamma}$

195. $\dfrac{s^3 + a_2 s^2 + a_1 s + a_0}{[(s+\alpha)^2 + \beta^2](s+\lambda)^2(s+\gamma)^2}$

$$\left[\frac{-\lambda^3 + a_2\lambda^2 - a_1\lambda + a_0}{[(\alpha-\lambda)^2 + \beta^2](\gamma-\lambda)^2}\,t + \frac{3\lambda^2 - 2a_2\lambda + a_1}{[(\alpha-\lambda)^2+\beta^2](\gamma-\lambda)^2} - \frac{2(-\lambda^3+a_2\lambda^2-a_1\lambda+a_0)}{[(\alpha-\lambda)^2+\beta^2](\gamma-\lambda)^3}\right.$$

$$\left. - \frac{2(\alpha-\lambda)(-\lambda^3+a_2\lambda^2-a_1\lambda+a_0)}{[(\alpha-\lambda)^2+\beta^2]^2(\gamma-\lambda)^2}\right]e^{-\lambda t} + \left[\frac{-\gamma^3+a_2\gamma^2-a_1\gamma+a_0}{[(\alpha-\gamma)^2+\beta^2](\lambda-\gamma)^2}\,t + \frac{3\gamma^2-2a_2\gamma+a_1}{[(\alpha-\gamma)^2+\beta^2](\lambda-\gamma)^2}\right.$$

$$\left. - \frac{2(\alpha-\gamma)(-\gamma^3+a_2\gamma^2-a_1\gamma+a_0)}{[(\alpha-\gamma)^2+\beta^2]^2(\lambda-\gamma)^2} - \frac{2(-\gamma^3+a_2\gamma^2-a_1\gamma+a_0)}{[(\alpha-\gamma)^2+\beta^2](\lambda-\gamma)^3}\right]e^{-\gamma t}$$

$$+ \frac{\sqrt{[\alpha^2(a_2-\alpha)+\beta^2(3\alpha-a_2)-a_1\alpha+a_0]^2 + \beta^2[\alpha(3\alpha-2a_2)-\beta^2+a_1]^2}}{\beta[(\lambda-\alpha)^2+\beta^2][(\gamma-\alpha)^2+\beta^2]}\,e^{-\alpha t}\sin(\beta t + \psi)$$

$$\psi = \tan^{-1}\frac{\beta[\alpha(3\alpha-2a_2)-\beta^2+a_1]}{\alpha^2(a_2-\alpha)+\beta^2(3\alpha-a_2)-a_1\alpha+a_0} + 2\tan^{-1}\frac{\beta}{\alpha-\lambda} + 2\tan^{-1}\frac{\beta}{\alpha-\gamma}$$

196. $\dfrac{1}{[(s+\alpha)^2+\beta^2]^2}$

$$\frac{1}{2\beta^3}e^{-\alpha t}(\sin\beta t - \beta t\cos\beta t)$$

197. $\dfrac{s+a_0}{[(s+\alpha)^2+\beta^2]^2}$

$$\frac{e^{-\alpha t}}{2\beta^3}[(a_0-\alpha+\beta^2 t)\sin\beta t - (a_0-\alpha)\beta t\cos\beta t]$$

198. $\dfrac{s^2+a_1 s+a_0}{[(s+\alpha)^2+\beta^2]^2}$

$$\frac{e^{-\alpha t}}{2\beta^3}\Big[[(\alpha^2+\beta^2)-(a_1\alpha-a_0)+(a_1-2\alpha)\beta^2 t]\sin\beta t - [(\alpha^2-\beta^2)-(a_1\alpha-a_0)]\beta t\cos\beta t\Big]$$

199. $\dfrac{s^3+a_2 s^2+a_1 s+a_0}{[(s+\alpha)^2+\beta^2]^2}$

$$\frac{e^{-\alpha t}}{2\beta^3}\Big\{[(\alpha^2+\beta^2)(a_2-\alpha)-\alpha(a_1+2\beta^2)+a_0+\beta^4 t(3\alpha^2-\beta^2-2a_2\alpha+a_1)]\sin\beta t$$

$$+ [2\beta^3 - \beta t[\alpha(3\beta^2-\alpha^2)+a_2(\alpha^2-\beta^2)-a_1\alpha+a_0]]\cos\beta t\Big\}$$

F(s)	f(t)
200. $\dfrac{\varphi(s)}{[(s+\alpha)^2+\beta^2]^2}$	$\dfrac{e^{-\alpha t}}{2\beta^3}\left[(\varphi_2-\beta\varphi_3)\cos\beta t+(\varphi_1+\beta\varphi_4)\sin\beta t+\beta(t\varphi_2\sin\beta t-\varphi_1 t\cos\beta t)\right]$ $\varphi(-\alpha+j\beta)=\varphi_1+j\varphi_2 \qquad \varphi'(-\alpha+j\beta)=\varphi_3+j\varphi_4$
201. $\dfrac{1}{(s^2+\beta^2)^2}$	$\dfrac{1}{2\beta^3}(\sin\beta t-\beta t\cos\beta t)$
202. $\dfrac{s+a_0}{(s^2+\beta^2)^2}$	$\dfrac{1}{2\beta^3}\left([a_0+\beta^2 t]\sin\beta t-a_0\beta t\cos\beta t\right)$
203. $\dfrac{s^2+a_1s+a_0}{(s^2+\beta^2)^2}$	$\dfrac{1}{2\beta^3}\left[[a_0+\beta^2(1+a_1 t)]\sin\beta t-(a_0-\beta^2)\beta t\cos\beta t\right]$
204. $\dfrac{1}{s(s^2+\beta^2)^2}$	$\dfrac{1}{\beta^4}(1-\cos\beta t)-\dfrac{1}{2\beta^3}t\sin\beta t$
205. $\dfrac{s+a_0}{s(s^2+\beta^2)^2}$	$\dfrac{a_0}{\beta^4}-\dfrac{\beta^2 t+2a_0}{2\beta^4}\cos\beta t-\dfrac{a_0 t-1}{2\beta^3}\sin\beta t$
206. $\dfrac{s^2+a_1s+a_0}{s(s^2+\beta^2)^2}$	$\dfrac{a_0}{\beta^4}-\dfrac{1}{2\beta^3}\sqrt{a_1^2\beta^2+(a_0-\beta^2)^2}\,t\sin(\beta t+\psi_1)-\dfrac{1}{2\beta^4}\sqrt{4a_0^2+a_1^2\beta^2}\cos(\beta t+\psi_2)$ $\psi_1=\tan^{-1}\dfrac{a_1\beta}{a_0-\beta^2} \qquad \psi_2=\tan^{-1}\dfrac{a_1\beta}{2a_0}$

207. $\dfrac{1}{s^2(s^2+\beta^2)^2}$

$$\dfrac{t}{\beta^4} + \dfrac{t}{2\beta^4}\cos\beta t + \dfrac{3}{2\beta^5}\sin\beta t$$

208. $\dfrac{s+a_0}{s^2(s^2+\beta^2)^2}$

$$\dfrac{a_0 t + 1}{\beta^4} + \dfrac{\sqrt{a_0^2+\beta^2}}{2\beta^4}\, t\cos(\beta t+\psi_1) - \dfrac{\sqrt{9a_0^2+4\beta^2}}{2\beta^5}\sin(\beta t+\psi_2)$$

$$\psi_1 = \tan^{-1}\dfrac{\beta}{a_0} \qquad \psi_2=\tan^{-1}\dfrac{2\beta}{3a_0}$$

209. $\dfrac{s^2+a_1 s + a_0}{s^2(s^2+\beta^2)^2}$

$$\dfrac{a_0 t + a_1}{\beta^4} + \dfrac{\sqrt{(a_0-\beta^2)^2+a_1^2\beta^2}}{2\beta^4}\, t\cos(\beta t+\psi_1) - \dfrac{\sqrt{(3a_0-\beta^2)^2+4a_1^2\beta^2}}{2\beta^5}\sin(\beta t+\psi_2)$$

$$\psi_1 = \tan^{-1}\dfrac{a_1\beta}{a_0-\beta^2} \qquad \psi_2=\tan^{-1}\dfrac{2a_1\beta}{3a_0-\beta^2}$$

210. $\dfrac{s^3+a_2 s^2+a_1 s+a_0}{s^2(s^2+\beta^2)^2}$

$$\dfrac{a_0 t + a_1}{\beta^4} + \dfrac{\sqrt{(a_0-\beta^2 a_2)^2+\beta^2(a_1-\beta^2)^2}}{2\beta^4}\, t\cos(\beta t+\psi_1) - \dfrac{\sqrt{(3a_0-a_2\beta^2)^2+4a_1^2\beta^2}}{2\beta^5}\sin(\beta t+\psi_2)$$

$$\psi_1 = \tan^{-1}\dfrac{\beta(a_1-\beta^2)}{a_0-a_2\beta^2} \qquad \psi_2=\tan^{-1}\dfrac{2a_1\beta}{3a_0-a_2\beta^2}$$

211. $\dfrac{1}{(s+\alpha)(s^2+\beta^2)^2}$

$$\dfrac{e^{-\alpha t}}{(\alpha^2+\beta^2)^2} - \dfrac{t\sin(\beta t+\psi_1)}{2\beta^2\sqrt{\alpha^2+\beta^2}} - \dfrac{\sqrt{\alpha^2+4\beta^2}}{2\beta^3(\alpha^2+\beta^2)}\cos(\beta t+\psi_2)$$

$$\psi_1 = \tan^{-1}\dfrac{\alpha}{\beta} \qquad \psi_2=\tan^{-1}\dfrac{\alpha(\alpha^2+3\beta^2)}{2\beta^3}$$

APPENDIX A: TABLE OF LAPLACE TRANSFORMS (cont.)

F(s)	f(t)
212. $\dfrac{s + a_0}{(s + \alpha)(s^2 + \beta^2)^2}$	$e^{-\alpha t}\dfrac{a_0 - \alpha}{(\alpha^2 + \beta^2)^2} - \dfrac{1}{2\beta^2}\sqrt{\dfrac{a_0^2 + \beta^2}{\alpha^2 + \beta^2}}\, t \sin(\beta t + \psi_1) + \dfrac{\sqrt{(\beta^2 - a_0\alpha)^2 + 4a_0^2\beta^2}}{2\beta^3(\alpha^2 + \beta^2)}\cos(\beta t + \psi_2)$ $\psi_1 = \tan^{-1}\dfrac{a}{\beta} + \tan^{-1}\dfrac{\beta}{a_0} \qquad \psi_2 = \tan^{-1}\dfrac{\beta^2 - a_0\alpha}{2\alpha_0\beta} - 2\tan^{-1}\dfrac{\beta}{\alpha}$
213. $\dfrac{s^2 + a_1 s + a_0}{(s + \alpha)(s^2 + \beta^2)^2}$	$e^{-\alpha t}\left[\dfrac{\alpha^2 + a_0 - a_1\alpha}{(\alpha^2 + \beta^2)^2}\right] - \dfrac{1}{2\beta^2}\sqrt{\dfrac{(a_0 - \beta^2)^2 + a_1^2\beta^2}{\alpha^2 + \beta^2}}\, t \sin(\beta t + \psi_1)$ $\qquad + \dfrac{\sqrt{4a_0^2\beta^2 + [\alpha(a_0 + \beta^2) - a_1\beta^2]^2}}{2\beta^3(\alpha^2 + \beta^2)}\sin(\beta t + \psi_2)$ $\psi_1 = \tan^{-1}\dfrac{\alpha}{\beta} + \tan^{-1}\dfrac{a_1\beta}{a_0 - \beta^2} \qquad \psi_2 = \tan^{-1}\dfrac{2a_0\beta}{\alpha(a_0 + \beta^2) - a_1\beta^2} - 2\tan^{-1}\dfrac{\beta}{\alpha}$
214. $\dfrac{s^3 + a_2 s^2 + a_1 s + a_0}{(s + \alpha)(s^2 + \beta^2)^2}$	$\dfrac{-\alpha^3 + a_2\alpha^2 - a_1\alpha + a_0}{(\alpha^2 + \beta^2)^2}\,e^{-\alpha t} - \dfrac{1}{2\beta^2}\sqrt{\dfrac{\beta^2(a_1 - \beta^2)^2 + (a_0 - a_2\beta^2)^2}{\alpha^2 + \beta^2}}\, t \sin(\beta t + \psi_1)$ $\qquad + \dfrac{\sqrt{4\beta^2(\alpha\beta^2 + a_0)^2 + [\beta^2(\beta^2 + a_1 - a_2\alpha) - a_0\alpha]^2}}{2\beta^3(\alpha^2 + \beta^2)}\sin(\beta t + \psi_2)$ $\psi_1 = \tan^{-1}\dfrac{\alpha}{\beta} + \tan^{-1}\dfrac{\beta(a_1 - \beta^2)}{a_0 - a_2\beta^2}$ $\psi_2 = \tan^{-1}\dfrac{\alpha}{\beta} - \tan^{-1}\dfrac{\beta}{\alpha} + \tan^{-1}\dfrac{\beta^2(\beta^2 + a_1 - a_2\alpha^2) - a_0\alpha}{2\beta(\alpha\beta^2 + a_0)}$
215. $\dfrac{1}{s(s + \alpha)(s^2 + \beta^2)^2}$	$\dfrac{1}{\alpha\beta^4} - \dfrac{e^{-\alpha t}}{\alpha(\alpha^2 + \beta^2)^2} + \dfrac{t\cos(\beta t + \psi_1)}{2\beta^3\sqrt{\alpha^2 + \beta^2}} - \dfrac{\sqrt{4\alpha^2 + 9\beta^2}}{2\beta^4(\alpha^2 + \beta^2)}\cos(\beta t + \psi_2)$ $\psi_1 = \tan^{-1}\dfrac{\alpha}{\beta} \qquad \psi_2 = 2\tan^{-1}\dfrac{\beta}{\alpha} + \tan^{-1}\dfrac{3\beta}{2\alpha}$

216. $\dfrac{s + a_0}{s(s + \alpha)(s^2 + \beta^2)^2}$

$$\frac{a_0}{\alpha\beta^4} + \frac{(\alpha - a_0)e^{-\alpha t}}{\alpha(\alpha^3 + \beta^2)^2} + \frac{1}{2\beta^3}\sqrt{\frac{a_0^2 + \beta^2}{\alpha^2 + \beta^2}}\; t\cos(\beta t + \psi_1) - \frac{\sqrt{4(a_0\alpha - \beta^2)^2 + \beta^2(\alpha + 3a_0)^2}}{2\beta^4(\alpha^2 + \beta^2)}\cos(\beta t + \psi_2)$$

$$\psi_1 = \tan^{-1}\frac{\alpha}{\beta} + \tan^{-1}\frac{\beta}{a_0} \qquad \psi_2 = \tan^{-1}\frac{\beta(\alpha + 3a_0)}{2(a_0\alpha - \beta^2)} - 2\tan^{-1}\frac{\beta}{\alpha}$$

217. $\dfrac{s^2 + a_1 s + a_0}{s(s + \alpha)(s^2 + \beta^2)^2}$

$$\frac{a_0}{\alpha\beta^4} - \frac{\alpha^2 - a_1\alpha + a_0}{\alpha(\alpha^2 + \beta^2)^2}\,e^{-\alpha t} + \frac{1}{2\beta^3}\sqrt{\frac{(a_0 - \beta^2)^2 + a_1^2\beta^2}{\alpha^2 + \beta^2}}\; t\cos(\beta t + \psi_1)$$

$$- \frac{\sqrt{4(\alpha a_0 - a_1\beta^2)^2 + \beta^2(3a_0 + \alpha a_1 - \beta^2)^2}}{2\beta^4(\alpha^2 + \beta^2)}\cos(\beta t + \psi_2)$$

$$\psi_1 = \tan^{-1}\frac{\alpha}{\beta} + \tan^{-1}\frac{a_1\beta}{a_0 - \beta^2} \qquad \psi_2 = \tan^{-1}\frac{2(a_1\beta^2 - \alpha a_0)}{\beta(3a_0 + \alpha a_1 - \beta^2)} + \tan^{-1}\frac{\alpha}{\beta} - \tan^{-1}\frac{\beta}{\alpha}$$

218. $\dfrac{s^3 + a_2 s^2 + a_1 s + a_0}{s(s + \alpha)(s^2 + \beta^2)^2}$

$$\frac{a_0}{\alpha\beta^4} + \frac{\alpha^3 - a_2\alpha^2 + a_1\alpha - a_0}{\alpha(\alpha^2 + \beta^2)^2}\,e^{-\alpha t} + \frac{1}{2\beta^3}\sqrt{\frac{(a_0 - \beta^2)^2 + \beta^2(a_1 - \beta^2)^2}{\alpha^2 + \beta^2}}\; t\cos(\beta t + \psi_1)$$

$$- \frac{\sqrt{4(\alpha a_0 - a_1\beta^2)^2 + \beta^2[3a_0 + a_1\alpha - \beta^2(a_2 - \alpha)]^2}}{2\beta^4(\alpha^2 + \beta^2)}\cos(\beta t + \psi_2)$$

$$\psi_1 = \tan^{-1}\frac{\alpha}{\beta} + \tan^{-1}\frac{\beta(a_1 - \beta^2)}{a_0 - \beta^2} \qquad \psi_2 = \tan^{-1}\frac{2(a_1\beta^2 - \alpha a_0)}{\beta[3a_0 + \alpha a_1 - \beta^2(a_2 - \alpha)]} + \tan^{-1}\frac{\alpha}{\beta} - \tan^{-1}\frac{\beta}{\alpha}$$

219. $\dfrac{1}{s^2(s + \alpha)(s^2 + \beta^2)^2}$

$$\frac{1}{\alpha\beta^4}\left[t - \frac{1}{\alpha}\right] + \frac{e^{-\alpha t}}{\alpha^2(\alpha^2 + \beta^2)^2} + \frac{t\sin(\beta t + \psi_1)}{2\beta^4\sqrt{\alpha^2 + \beta^2}} + \frac{\sqrt{9\alpha^2 + 16\beta^2}}{2\beta^5(\alpha^2 + \beta^2)}\sin(\beta t + \psi_2)$$

$$\psi_1 = \tan^{-1}\frac{\alpha}{\beta} \qquad \psi_2 = \tan^{-1}\frac{4\beta}{3\alpha} + 2\tan^{-1}\frac{\alpha}{\beta}$$

	$F(s)$	$f(t)$
220.	$\dfrac{s + a_0}{s^2(s+\alpha)(s^2+\beta^2)^2}$	$\dfrac{1}{\alpha\beta^4}\left[a_0 t - \dfrac{a_0}{\alpha} + 1\right] + \dfrac{(a_0-\alpha)e^{-\alpha t}}{\alpha^2(\alpha^2+\beta^2)^2} + \dfrac{1}{2\beta^4}\sqrt{\dfrac{a_0^2+\beta^2}{\alpha^2+\beta^2}}\, t\sin(\beta t + \psi_1)$ $+\dfrac{\sqrt{9(a_0\alpha - \beta^2)^2 + 4\beta^2(\alpha + 2a_0)^2}}{2\beta^5(\alpha^2+\beta^2)}\sin(\beta t + \psi_2)$ $\psi_1 = \tan^{-1}\dfrac{\alpha}{\beta} + \tan^{-1}\dfrac{\beta}{a_0}$ $\psi_2 = \tan^{-1}\dfrac{2\beta(\alpha + 2a_0)}{3(a_0\alpha - \beta^2)} + 2\tan^{-1}\dfrac{\alpha}{\beta}$
221.	$\dfrac{s^2 + a_1 s + a_0}{s^2(s+\alpha)(s^2+\beta^2)^2}$	$\dfrac{1}{\alpha\beta^4}\left[a_0 t - \dfrac{a_0}{\alpha} + a_1\right] + \dfrac{\alpha^2 - a_1\alpha + a_0}{\alpha^2(\alpha^2+\beta^2)^2}e^{-\alpha t} + \dfrac{1}{2\beta^4}\sqrt{\dfrac{(a_0-\beta^2)^2 + a_1^2\beta^2}{\alpha^2+\beta^2}}\, t\sin(\beta t + \psi_1)$ $+\dfrac{\sqrt{[3\alpha a_0 - \beta^2(3a_1 + \alpha)]^2 + 4\beta^2[\beta^2 - \alpha a_1 - 2a_0]^2}}{2\beta^5(\alpha^2+\beta^2)}\sin(\beta t + \psi_2)$ $\psi_1 = \tan^{-1}\dfrac{\alpha}{\beta} + \tan^{-1}\dfrac{a_1\beta}{a_0 - \beta^2}$ $\psi_2 = \tan^{-1}\dfrac{3\alpha a_0 - \beta^2(3a_1 + \alpha)}{2\beta(\beta^2 - \alpha a_1 - 2a_0)} + \tan^{-1}\dfrac{\alpha}{\beta} - \tan^{-1}\dfrac{\beta}{\alpha}$
222.	$\dfrac{s^3 + a_2 s^2 + a_1 s + a_0}{s^2(s+\alpha)(s^2+\beta^2)^2}$	$\dfrac{1}{\alpha\beta^4}\left[a_0 t + a_1 - \dfrac{a_0}{\alpha}\right] + \dfrac{-\alpha^3 + a_2\alpha^2 - a_1\alpha + a_0}{\alpha^2(\alpha^2+\beta^2)^2}e^{-\alpha t} + \dfrac{1}{2\beta^4}\sqrt{\dfrac{(a_0 - a_2\beta^2)^2 + \beta^2(a_1 - \beta^2)^2}{\alpha^2+\beta^2}}$ $\times\, t\sin(\beta t + \psi_1) + \dfrac{\sqrt{[3\alpha a_0 - \beta^2(3a_1 + \alpha a_2 - \beta^2)]^2 + 4\beta^2[a_2\beta^2 - 2a_1 + a_1\alpha]^2}}{2\beta^5(\alpha^2+\beta^2)}\sin(\beta t + \psi_2)$ $\psi_1 = \tan^{-1}\dfrac{\alpha}{\beta} + \tan^{-1}\dfrac{\beta(a_1 - \beta^2)}{a_0 - a_2\beta^2}$ $\psi_2 = \tan^{-1}\dfrac{3\alpha a_0 - \beta^2(3a_1 + \alpha a_2 - \beta^2)}{2\beta(a_2\beta^2 - 2a_0 + a_1\alpha)} + \tan^{-1}\dfrac{\alpha}{\beta} - \tan^{-1}\dfrac{\beta}{\alpha}$
223.	$\dfrac{s + a_0}{(s+\alpha)^3}$	$\left[\dfrac{(a_0 - \alpha)t}{2} + 1\right]te^{-\alpha t}$

224.	$\dfrac{s^2 + a_1 s + a_0}{(s+\alpha)^3}$	$\left[\dfrac{(\alpha^2 - a_1\alpha + a_0)t^2}{2} + (a_1 - 2\alpha)t + 1\right]e^{-\alpha t}$
225.	$\dfrac{1}{s(s+\alpha)^3}$	$\dfrac{1}{\alpha^3} - \dfrac{1}{\alpha}\left[\dfrac{t^2}{2} + \dfrac{t}{\alpha} + \dfrac{1}{\alpha^2}\right]e^{-\alpha t}$
226.	$\dfrac{s+a_0}{s(s+\alpha)^3}$	$\dfrac{a_0}{\alpha^3} - \dfrac{1}{\alpha}\left[\dfrac{(a_0-\alpha)t^2}{2} + \dfrac{a_0 t}{\alpha} + \dfrac{a_0}{\alpha^2}\right]e^{-\alpha t}$
227.	$\dfrac{s^2 + a_1 s + a_0}{s(s+\alpha)^3}$	$\dfrac{a_0}{\alpha^3} - \dfrac{1}{\alpha}\left[\dfrac{(\alpha^2 - a_1\alpha + a_0)t^2}{2} + \dfrac{(a_0 - \alpha^2)t}{\alpha} + \dfrac{a_0}{\alpha^2}\right]e^{-\alpha t}$
228.	$\dfrac{s^3 + a_2 s^2 + a_1 s + a_0}{s(s+\alpha)^3}$	$\dfrac{a_0}{\alpha^3} - \dfrac{1}{\alpha}\left[\dfrac{(a_0 - a_1\alpha + a_2\alpha^2 - \alpha^3)t^2}{2} + \dfrac{(2\alpha^3 - a_2\alpha^2 + a_0)t}{\alpha} + \dfrac{(a_0 - \alpha^3)}{\alpha^2}\right]e^{-\alpha t}$
229.	$\dfrac{1}{s^2(s+\alpha)^3}$	$\dfrac{1}{\alpha^3}\left[t - \dfrac{3}{\alpha}\right] + \dfrac{1}{\alpha^2}\left[\dfrac{t^2}{2} + \dfrac{2}{\alpha}t + \dfrac{3}{\alpha^2}\right]e^{-\alpha t}$
230.	$\dfrac{s+a_0}{s^2(s+\alpha)^3}$	$\dfrac{1}{\alpha^3}\left[a_0 t + 1 - \dfrac{3a_0}{\alpha}\right] + \dfrac{1}{\alpha^2}\left[\dfrac{(a_0-\alpha)t^2}{2} + \dfrac{(2a_0-\alpha)t}{\alpha} - \dfrac{1}{\alpha} + \dfrac{3a_0}{\alpha^2}\right]e^{-\alpha t}$
231.	$\dfrac{s^2 + a_1 s + a_0}{s^2(s+\alpha)^3}$	$\dfrac{1}{\alpha^3}\left[\dfrac{a_1\alpha - 3a_0}{\alpha} + a_0 t\right] + \left[\dfrac{(\alpha^2 - a_1\alpha + a_0)t^2}{2\alpha^2} + \dfrac{(2a_0 - a_1\alpha)t}{\alpha^3} + \dfrac{3a_0 - a_1\alpha}{\alpha^4}\right]e^{-\alpha t}$
232.	$\dfrac{s^3 + a_2 s^2 + a_1 s + a_0}{s^2(s+\alpha)^3}$	$\dfrac{1}{\alpha^3}\left[a_0 t + a_1 - \dfrac{3a_0}{\alpha}\right] + \dfrac{1}{\alpha^2}\left[\dfrac{(a_0 - a_1\alpha + a_2\alpha^2 - \alpha^3)t^2}{2} + \dfrac{(2a_0 - a_1\alpha + a_2\alpha^2 - \alpha^3)t}{\alpha} + \dfrac{3a_0 - a_1\alpha}{\alpha^2}\right]e^{-\alpha t}$
233.	$\dfrac{1}{(s+\gamma)(s+\alpha)^3}$	$\dfrac{e^{-\gamma t}}{(\alpha-\gamma)^3} + \dfrac{1}{\gamma-\alpha}\left[\dfrac{t^2}{2} - \dfrac{t}{\gamma-\alpha} + \dfrac{1}{(\gamma-\alpha)^2}\right]e^{-\alpha t}$

APPENDIX A: TABLE OF LAPLACE TRANSFORMS (cont.)

	$F(s)$	$f(t)$
234.	$\dfrac{s + a_0}{(s + \gamma)(s + \alpha)^3}$	$\dfrac{a_0 - \gamma}{(\alpha - \gamma)^3} e^{-\gamma t} + \left[\dfrac{(a_0 - \alpha)t^2}{2(\gamma - \alpha)} + \dfrac{(\gamma - a_0)t}{(\gamma - \alpha)^2} + \dfrac{a_0 - \gamma}{(\gamma - \alpha)^3}\right] e^{-\alpha t}$
235.	$\dfrac{s^2 + a_1 s + a_0}{(s + \gamma)(s + \alpha)^3}$	$\dfrac{\gamma^2 - a_1\gamma + a_0}{(\alpha - \gamma)^3} e^{-\gamma t} + \left[\dfrac{(\alpha^2 - a_1\alpha + a_0)t^2}{2} + \dfrac{(\alpha^2 - 2\gamma\alpha + a_1\gamma - a_0)t}{\gamma - \alpha} + \dfrac{(\gamma^2 - a_1\gamma + a_0)}{(\gamma - \alpha)^2}\right] \dfrac{e^{-\alpha t}}{\gamma - \alpha}$
236.	$\dfrac{s^3 + a_2 s^2 + a_1 s + a_0}{(s + \gamma)(s + \alpha)^3}$	$\dfrac{1}{\gamma - \alpha}\left[\dfrac{(a_0 - a_1\alpha + a_2\alpha^2 - \alpha^3)t^2}{2} + \dfrac{[\alpha(\alpha - \gamma)(a_2 - 2\alpha) + \gamma\{\alpha(\alpha - a_2) + a_1\} - a_0]t}{\gamma - \alpha}\right.$ $\left. + \dfrac{a_0 - a_1\gamma + a_2\gamma^2 - 3\alpha\gamma(\gamma - \alpha) - \alpha^3}{(\gamma - \alpha)^2}\right]e^{-\alpha t} + \dfrac{a_0 - a_1\gamma + a_2\gamma^2 - \gamma^3}{(\alpha - \gamma)^3} e^{-\gamma t}$
237.	$\dfrac{1}{s^2(s^2 - \beta^2)}$	$\dfrac{1}{\beta^3}\sinh\beta t - \dfrac{1}{2\beta^2}t$
238.	$\dfrac{1}{s^3(s^2 + \beta^2)}$	$\dfrac{1}{\beta^4}(\cos\beta t - 1) + \dfrac{1}{2\beta^2}t$
239.	$\dfrac{1}{s^3(s^2 - \beta^2)}$	$\dfrac{1}{\beta^4}(\cos\beta t - 1) - \dfrac{1}{2\beta^2}t$
240.	$\tan^{-1}\dfrac{\beta}{s}$	$\dfrac{\sin\beta t}{t}$
241.	$\ln\dfrac{s + \beta}{s + \alpha}$	$\dfrac{e^{-\alpha t} - e^{-\beta t}}{t}$

242. $\dfrac{s^n}{(s+\alpha)^{n+1}}$

$e^{-\alpha t}\displaystyle\sum_{k=0}^{n}\dfrac{n!\,(-\alpha)^k}{(n-k)!\,(k!)^2}\,t^k \qquad n>0$

243. $\dfrac{a_3 s^3 + a_2 s^2 + a_1 s + a_0}{s(s+\gamma)(s+\delta)[(s+\alpha)^2+\beta^2]}$

$\dfrac{a_0}{\gamma\delta(\alpha^2+\beta^2)} + \dfrac{a_0 - a_1\gamma + a_2\gamma^2 - a_3\gamma^3}{\gamma(\gamma-\delta)[(\alpha-\gamma)^2+\beta^2]}e^{-\gamma t} + \dfrac{a_0 - a_1\delta + a_2\delta^2 - a_3\delta^3}{\delta(\delta-\gamma)[(\alpha-\delta)^2+\beta^2]}e^{-\delta t}$

$+ \dfrac{1}{\beta}\sqrt{\dfrac{[1]^2+\beta^2[2]^2}{(\alpha^2+\beta^2)[(\gamma-\alpha)^2+\beta^2][(\delta-\alpha)^2+\beta^2]}}\;e^{-\alpha t}\cos(\beta t+\psi)$

$\psi = \tan^{-1}\dfrac{\beta[2]}{[1]} + \tan^{-1}\dfrac{\beta}{\alpha} + \tan^{-1}\dfrac{\gamma-\alpha}{\beta} - \tan^{-1}\dfrac{\beta}{\delta-\alpha}$

[Note: See page 363 at the end of this Appendix for a list of abbreviations used in this and all ensuing transform pairs.]

244. $\dfrac{a_4 s^4 + a_3 s^3 + a_2 s^2 + a_1 s + a_0}{(s+\gamma)(s+\delta)(s+\mu)[(s+\alpha)^2+\beta^2]}$

$\dfrac{a_0 - a_1\gamma + a_2\gamma^2 - a_3\gamma^3 + a_4\gamma^4}{(\delta-\gamma)(\mu-\gamma)[(\alpha-\gamma)^2+\beta^2]}e^{-\gamma t} + \dfrac{a_0 - a_1\delta + a_2\delta^2 - a_3\delta^3 + a_4\delta^4}{(\gamma-\delta)(\mu-\delta)[(\alpha-\delta)^2+\beta^2]}e^{-\delta t}$

$+ \dfrac{a_0 - a_1\mu + a_2\mu^2 - a_3\mu^3 + a_4\mu^4}{(\gamma-\mu)(\delta-\mu)[(\alpha-\mu)^2+\beta^2]}e^{-\mu t}$

$+ \dfrac{1}{\beta}\sqrt{\dfrac{[5]^2+\beta^2[6]^2}{[(\gamma-\alpha)^2+\beta^2][(\delta-\alpha)^2+\beta^2][(\mu-\alpha)^2+\beta^2]}}\;e^{-\alpha t}\sin(\beta t+\psi)$

$\psi = \tan^{-1}\dfrac{\beta[6]}{[5]} - \tan^{-1}\dfrac{\beta}{\gamma-\alpha} - \tan^{-1}\dfrac{\beta}{\delta-\alpha} - \tan^{-1}\dfrac{\beta}{\mu-\alpha}$

APPENDIX A: TABLE OF LAPLACE TRANSFORMS (cont.)

$F(s)$	$f(t)$

245.

$$F(s) = \frac{a_4 s^4 + a_3 s^3 + a_2 s^2 + a_1 s + a_0}{s(s+\gamma)(s+\delta)(s+\mu)[(s+\alpha)^2+\beta^2]}$$

$$f(t) = \frac{a_0}{\gamma\delta\mu(\alpha^2+\beta^2)} - \frac{a_0 - a_1\gamma + a_2\gamma^2 - a_3\gamma^3 + a_4\gamma^4}{\gamma(\delta-\gamma)(\mu-\gamma)[(\alpha-\gamma)^2+\beta^2]}e^{-\gamma t}$$

$$- \frac{a_0 - a_1\delta + a_2\delta^2 - a_3\delta^3 + a_4\delta^4}{\delta(\gamma-\delta)(\mu-\delta)[(\alpha-\delta)^2+\beta^2]}e^{-\delta t} - \frac{a_0 - a_1\mu + a_2\mu^2 - a_3\mu^3 + a_4\mu^4}{\mu(\gamma-\mu)(\delta-\mu)[(\alpha-\mu)^2+\beta^2]}e^{-\mu t}$$

$$+ \frac{1}{\beta}\sqrt{\frac{[5]^2+\beta^2[6]^2}{(\alpha^2+\beta^2)[(\gamma-\alpha)^2+\beta^2][(\delta-\alpha)^2+\beta^2][(\mu-\alpha)^2+\beta^2]}}\; e^{-\alpha t}\cos(\beta t+\psi)$$

$$\psi = \tan^{-1}\frac{\beta[6]}{[5]} + \tan^{-1}\frac{\delta-\alpha}{\beta} + \tan^{-1}\frac{\gamma-\alpha}{\beta} - \tan^{-1}\frac{\beta}{\mu-\alpha} - \tan^{-1}\frac{\alpha}{\beta}$$

246.

$$F(s) = \frac{a_4 s^4 + a_3 s^3 + a_2 s^2 + a_1 s + a_0}{(s+\gamma)(s+\delta)(s+\mu)(s+\eta)[(s+\alpha)^2+\beta^2]}$$

$$f(t) = \frac{a_0 - a_1\gamma + a_2\gamma^2 - a_3\gamma^3 + a_4\gamma^4}{(\delta-\gamma)(\mu-\gamma)(\eta-\gamma)[(\alpha-\gamma)^2+\beta^2]}e^{-\gamma t} + \frac{a_0 - a_1\delta + a_2\delta^2 - a_3\delta^3 + a_4\delta^4}{(\gamma-\delta)(\mu-\delta)(\eta-\delta)[(\alpha-\delta)^2+\beta^2]}e^{-\delta t}$$

$$+ \frac{a_0 - a_1\mu + a_2\mu^2 - a_3\mu^3 + a_4\mu^4}{(\gamma-\mu)(\delta-\mu)(\eta-\mu)[(\alpha-\mu)^2+\beta^2]}e^{-\mu t} + \frac{a_0 - a_1\eta + a_2\eta^2 - a_3\eta^3 + a_4\eta^4}{(\gamma-\eta)(\delta-\eta)(\mu-\eta)[(\alpha-\eta)^2+\beta^2]}e^{-\eta t}$$

$$+ \frac{1}{\beta}\sqrt{\frac{[5]^2+\beta^2[6]^2}{[(\gamma-\alpha)^2+\beta^2][(\delta-\alpha)^2+\beta^2][(\mu-\alpha)^2+\beta^2][(\eta-\alpha)^2+\beta^2]}}\; e^{-\alpha t}\sin(\beta t+\psi)$$

$$\psi = \tan^{-1}\frac{\beta[6]}{[5]} - \tan^{-1}\frac{\beta}{\gamma-\alpha} - \tan^{-1}\frac{\beta}{\delta-\alpha} - \tan^{-1}\frac{\beta}{\mu-\alpha} - \tan^{-1}\frac{\beta}{\eta-\alpha}$$

247.

$$\frac{a_4s^4 + a_3s^3 + a_2s^2 + a_1s + a_0}{s(s+\gamma)(s+\delta)(s+\mu)(s+\eta)[(s+\alpha)^2+\beta^2]}$$

$$\frac{a_0}{\gamma\delta\mu\eta(\alpha^2+\beta^2)} - \frac{a_0 - a_1\gamma + a_2\gamma^2 - a_3\gamma^3 + a_4\gamma^4}{\gamma(\delta-\gamma)(\mu-\gamma)(\eta-\gamma)[(\alpha-\gamma)^2+\beta^2]}e^{-\gamma t}$$

$$- \frac{a_0 - a_1\delta + a_2\delta^2 - a_3\delta^3 + a_4\delta^4}{\delta(\gamma-\delta)(\mu-\delta)(\eta-\delta)[(\alpha-\delta)^2+\beta^2]}e^{-\delta t}$$

$$- \frac{a_0 - a_1\mu + a_2\mu^2 - a_3\mu^3 + a_4\mu^4}{\mu(\gamma-\mu)(\delta-\mu)(\eta-\mu)[(\alpha-\mu)^2+\beta^2]}e^{-\mu t}$$

$$- \frac{a_0 - a_1\eta + a_2\eta^2 - a_3\eta^3 + a_4\eta^4}{\eta(\gamma-\eta)(\delta-\eta)(\mu-\eta)[(\alpha-\eta)^2+\beta^2]}e^{-\eta t}$$

$$- \frac{1}{\beta}\sqrt{\frac{[5]^2+\beta^2[6]^2}{(\alpha^2+\beta^2)[(\gamma-\alpha)^2+\beta^2][(\delta-\alpha)^2+\beta^2][(\mu-\alpha)^2+\beta^2][(\eta-\alpha)^2+\beta^2]}}\,e^{-\alpha t}\sin(\beta t+\psi)$$

$$\psi = \tan^{-1}\frac{\beta[6]}{[5]} + \tan^{-1}\frac{\beta}{\alpha} - \tan^{-1}\frac{\beta}{\gamma-\alpha} - \tan^{-1}\frac{\beta}{\delta-\alpha} - \tan^{-1}\frac{\beta}{\mu-\alpha} - \tan^{-1}\frac{\beta}{\eta-\alpha}$$

248.

$$\frac{a_3s^3 + a_2s^2 + a_1s + a_0}{[(s+\alpha)^2+\beta^2][(s+\sigma)^2+\tau^2]}$$

$$\frac{1}{\beta}\sqrt{\frac{[1]^2+\beta^2[2]^2}{[(\sigma-\alpha)^2+\tau^2-\beta^2]^2+4\beta^2(\sigma-\alpha)^2}}\,e^{-\alpha t}\sin(\beta t+\psi_1)$$

$$+ \frac{1}{\tau}\sqrt{\frac{[3]^2+\tau^2[4]^2}{[(\sigma-\alpha)^2+\beta^2-\tau^2]^2+4\tau^2(\sigma-\alpha)^2}}\,e^{-\sigma t}\sin(\tau t+\psi_2)$$

$$\psi_1 = \tan^{-1}\frac{\beta[2]}{[1]} - \tan^{-1}\frac{2\beta(\sigma-\alpha)}{(\sigma-\alpha)^2+\tau^2-\beta^2}$$

$$\psi_2 = \tan^{-1}\frac{\tau[4]}{[3]} - \tan^{-1}\frac{2\tau(\alpha-\sigma)}{(\sigma-\alpha)^2+\beta^2-\tau^2}$$

$F(s)$	$f(t)$
249. $\dfrac{a_3 s^3 + a_2 s^2 + a_1 s + a_0}{s[(s+\alpha)^2 + \beta^2][(s+\sigma)^2 + \tau^2]}$	$\dfrac{a_0}{(\alpha^2+\beta^2)(\sigma^2+\tau^2)} - \dfrac{1}{\beta}\sqrt{\dfrac{[1]^2+\beta^2[2]^2}{(\alpha^2+\beta^2)\{4\beta^2(\sigma-\alpha)^2+[(\sigma-\alpha)^2+\tau^2-\beta^2]^2\}}}\, e^{-\alpha t}\sin(\beta t + \psi_1)$ $-\dfrac{1}{\tau}\sqrt{\dfrac{[3]^2+\tau^2[4]^2}{(\sigma^2+\tau^2)\{4\tau^2(\sigma-\alpha)^2+[(\sigma-\alpha)^2+\beta^2-\tau^2]^2\}}}\, e^{-\sigma t}\sin(\tau t + \psi_2)$ $\psi_1 = \tan^{-1}\dfrac{\beta[2]}{[1]} + \tan^{-1}\dfrac{\beta}{\alpha} - \tan^{-1}\dfrac{2\beta(\sigma-\alpha)}{(\sigma-\alpha)^2+\tau^2-\beta^2}$ $\psi_2 = \tan^{-1}\dfrac{\tau[4]}{[3]} + \tan^{-1}\dfrac{\tau}{\sigma} - \tan^{-1}\dfrac{2\tau(\alpha-\sigma)}{(\sigma-\alpha)^2+\beta^2-\tau^2}$
250. $\dfrac{a_3 s^3 + a_2 s^2 + a_1 s + a_0}{(s+\gamma)[(s+\alpha)^2 + \beta^2][(s+\sigma)^2 + \tau^2]}$	$\dfrac{a_0 - a_1\gamma + a_2\gamma^2 - a_3\gamma^3}{[(\alpha - \gamma)^2 + \beta^2][(\sigma - \gamma)^2 + \tau^2]}\, e^{-\gamma t}$ $+\dfrac{1}{\beta}\sqrt{\dfrac{[1]^2+\beta^2[2]^2}{[(\gamma-\alpha)^2+\beta^2]\{4\beta^2(\sigma-\alpha)^2+[(\sigma-\alpha)^2+\tau^2-\beta^2]^2\}}}\, e^{-\alpha t}\sin(\beta t + \psi_1)$ $+\dfrac{1}{\tau}\sqrt{\dfrac{[3]^2+\tau^2[4]^2}{[(\gamma-\sigma)^2+\tau^2]\{4\tau^2(\sigma-\alpha)^2+[(\sigma-\alpha)^2+\beta^2-\tau^2]^2\}}}\, e^{-\sigma t}\sin(\tau t + \psi_2)$ $\psi_1 = \tan^{-1}\dfrac{\beta[2]}{[1]} - \tan^{-1}\dfrac{\beta}{\gamma - \alpha} - \tan^{-1}\dfrac{2\beta(\sigma-\alpha)}{(\sigma-\alpha)^2+\tau^2-\beta^2}$ $\psi_2 = \tan^{-1}\dfrac{\tau[4]}{[3]} - \tan^{-1}\dfrac{\tau}{\gamma - \sigma} - \tan^{-1}\dfrac{2\tau(\alpha-\sigma)}{(\sigma-\alpha)^2+\beta^2-\tau^2}$

251.

$$\frac{a_4 s^4 + a_3 s^3 + a_2 s^2 + a_1 s + a_0}{s(s+\gamma)[(s+\alpha)^2 + \beta^2][(s+\sigma)^2 + \tau^2]}$$

$$\frac{a_0 - a_1\gamma + a_2\gamma^2 - a_3\gamma^3 + a_4\gamma^4}{\gamma(\alpha^2 + \beta^2)(\sigma^2 + \tau^2) - \gamma[(\alpha - \gamma)^2 + \beta^2][(\sigma - \gamma)^2 + \tau^2]} e^{-\gamma t}$$

$$- \frac{1}{\beta}\sqrt{\frac{[5]^2 + \beta^2[6]^2}{(\alpha^2 + \beta^2)[(\gamma - \alpha)^2 + \beta^2]\{4\beta^2(\sigma - \alpha)^2 + [(\sigma - \alpha)^2 + \tau^2 - \beta^2]^2\}}}\, e^{-\alpha t}\sin(\beta t + \psi_1)$$

$$- \frac{1}{\tau}\sqrt{\frac{[7]^2 + \tau^2[8]^2}{(\sigma^2 + \tau^2)[(\gamma - \sigma)^2 + \tau^2]\{4\tau^2(\sigma - \alpha)^2 + [(\sigma - \alpha)^2 + \beta^2 - \tau^2]^2\}}}\, e^{-\sigma t}\sin(\tau t + \psi_2)$$

$$\psi_1 = \tan^{-1}\frac{\beta[6]}{[5]} + \tan^{-1}\frac{\gamma - \alpha}{\beta} - \tan^{-1}\frac{\alpha}{\beta} - \tan^{-1}\frac{2\beta(\sigma - \alpha)}{(\sigma - \alpha)^2 + \tau^2 - \beta^2}$$

$$\psi_2 = \tan^{-1}\frac{\tau[8]}{[7]} + \tan^{-1}\frac{\gamma - \sigma}{\tau} - \tan^{-1}\frac{\sigma}{\tau} - \tan^{-1}\frac{2\tau(\alpha - \sigma)}{(\sigma - \alpha)^2 + \beta^2 - \tau^2}$$

252.

$$\frac{a_4 s^4 + a_3 s^3 + a_2 s^2 + a_1 s + a_0}{(s+\gamma)(s)(s+\delta)[(s+\alpha)^2 + \beta^2][(s+\sigma)^2 + \tau^2]}$$

$$\frac{a_0 - a_1\gamma + a_2\gamma^2 - a_3\gamma^3 + a_4\gamma^4}{(\delta - \gamma)[(\alpha - \gamma)^2 + \beta^2][(\sigma - \gamma)^2 + \tau^2]} e^{-\gamma t} + \frac{a_0 - a_1\delta + a_2\delta^2 - a_3\delta^3 + a_4\delta^4}{(\gamma - \delta)[(\alpha - \delta)^2 + \beta^2][(\sigma - \delta)^2 + \tau^2]} e^{-\delta t}$$

$$+ \frac{1}{\beta}\sqrt{\frac{[5]^2 + \beta^2[6]^2}{[(\gamma - \alpha)^2 + \beta^2][(\delta - \alpha)^2 + \beta^2]\{4\beta^2(\sigma - \alpha)^2 + [(\sigma - \alpha)^2 + \tau^2 - \beta^2]^2\}}}\, e^{-\alpha t}\sin(\beta t + \psi_1)$$

$$+ \frac{1}{\tau}\sqrt{\frac{[7]^2 + \tau^2[8]^2}{[(\gamma - \sigma)^2 + \tau^2][(\delta - \sigma)^2 + \tau^2]\{4\tau^2(\sigma - \alpha)^2 + [(\sigma - \alpha)^2 + \beta^2 - \tau^2]^2\}}}\, e^{-\sigma t}\sin(\tau t + \psi_2)$$

$$\psi_1 = \tan^{-1}\frac{\beta[6]}{[5]} - \tan^{-1}\frac{\beta}{\gamma - \alpha} - \tan^{-1}\frac{\beta}{\delta - \alpha} - \tan^{-1}\frac{2\beta(\sigma - \alpha)}{(\sigma - \alpha)^2 + \tau^2 - \beta^2}$$

$$\psi_2 = \tan^{-1}\frac{\tau[8]}{[7]} - \tan^{-1}\frac{\tau}{\gamma - \sigma} - \tan^{-1}\frac{\tau}{\delta - \sigma} - \tan^{-1}\frac{2\tau(\alpha - \sigma)}{(\sigma - \alpha)^2 + \beta^2 - \tau^2}$$

APPENDIX A: TABLE OF LAPLACE TRANSFORMS (cont.)

$F(s)$	$f(t)$
253. $\dfrac{a_4 s^4 + a_3 s^3 + a_2 s^2 + a_1 s + a_0}{s(s+\gamma)(s+\delta)[(s+\alpha)^2+\beta^2][(s+\sigma)^2+\tau^2]}$	(see below)

$$\frac{a_0}{\gamma\delta(\alpha^2+\beta^2)(\sigma^2+\tau^2)} - \frac{a_0 - a_1\gamma + a_2\gamma^2 - a_3\gamma^3 + a_4\gamma^4}{\gamma\delta(\alpha^2+\beta^2)(\sigma^2+\tau^2)}\,e^{-\gamma t}$$

$$-\,\frac{a_0 - a_1\delta + a_2\delta^2 - a_3\delta^3 + a_4\delta^4}{\delta(\gamma-\delta)[(\alpha-\delta)^2+\beta^2][(\sigma-\delta)^2+\tau^2]}\,e^{-\delta t}$$

$$-\,\frac{1}{\beta}\sqrt{\frac{[5]^2+\beta^2[6]^2}{(\alpha^2+\beta^2)[(\gamma-\alpha)^2+\beta^2][(\delta-\alpha)^2+\beta^2]\{4\beta^2(\sigma-\alpha)^2+[(\sigma-\alpha)^2+\tau^2-\beta^2]^2\}}}\;e^{-\alpha t}\sin(\beta t + \psi_1)$$

$$-\,\frac{1}{\tau}\sqrt{\frac{[7]^2+\tau^2[8]^2}{(\sigma^2+\tau^2)[(\gamma-\sigma)^2+\tau^2][(\delta-\sigma)^2+\tau^2]\{4\tau^2(\sigma-\alpha)^2+[(\sigma-\alpha)^2+\beta^2-\tau^2]^2\}}}\;e^{-\sigma t}\sin(\tau t + \psi_2)$$

$$\psi_1 = \tan^{-1}\frac{\beta[6]}{[5]} - \tan^{-1}\frac{\alpha}{\beta} - \tan^{-1}\frac{\beta}{\delta-\alpha} - \tan^{-1}\frac{2\beta(\sigma-\alpha)}{(\sigma-\alpha)^2+\tau^2-\beta^2} + \tan^{-1}\frac{\gamma-\alpha}{\beta}$$

$$\psi_2 = \tan^{-1}\frac{\tau[8]}{[7]} - \tan^{-1}\frac{\sigma}{\tau} - \tan^{-1}\frac{\tau}{\delta-\sigma} - \tan^{-1}\frac{2\tau(\alpha-\sigma)}{(\sigma-\alpha)^2+\beta^2-\tau^2} + \tan^{-1}\frac{\gamma-\sigma}{\tau}$$

254.

$$\frac{a_4 s^4 + a_3 s^3 + a_2 s^2 + a_1 s + a_0}{(s+\gamma)(s+\delta)(s+\mu)[(s+\alpha^2)+\beta^2][(s+\sigma)^2+\tau^2]}$$

$$\frac{a_0 - a_1\gamma + a_2\gamma^2 - a_3\gamma^3 + a_4\gamma^4}{(\delta-\gamma)(\mu-\gamma)[(\alpha-\gamma)^2+\beta^2][(\sigma-\gamma)^2+\tau^2]}e^{-\gamma t}$$

$$+\frac{a_0 - a_1\delta + a_2\delta^2 - a_3\delta^3 + a_4\delta^4}{(\gamma-\delta)(\mu-\delta)[(\alpha-\delta)^2+\beta^2][(\sigma-\delta)^2+\tau^2]}e^{-\delta t}$$

$$+\frac{a_0 - a_1\mu + a_2\mu^2 - a_3\mu^3 + a_4\mu^4}{(\gamma-\mu)(\delta-\mu)[(\alpha-\mu)^2+\beta^2][(\sigma-\mu)^2+\tau^2]}e^{-\mu t}$$

$$+\frac{1}{\beta}\sqrt{\frac{[5]^2+\beta^2[6]^2}{[(\gamma-\alpha)^2+\beta^2][(\delta-\alpha)^2+\beta^2][(\mu-\alpha)^2+\beta^2]\{4\beta^2(\sigma-\alpha)^2+[(\sigma-\alpha)^2+\tau^2-\beta^2]^2\}}}\;e^{-\alpha t}\sin(\beta t + \psi_1)$$

$$+\frac{1}{\tau}\sqrt{\frac{[7]^2+\tau^2[8]^2}{[(\gamma-\sigma)^2+\tau^2][(\delta-\sigma)^2+\tau^2][(\mu-\sigma)^2+\tau^2]\{4\tau^2(\sigma-\alpha)^2+[(\sigma-\alpha)^2+\beta^2-\tau^2]^2\}}}\;e^{-\sigma t}\sin(\tau t + \psi_2)$$

$$\psi_1 = \tan^{-1}\frac{\beta[6]}{[5]} - \tan^{-1}\frac{\beta}{\gamma-\alpha} - \tan^{-1}\frac{\beta}{\delta-\alpha} - \tan^{-1}\frac{\beta}{\mu-\alpha} - \tan^{-1}\frac{2\beta(\sigma-\alpha)}{(\sigma-\alpha)^2+\tau^2-\beta^2}$$

$$\psi_2 = \tan^{-1}\frac{\tau[8]}{[7]} - \tan^{-1}\frac{\tau}{\gamma-\sigma} - \tan^{-1}\frac{\tau}{\delta-\sigma} - \tan^{-1}\frac{\tau}{\mu-\sigma} - \tan^{-1}\frac{2\tau(\alpha-\sigma)}{(\sigma-\alpha)^2+\beta^2-\tau^2}$$

255.

$$\frac{a_4 s^4 + a_3 s^3 + a_2 s^2 + a_1 s + a_0}{s(s+\gamma)(s+\delta)(s+\mu)[(s+\alpha)^2+\beta^2][(s+\sigma)^2+\tau^2]}$$

$$\frac{a_0}{\gamma\delta\mu(\alpha^2+\beta^2)(\sigma^2+\tau^2)} - \frac{a_0 - a_1\gamma + a_2\gamma^2 - a_3\gamma^3 + a_4\gamma^4}{\gamma(\delta-\gamma)(\mu-\gamma)[(\alpha-\gamma)^2+\beta^2][(\sigma-\gamma)^2+\tau^2]}e^{-\gamma t}$$

$$- \frac{a_0 - a_1\delta + a_2\delta^2 - a_3\delta^3 + a_4\delta^4}{\delta(\gamma-\delta)(\mu-\delta)[(\alpha-\delta)^2+\beta^2][(\sigma-\delta)^2+\tau^2]}e^{-\delta t}$$

$$- \frac{a_0 - a_1\mu + a_2\mu^2 - a_3\mu^3 + a_4\mu^4}{\mu(\gamma-\mu)(\delta-\mu)[(\alpha-\mu)^2+\beta^2][(\sigma-\mu)^2+\tau^2]}e^{-\mu t}$$

$$- \frac{1}{\beta}\sqrt{\frac{[5]^2+\beta^2[6]^2}{(\alpha^2+\beta^2)[(\gamma-\alpha)^2+\beta^2][(\delta-\alpha)^2+\beta^2]}\cdot\frac{1}{[(\mu-\alpha)^2+\beta^2]\{4\beta^2(\sigma-\alpha)^2+[(\sigma-\alpha)^2+\tau^2-\beta^2]^2\}}}\; e^{-\alpha t}\sin(\beta t+\psi_1)$$

$$- \frac{1}{\tau}\sqrt{\frac{[7]^2+\tau^2[8]^2}{(\sigma^2+\tau^2)[(\gamma-\sigma)^2+\tau^2][(\delta-\sigma)^2+\tau^2]}\cdot\frac{1}{[(\mu-\sigma)^2+\tau^2]\{4\tau^2(\sigma-\alpha)^2+[(\sigma-\alpha)^2+\beta^2-\tau^2]^2\}}}\; e^{-\sigma t}\sin(\tau t+\psi_2)$$

$$\psi_1 = \tan^{-1}\frac{\beta[6]}{[5]} - \tan^{-1}\frac{\alpha}{\beta} + \tan^{-1}\frac{\beta}{\gamma-\alpha} + \tan^{-1}\frac{\delta-\alpha}{\beta} - \tan^{-1}\frac{\beta}{\mu-\alpha} - \tan^{-1}\frac{2\beta(\sigma-\alpha)}{(\sigma-\alpha^2)+\tau^2-\beta^2}$$

$$\psi_2 = \tan^{-1}\frac{\tau[8]}{[7]} - \tan^{-1}\frac{\sigma}{\tau} - \tan^{-1}\frac{\tau}{\gamma-\sigma} + \tan^{-1}\frac{\delta-\sigma}{\tau} - \tan^{-1}\frac{\tau}{\mu-\sigma} - \tan^{-1}\frac{2\tau(\alpha-\sigma)}{(\sigma-\alpha)^2+\beta^2-\tau^2}$$

$$\frac{a_0 - a_1\gamma + a_2\gamma^2 - a_3\gamma^3 + a_4\gamma^4 - a_5\gamma^5}{(\delta-\gamma)(\mu-\gamma)(\eta-\gamma)[(\alpha-\gamma)^2 + \beta^2][(\sigma-\gamma)^2 + \tau^2]}\, e^{-\gamma}$$

$$+\,\frac{a_0 - a_1\delta + a_2\delta^2 - a_3\delta^3 + a_4\delta^4 - a_5\delta^5}{(\gamma-\delta)(\mu-\delta)(\eta-\delta)[(\alpha-\delta)^2 + \beta^2][(\sigma-\delta)^2 + \tau^2]}\, e^{-\delta}$$

$$+\,\frac{a_0 - a_1\mu + a_2\mu^2 - a_3\mu^3 + a_4\mu^4 - a_5\mu^5}{(\gamma-\mu)(\delta-\mu)(\eta-\mu)[(\alpha-\mu)^2 + \beta^2][(\sigma-\mu)^2 + \tau^2]}\, e^{-\mu}$$

$$+\,\frac{a_0 - a_1\eta + a_2\eta^2 - a_3\eta^3 + a_4\eta^4 - a_5\eta^5}{(\gamma-\eta)(\delta-\eta)(\mu-\eta)[(\alpha-\eta)^2 + \beta^2][(\sigma-\eta)^2 + \tau^2]}\, e^{-\eta}$$

$$+\,\frac{1}{\beta}\sqrt{\frac{[9]^2 + \beta^2[10]^2}{[(\gamma-\alpha)^2+\beta^2][(\delta-\alpha)^2+\beta^2][(\mu-\alpha)^2+\beta^2][(\eta-\alpha)^2+\beta^2]\{4\beta^2(\sigma-\alpha)^2 + [(\sigma-\alpha)^2+\tau^2-\beta^2]^2\}}}\; e^{-\alpha t}\sin(\beta t + \psi_1)$$

$$+\,\frac{1}{\tau}\sqrt{\frac{[11]^2 + \tau^2[12]^2}{[(\gamma-\sigma)^2+\tau^2][(\delta-\sigma)^2+\tau^2][(\mu-\sigma)^2+\tau^2][(\eta-\sigma)^2+\tau^2]\{4\tau^2(\sigma-\alpha)^2 + [(\sigma-\alpha)^2+\beta^2-\tau^2]^2\}}}\; e^{-\sigma t}\sin(\tau t + \psi_2)$$

$$\psi_1 = \tan^{-1}\frac{\beta[10]}{[9]} - \tan^{-1}\frac{2\beta(\sigma-\alpha)}{(\sigma-\alpha)^2+\tau^2-\beta^2} - \tan^{-1}\frac{\beta}{\gamma-\alpha} - \tan^{-1}\frac{\beta}{\delta-\alpha} - \tan^{-1}\frac{\beta}{\mu-\alpha} - \tan^{-1}\frac{\beta}{\eta-\alpha}$$

$$\psi_2 = \tan^{-1}\frac{\tau[12]}{[11]} - \tan^{-1}\frac{2\tau(\alpha-\sigma)}{(\sigma-\alpha)^2+\beta^2-\tau^2} - \tan^{-1}\frac{\tau}{\gamma-\sigma} - \tan^{-1}\frac{\tau}{\delta-\sigma} - \tan^{-1}\frac{\tau}{\mu-\sigma} - \tan^{-1}\frac{\tau}{\eta-\sigma}$$

256.

$$\frac{a_5 s^5 + a_4 s^4 + a_3 s^3 + a_2 s^2 + a_1 s + a_0}{(s+\gamma)(s)(s+\delta)(s+\mu)(s+\eta)[(s+\alpha)^2 + \beta^2][(s+\sigma)^2 + \tau^2]}$$

257.

$$\frac{a_5 s^5 + a_4 s^4 + a_3 s^3 + a_2 s^2 + a_1 s + a_0}{s(s+\gamma)(s+\delta)(s+\mu)(s+\eta)[(s+\alpha)^2 + \beta^2][(s+\sigma)^2 + \tau^2]}$$

$$\frac{a_0}{\gamma\delta\mu\eta(\alpha^2+\beta^2)(\sigma^2+\tau^2)}$$

$$-\frac{a_0 - a_1\gamma + a_2\gamma^2 - a_3\gamma^3 + a_4\gamma^4 - a_5\gamma^5}{\gamma(\delta-\gamma)(\mu-\gamma)(\eta-\gamma)[(\alpha-\gamma)^2+\beta^2][(\sigma-\gamma)^2+\tau^2]}\,e^{-\gamma t}$$

$$-\frac{a_0 - a_1\delta + a_2\delta^2 - a_3\delta^3 + a_4\delta^4 - a_5\delta^5}{\delta(\gamma-\delta)(\mu-\delta)(\eta-\delta)[(\alpha-\delta)^2+\beta^2][(\sigma-\delta)^2+\tau^2]}\,e^{-\delta t}$$

$$-\frac{a_0 - a_1\mu + a_2\mu^2 - a_3\mu^3 + a_4\mu^4 - a_5\mu^5}{\mu(\gamma-\mu)(\delta-\mu)(\eta-\mu)[(\alpha-\mu)^2+\beta^2][(\sigma-\mu)^2+\tau^2]}\,e^{-\mu t}$$

$$-\frac{a_0 - a_1\eta + a_2\eta^2 - a_3\eta^3 + a_4\eta^4 - a_5\eta^5}{\eta(\gamma-\eta)(\delta-\eta)(\mu-\eta)[(\alpha-\eta)^2+\beta^2][(\sigma-\eta)^2+\tau^2]}\,e^{-\eta t}$$

$$-\frac{1}{\beta}\sqrt{\frac{[9]^2+\beta^2[10]^2}{(\alpha^2+\beta^2)[(\gamma-\alpha)^2+\beta^2][(\delta-\alpha)^2+\beta^2][(\mu-\alpha)^2+\beta^2][(\eta-\alpha)^2+\beta^2]\{4\beta^2(\sigma-\alpha)^2 + [(\sigma-\alpha)^2+\tau^2-\beta^2]^2\}}}\;e^{-\alpha t}\sin(\beta t + \psi_1)$$

$$-\frac{1}{\tau}\sqrt{\frac{[11]^2+\tau^2[12]^2}{(\sigma^2+\tau^2)[(\gamma-\sigma)^2+\tau^2][(\delta-\sigma)^2+\tau^2][(\mu-\sigma)^2+\tau^2][(\eta-\sigma)^2+\tau^2][4\tau^2(\sigma-\alpha)^2 + [(\sigma-\alpha)^2+\beta^2-\tau^2]^2\}}}\;e^{-\sigma t}\sin(\tau t + \psi_2)$$

$$\psi_1 = \tan^{-1}\frac{\beta[10]}{[9]} + \tan^{-1}\frac{\beta}{\alpha} - \tan^{-1}\frac{2\beta(\sigma-\alpha)}{(\sigma-\alpha)^2+\tau^2-\beta^2} - \tan^{-1}\frac{\beta}{\gamma-\alpha} - \tan^{-1}\frac{\beta}{\delta-\alpha} - \tan^{-1}\frac{\beta}{\mu-\alpha} - \tan^{-1}\frac{\beta}{\eta-\alpha}$$

$$\psi_2 = \tan^{-1}\frac{\tau[12]}{[11]} + \tan^{-1}\frac{\tau}{\sigma} - \tan^{-1}\frac{2\tau(\alpha-\sigma)}{(\sigma-\alpha)^2+\beta^2-\tau^2} - \tan^{-1}\frac{\tau}{\gamma-\sigma} - \tan^{-1}\frac{\tau}{\delta-\sigma} - \tan^{-1}\frac{\tau}{\mu-\sigma} - \tan^{-1}\frac{\tau}{\eta-\sigma}$$

THE FOLLOWING ABBREVIATIONS APPEAR IN TRANSFORM PAIRS 243–257

$[1] = a_0 - a_1\alpha + a_2(\alpha^2 - \beta^2) + a_3\alpha[2\beta^2 - (\alpha^2 - \beta^2)]$

$[2] = a_1 - 2a_2\alpha + \alpha_3[2\alpha^2 + (\alpha^2 - \beta^2)]$

$[3] = a_0 - a_1\sigma + a_2(\sigma^2 - \tau^2) + a_3\sigma[2\tau^2 - (\sigma^2 - \tau^2)]$

$[4] = a_1 - 2a_2\sigma + a_3[2\sigma^2 + (\sigma^2 - \tau^2)]$

$[5] = a_0 - a_1\alpha + a_2(\alpha^2 - \beta^2) + a_3\alpha[2\beta^2 - (\alpha^2 - \beta^2)] + a_4[(\alpha^2 - \beta^2)^2 - 4\alpha^2\beta^2]$

$[6] = a_1 - 2a_2\alpha + a_3[2\alpha^2 + (\alpha^2 - \beta^2)] - 4a_4\alpha(\alpha^2 - \beta^2)$

$[7] = a_0 - a_1\sigma + a_2(\sigma^2 - \tau^2) + a_3\sigma[2\tau^2 - (\sigma^2 - \tau^2)] + a_4[(\sigma^2 - \tau^2)^2 - 4\sigma^2\tau^2]$

$[8] = a_1 - 2a_2\sigma + a_3[2\sigma^2 + (\sigma^2 - \tau^2)] - 4a_4\sigma(\sigma^2 - \tau^2)$

$[9] = a_0 - a_1\alpha + a_2(\alpha^2 - \beta^2) + a_3\alpha[2\beta^2 - (\alpha^2 - \beta^2)] + a_4[(\alpha^2 - \beta^2)^2 - 4\alpha^2\beta^2]$
$$+ a_5\alpha\{4\beta^2(\alpha^2 - \beta^2) - [(\alpha^2 - \beta^2)^2 - 4\alpha^2\beta^2]\}$$

$[10] = a_1 - 2a_2\alpha + \alpha_3[2\alpha^2 + (\alpha^2 - \beta^2)] - 4a_4\alpha(\alpha^2 - \beta^2)$
$$+ a_5\{4\alpha^2(\alpha^2 - \beta^2) + [(\alpha^2 - \beta^2)^2 - 4\alpha^2\beta^2]\}$$

$[11] = a_0 - a_1\sigma + a_2(\sigma^2 - \tau^2) + a_3\sigma[2\tau^2 - (\sigma^2 - \tau^2)] + a_4[(\sigma^2 - \tau^2)^2 - 4\sigma^2\tau^2]$
$$+ a_5\sigma\{4\tau^2(\sigma^2 - \tau^2) - [(\sigma^2 - \tau^2)^2 - 4\sigma^2\tau^2]\}$$

$[12] = a_1 - 2a_2\sigma + a_3[2\sigma^2 + (\sigma^2 - \tau^2)] - 4a_4\sigma(\sigma^2 - \tau^2)$
$$+ a_5\{4\sigma^2(\sigma^2 - \tau^2) + [(\sigma^2 - \tau^2)^2 - 4\sigma^2\tau^2]\}$$

APPENDIX B

THE ROUTH STABILITY CRITERION[1]

B-I THE ROUTH ARRAY

It has been shown, in Chapter 4, that the stability of any control system is a direct consequence of the type of closed-loop poles involved, i.e., if the system contains only left half-plane poles, the closed-loop stability is assured. If, however, one or more right half-plane poles exist, the system is unstable. Finally, if conjugate imaginary poles are generated, the corresponding system is marginally stable such that sustained oscillations are observed. (It should be noted that repeated poles at the origin and repeated imaginary poles also lead to instability; the former is quite simple to identify, however, and the latter will be considered in Section B-2.

Since the main problem associated with the transition from open-loop analysis is that of factoring the system transfer function into poles and zeros, it would be desirable to deduce information regarding absolute stability directly from the characteristic equation of the transfer function. Routh's stability criterion provides a technique, based only upon the characteristic equation coefficients, for determining the total number of right half-plane poles, thus obviating the polynomial factoring requirement.

The Routh array is generated and processed as follows:

1. Arrange the polynomial in descending orders of s, i.e.

$$a_n s^n + a_{n-1} s^{n-1} + a_{n-2} s^{n-2} + \cdots + a_2 s^2 + a_1 s + a_0 \qquad \text{(B-1.1)}$$

2. Beginning with the highest-order term coefficient, form an array consisting of two rows. The first row contains the first, third, fifth, etc., coefficients, and the second row contains the second, fourth, sixth, etc. The first and second rows are identified as the s^n and s^{n-1} rows respectively.

$$\begin{array}{ccc} a_n & a_{n-2} & a_{n-4} \quad \cdots \\ \\ a_{n-1} & a_{n-3} & a_{n-5} \quad \cdots \end{array} \qquad \text{(B-1.2)}$$

The first two rows of the Routh array Eq. (B-1.2) are written to include all coefficients of Eq. (B-1.1).

3. The third Routh-array row is constructed by a process of cross multiplication as illustrated in Eq. (B-1.3).

$$
\begin{array}{llll}
s^n & a_n & a_{n-2} & a_{n-4} \quad \cdots \\[2mm]
s^{n-1} & a_{n-1} & a_{n-3} & a_{n-5} \quad \cdots \\[2mm]
s^{n-2} & \dfrac{a_{n-1}a_{n-2} - a_n a_{n-3}}{a_{n-1}} & \dfrac{a_{n-1}a_{n-4} - a_n a_{n-5}}{a_{n-1}} & \cdots
\end{array} \qquad \text{(B-1.3)}
$$

A convenient device for remembering the polarities involved in the multiplication is that of considering the letter A of "array" and decomposing the letter into a slightly less-recognizable form, $\wedge$. The symbolic A states that the quantities of the array along the general lines 45°—225° are considered positive, and are diminished by the product of the quantities taken along the diagonal 135°—315°. The cross-multiplication terms are then divided by the first-column term of the preceding row.

This cross multiplication process is continued until no more rows can be generated. Any complete row can be multiplied by an arbitrary constant without altering the final result.

4. The number of sign changes, going from top to bottom, of the first *column* are now considered. In particular, the number of sign changes in the elements of the first column is equal to the number of right half-plane singularities that exist in the original polynomial. Thus, if a final Routh array was computed as

$$
\begin{array}{ccc}
a & b & c \\[1mm]
d & e & f \\[1mm]
g & h & \\[1mm]
-i & j & \\[1mm]
k & & \\[1mm]
l & &
\end{array} \qquad \text{(B-1.4)}
$$

two unstable zeros would be found in the original polynomial, i.e., two sign changes are encountered in the elements of the first column ($+g$ to $-i$ represents the first, and $-i$ to $+k$ represents the second).

We now apply the Routh stability rules to the analyses of two example polynomials.

EXAMPLE 1: *Stable System*

Assuming the polynomial equation

$$H(s) = s^5 + 11s^4 + 53s^3 + 165s^2 + 300s + 250 \qquad \text{(B-1.5)}$$

the corresponding Routh array is

s^5	1	53	300
s^4	1	15	22.73 (after dividing by 11)
s^3	1	7.30	(after dividing by 38)
s^2	1	2.95	(after dividing by 7.70)
s^1	4.35		
s^0	2.95		(B-1.6)

Since the Routh array of Eq. (B-1.6) contains no sign changes in the first column, the corresponding equation contains no right half-plane roots. This fact is verified by factoring Eq. (B-1.6), i.e.

$$H(s) = (s + 1 + j3)(s + 1 - j3)(s + 2 - j1)(s + 2 - j1)(s + 5) \quad \text{(B-1.7)}$$

EXAMPLE 2: *Unstable System*

Consider now the unstable polynomial

$$(s - 2)(s - 1 + j2)(s - 1 - j2)(s + 10) \qquad \text{(B-1.8)}$$

or equivalently

$$s^4 + 6s^3 - 31s^2 + 80s - 100 \qquad \text{(B-1.9)}$$

Generating the appropriate Routh array

s^4	1	−31	−100
s^3	1	13.33	
s^2	−1	−2.25	(B-1.10)
s^1	1		
s^0	−2.25		

Three sign variations are exhibited by the first-column elements, thus verifying Eq. (B-1.8).

Note that, although the Routh array can be employed to deduce stability characteristics, no insight is provided as to the unstable pole locations. Thus, two positive real-axis poles and two complex right half-plane poles will both yield identical results when submitted to the Routh-array analysis. Often, however, this information will suffice to achieve the purpose of the analytical study, i.e., that of deducing absolute systems stability.

B-2 EXCEPTIONS TO THE RULE

Two main exceptions to the rules of Routh array construction discussed in the previous section frequently appear. Both deal with the generation of zeros in the third and subsequent rows.

The first exception arises if the first element of any row is zero, followed by additional nonzero row elements. When this phenomenon occurs, no additional rows can be formed, because each of the subsequent terms become infinite. Two methods of eliminating this ambiguity are suggested.

1. In place of the first column zero, an arbitrarily small positive number ε is inserted. The criterion of stability remains invariant, and the number of unstable singularities are then computed by standard methods.

2. The original polynomial can be multiplied by a left half-plane singularity $s + \alpha$. The resulting polynomial, when analyzed by the Routh-array technique, will not, in general, generate a zero element. Since the singularity that was introduced is stable, the stability criterion remains unaltered.

To illustrate the first exception, we will consider the polynomial equation

$$M(s) = s^5 + s^4 + s^3 + s^2 + 4s + 1 \qquad \textbf{(B-2.1)}$$

The first three rows of the Routh array are

$$
\begin{array}{llll}
s^5 & 1 & 1 & 4 \\
s^4 & 1 & 1 & 1 \\
s^3 & 0 & 3 &
\end{array}
\qquad \textbf{(B-2.2)}
$$

No additional rows can be formed, due to the zero shown in the s^3 row. Substituting the small positive real number ε for the initial s^3 coefficient, and completing the array

$$
\begin{array}{lccc}
s^5 & 1 & 1 & 4 \\
s^4 & 1 & 1 & 1 \\
s^3 & \varepsilon & 3 & \\
s^2 & \dfrac{\varepsilon - 3}{\varepsilon} & 1 & \\
s^1 & 3 - \dfrac{\varepsilon^2}{\varepsilon - 3} & & \\
s^0 & 1 & &
\end{array}
\qquad \textbf{(B-2.3)}
$$

For $\varepsilon \ll 1$, two sign changes occur in the first-column coefficients, and the original system is judged unstable with a pair of right half-plane singularities.

The second exception to the rules of Section B-1 occurs when all coefficients of one row vanish. (This case also includes the situation in which a row consists of a single element that is zero.) Unlike the first exception, however, this condition has a very real implication in terms of the original system singularity configuration. If an entire row of the Routh array consists of vanishing elements, then the original polynomial contains singularities that are symmetrically disposed about the s-plane origin. Thus, polynomials containing terms of the forms $(s + \alpha)(s - \alpha)$, $(s + j\omega)(s - j\omega)$, and $(s + \alpha + j\beta)(s + \alpha - j\beta)(s - \alpha + j\beta)(s - \alpha - j\beta)$ will all yield Routh arrays falling under the second exception.

The second exception is circumvented as follows: From the last *nonvanishing* row, an auxiliary polynomial is formed. The auxiliary expression is then differentiated with respect to s, and the coefficients of the differentiated polynomial are substituted for the elements of the zero-coefficient row. Once the substitution is complete, the remainder of the Routh array is generated as described earlier, and the stability criterion is used in the usual manner.

A very useful side product of the second exception is that the roots of the auxiliary equation define the original system singularities which are symmetrically disposed about the origin. For example, consider the polynomial equation

$$G(s) = s^4 + 3s^3 + 3s^2 + 3s + 2 \qquad \text{(B-2.4)}$$

The first three rows of the Routh array become

$$
\begin{array}{llll}
s^4 & 1 & 3 & 2 \\
s & 1 & 1 & \text{(after dividing by 3)} \\
s^2 & 1 & 1 & \text{(after dividing by 2)}
\end{array}
$$

The s^1 row vanishes; thus, this condition is an example of the second exception. Forming an auxiliary polynomial from the last nonvanishing row (s^2 row)

$$s^2 + 1 = 0 \qquad \text{(B-2.5)}$$

Differentiating with respect to s, we obtain $2s = 0$. The coefficients 2, 0 are therefore substituted for the elements of the s^1 row and the array is completed.

$$
\begin{array}{lll}
s^4 & 1 & 3 \quad 2 \\
s^3 & 1 & 1 \\
s^2 & 1 & 1 \\
s^1 & 2 \\
s^0 & 1
\end{array}
\qquad \text{(B-2.6)}
$$

No sign variations exist in the first column; thus the system is stable. Solving Eq. (B-2.5), roots of the form $s = \pm j1$ are illustrated; these are also roots of $G(s)$ in Eq. (B-2.4).

As a final example, consider the polynomial equation

$$F(s) = s^5 + s^4 + 4s + 4 \qquad \text{(B-2.7)}$$

The corresponding Routh array contains zeros in the s^3 row, i.e.

$$
\begin{array}{llll}
s^5 & 1 & 0 & 4 \\
s^4 & 1 & 0 & 4 \\
s^3 & 0 & 0 &
\end{array}
\qquad \text{(B-2.8)}
$$

Forming an auxiliary equation from the last nonvanishing row,

$$s^4 + 4 = 0 \qquad \text{(B-2.9)}$$

From Section 2-3 (Chapter 2), we know that Eq. (B-2.9) has the solutions $s = -1 \pm j1$, $1 \pm j1$. Differentiating Eq. (B-2.9) we obtain $4s^3 = 0$. Substituting the coefficients 4, 0 into the s^3 row and completing the Routh array

$$
\begin{array}{lccc}
s^5 & 1 & 0 & 4 \\
s^4 & 1 & 0 & 4 \\
s^3 & 4 & 0 & \\
s^2 & \varepsilon & 4 & \\
s^1 & \dfrac{-16}{\varepsilon} & & \\
s^0 & 4 & &
\end{array}
\qquad \text{(B-2.10)}
$$

Two sign changes, corresponding to the unstable roots $s = 1 \pm j1$ are indicated as expected.

B-3 CALCULATING THE CONDITIONS OF INSTABILITY

In the design of closed-loop control systems, one of the first and most important considerations is that of characterizing the specific value of open-loop gain that results in a marginally stable response. For the majority of practical systems, complex roots of the characteristic equation are observed to migrate, with increasing open-loop gain, into the right half plane. Routh's criterion can be used to compute both the value of gain that results in marginal stability and the point upon the $j\omega$ axis at which the transition occurs. (Stated in slightly different terms, the $j\omega$ crossover point represents the frequency with which the marginally stable system will oscillate when excited by a transient forcing function.)

To illustrate, let us consider the unity-feedback system with the open-loop transfer function

$$KG(s) = \frac{K(s + 0.8)}{s^2(s + 4)(s + 6)} \tag{B-3.1}$$

The corresponding closed-loop transfer function is

$$\frac{C}{R}(s) = \frac{K(s + 0.8)}{s^2(s + 4)(s + 6) + K(s + 0.8)} \tag{B-3.2}$$

and, after expanding the denominator and equating to zero

$$s^4 + 10s^3 + 24s^2 + Ks + 0.8K = 0 \tag{B-3.3}$$

The roots of the characteristic equation will migrate as the loop gain K varies from zero to infinity. To deduce that value of K which yields marginally stable roots, a normal Routh array is generated in terms of the arbitrary gain factor K. Thus

$$
\begin{array}{cccc}
s^4 & 1 & 24 & 0.8K \\[2mm]
s^3 & 10 & K & \\[2mm]
s^2 & \dfrac{240 - K}{10} & 0.8K & \\[4mm]
s^1 & \dfrac{[(240 - K)/10]K - 8K}{(240 - K)/10} &
\end{array}
\tag{B-3.4}
$$

As shown in the previous section, a vanishing s^1 row indicates that two roots are present in Eq. (B-3.3) that are symmetrically disposed about the origin. These are usually of the form $s = \pm j\omega$ (but may on rare occasion be of the type $s = \pm\alpha$). The former situation defines the point of marginal stability. Equating the s^1 row of Eq. (B-3.4) to zero, and solving for K.

$$(240 - K)K - 80K = 0$$

$$K = 160 \tag{B-3.5}$$

Hence, for a gain constant of 160, roots are generated that are symmetrical with respect to the origin. Substituting this value into an auxiliary polynomial formed from the last nonvanishing row of Eq. (B-3.4)

$$\frac{240 - K}{10} s^2 + 0.8K = 0 \tag{B-3.6}$$

$$s^2 + 16 = 0$$

Solving Eq. (B-3.6) we obtain $s = \pm j4$. Thus, the frequency of oscillation associated with Eq. (B-3.2) at the point of marginal stability is 4 radians/sec.

BIBLIOGRAPHY

1. Routh, E. J., *Dynamics of a System of Rigid Bodies: Part II, Advanced*. London, Macmillan & Co., Ltd., 1905.

PARTIAL PROBLEM SOLUTIONS

CHAPTER 3

3.1   (a) $-V_{\text{in}} + IR + L_1\dfrac{dI}{dt} + \dfrac{1}{C}\int I\,dt + L_2\dfrac{dI}{dt} = 0$, $V_{\text{out}} = L_2\dfrac{dI}{dt}$

       (c) $-V_{\text{in}} + IR_1 + L_1\dfrac{dI}{dt} + \dfrac{1}{C_1}\int I\,dt + IR_2 + L_2\dfrac{dI}{dt} + \dfrac{1}{C_2}\int I\,dt = 0$

       $-V_{\text{in}} + (R_1 + R_2)I + (L_1 + L_2)\dfrac{dI}{dt} + \left(\dfrac{1}{C_1} + \dfrac{1}{C_2}\right)\int I\,dt = 0$

       $V_{\text{out}} = IR_2 + L_2\dfrac{dI}{dt} + \dfrac{1}{C_2}\int I\,dt$

3.2 (a) $V_{in} = 1.1 \times 10^6 I + 2 \times 10^6 \int I \, dt$, $V_{out} = 10^6 I$

(c) $\dfrac{V_{in} - V_1}{37 \times 10^3} + 2 \times 10^{-7} \dfrac{d(V_{in} - V_1)}{dt} = 10^{-6} \dfrac{d(V_1 - V_{out})}{dt}$

$10^{-6} \dfrac{d(V_1 - V_{out})}{dt} = \dfrac{V_{out} - V_2}{5 \times 10^3}$, $\dfrac{V_{out} - V_2}{5 \times 10^3} = 2 \times 10^{-6} \dfrac{dV_2}{dt}$

3.3 (b) Loop 1: $-V_{in} + I_1 R_1 + L_1 \dfrac{dI_1}{dt} + L_3 \dfrac{d(I_1 - I_2)}{dt} + \dfrac{1}{C_2} \int (I_1 - I_2) \, dt$

$- M_{21} \dfrac{dI_2}{dt} + M_{31} \dfrac{d(I_1 - I_2)}{dt} + M_{13} \dfrac{dI_1}{dt} - M_{23} \dfrac{dI_2}{dt} = 0$

Loop 2: $\dfrac{1}{C_2} \int (I_2 - I_1) \, dt + L_3 \dfrac{d(I_2 - I_1)}{dt} + L_2 \dfrac{dI_2}{dt} + R_2 I_2$

$+ \dfrac{1}{C_1} \int I_2 \, dt + I_2 R_3 - M_{13} \dfrac{dI_1}{dt} + M_{23} \dfrac{dI_2}{dt} - M_{12} \dfrac{dI_1}{dt} + M_{32} \dfrac{d(I_2 - I_1)}{dt} = 0$

3.6 (b) $65 - 30x - 20 \dfrac{dx}{dt} = 3 \dfrac{d^2 x}{dt^2}$

(d) $M_1 \dfrac{d^2 x_1}{dt^2} = - K_1 x_1 - K_2 (x_1 - x_2) - B_1 \left(\dfrac{dx_1}{dt} - \dfrac{dx_2}{dt} \right)$

$M_2 \dfrac{d^2 x_2}{dt^2} = F - K_2 (x_2 - x_1) - B_1 \left(\dfrac{dx_2}{dt} - \dfrac{dx_1}{dt} \right)$

$- K_3 (x_2 - x_3) - B_2 \left(\dfrac{dx_2}{dt} - \dfrac{dx_3}{dt} \right)$

$M_3 \dfrac{d^2 x_3}{dt^2} = - K_3 (x_3 - x_2) - B_2 \left(\dfrac{dx_3}{dt} - \dfrac{dx_2}{dt} \right) - K_4 x_3 - B_3 \dfrac{dx_3}{dt}$

3.7 $L = J_1 \dfrac{d^2 \theta_1}{dt^2} + B_1 \dfrac{d\theta_1}{dt} + K_2 (\theta_1 - \theta_2)$

$0 = J_2 \dfrac{d^2 \theta_2}{dt^2} + B_2 + K_2 (\theta_2 - \theta_1)$

3.9 $F = M_2 \dfrac{d^2 x_2}{dt^2} + B \dfrac{dx_2}{dt} + K(x_2 - x_1)$

$0 = M_1 \dfrac{d^2 x_1}{dt^2} + B \dfrac{dx_1}{dt} + B_1 \dfrac{dx_1}{dt} + K(x_1 - x_2)$

$E_{arm} = \dfrac{E}{2} \cdot \dfrac{1}{d} x_2 = \dfrac{1}{C} \int I \, dt + (R_1 + R_{23}) I$, $R_{23} = \dfrac{R_2 R_3}{R_2 + R_3}$

$E_o = R_{23} I$

CHAPTER 4

4.2   (a) $\theta(s) = \dfrac{18}{(s^2 + 36)(s^2 + 3s + 4)}$; (c) $Y = \dfrac{5s^2}{s^3 + 1}$

(d) $x(s) = \dfrac{-2(s + 3)}{s^2 + 4s - 2}$; (e) $\theta(s) = \dfrac{s^2 + s + 1}{s(s^2 + 1)(s^4 + s^3 + 6s^2 + 12s + 1)}$

4.4   (a) $x(t) = \frac{1}{2} - e^{-t} + \frac{1}{2}e^{-2t}$

(b) $x(t) = \frac{1}{1296}e^{-6t} - \frac{1}{1296} + \frac{1}{216}t - \frac{1}{72}t^2 + \frac{1}{36}t^3$

(c) $x(t) = \frac{16}{3} - 8e^{-t} + \frac{8}{3}e^{-3t}$

(d) $x(t) = 6te^{-120t}$; (e) $x(t) = 1 - e^{-t} - te^{-t} - \frac{1}{2}t^2e^{-t}$

(f) $x(t) = \frac{1}{51}e^{12t} - \frac{1}{51}\cos 3t - \frac{4}{51}\sin 3t$

(g) $x(t) = \frac{1}{24}t^4$; (h) $x(t) = \frac{2}{3} - \frac{2}{3}e^{-t}\cos \sqrt{5}t - \frac{2}{3}\sqrt{5}e^{-t}\sin \sqrt{5}t$

(i) $x(t) = 1 - \cos t - t \sin t/2$

(j) $x(t) = \frac{1}{20}e^{-t} - \frac{1}{20}e^{-3t}\cos 4t - \frac{1}{40}e^{-3t}\sin 4t$

4.6   (a) $x(t) = 0.90 - 0.90e^{-1.67t}\cos 2.69t - 1.3e^{-1.67t}\sin 2.69t$

4.7   (a) $x(t) = \frac{1}{2}\sinh 2t$;   (b) $x(t) = 2 \sinh t$

   $y(t) = \frac{1}{2}(1 - \frac{1}{2}\sinh 2t)$ $y(t) = 1 - 2 \cosh t$

4.8   (a) Initial $= 100$, final $= 50$; (c) Initial $= \infty$, Final $= 0$;

   Initial $= 0.27$, final $= 1.745$

4.9   (a) $x(t) = e^{-t} - e^{-2t}$

(b) $x(t) = \frac{1}{11} - \frac{1}{11}e^{-3t}\cos \sqrt{2}t - 3e^{-3t}\sin \sqrt{2}t/11\sqrt{2}$

(e) $x(t) = \delta(t) - 3e^{-3t}$ (f) $x(t) = \cos t/\sqrt{5}$

4.10   (a) $5/s - 4e^{-2s}/s - e^{-6s}/s$ (b) $1.5/s^2 - 1.5e^{-2s}/s^2 - 3e^{-6s}/s$

(c) $\dfrac{4}{s^2} - \dfrac{11/2}{s^2}e^{-s} + \dfrac{3/2}{s^2}e^{-3s} + \dfrac{2}{s}e^{-5s}$

CHAPTER 5

5.1   (a) $V_{\text{in}}(s) = (R + 1/Cs + Ls)I(s)$, $V_{\text{out}}(s) = (1/Cs + Ls)I(s)$

(b) $\dfrac{V_{\text{in}} - V_{\text{out}}}{sL_1} = \dfrac{V_{\text{out}}}{R_1 + 1/C_1s} + \dfrac{V_{\text{out}}}{sL_2} + \dfrac{V_{\text{out}}}{1/C_2s + L_3s}$

5.3   (a) $G(j\omega) = \dfrac{2\omega^2}{4\omega^2 + 1} + j\left(\dfrac{\omega}{4\omega^2 + 1}\right)$, $G(j1) = 0.45e^{j26.5°}$

   $G(j10) = 0.5e^{j2.9°}$

(b) $G(j\omega) = \dfrac{2\omega^2 + 1}{4\omega^2 + 1} - j\left(\dfrac{\omega}{4\omega^2 + 1}\right)$, $G(j1) = 0.633e^{-j18.4°}$,

   $G(j10) = 0.501e^{-j2.8°}$

CHAPTER 6

6.1 (a) $\theta(t) = -[x(t) + y(t) + 10z(t)]$;

(b) $\theta(t) = -\int [x(t) - 10y(t) - 5z(t)]\,dt$

(c) $\theta(t) = -\frac{1}{2}x(t) + 5y(t) - 10z(t)$;

(d) $\theta(t) = -\int [5x(t) + \frac{1}{4}y(t) + \frac{1}{2}z(t)]\,dt$

(e) $\theta(t) = \dfrac{x(t) - y(t)}{2}$; (f) $\theta(t) = -x(t) - 10^{-4}\dfrac{d^2y}{dt^2} - 10^{-4}\dfrac{dz}{dt}$

CHAPTER 7

7.1 (a) $\dfrac{C}{E}(s) = \dfrac{64(s + 1.5)}{(s + 1)(s + 2)(s^3 + 6s^2 + 4s + 6)[(s + 1.5)^2 + 3.75]}$

7.2 (a) $\dfrac{C}{E}(s) = G_1G_2(G_3 + G_4G_5)$; (b) $\dfrac{G_1(G_2 - G_3G_4)}{1 + G_1H}$; (c) $\dfrac{G_1G_2G_3}{1 - G_2G_3 + G_1G_2G_3H}$

7.3 (a) $\dfrac{C}{R}(s)$

$= \dfrac{1.88 \times 10^6(s + 1000)(s + 765)}{s^2(s + 400)(s + 200)(s + 650)(s + 765) + 1.88 \times 10^6(s + 1000)(s + 740)}$

7.4 (b) $x(s) = \dfrac{1000 - 50s(s^2 + 3s + 20)}{s[s^2(s^2 + 3s + 20) + 10]}$

CHAPTER 8

8.1 (a) $\tau = 0.25$, $\omega_b = 4$; (d) $\tau = 0.001$, $\omega_b = 1000$

8.3 (a) $\zeta = 0.28$, $\omega_n = 1.635$; (b) $\zeta = 0.34$, $\omega_n = 334$,

8.5 (a) $\zeta = 0.473$, $\omega_n = 17.5$; (b) $\zeta = 0.22$, $\omega_n = 274$

8.6 2.4, 476, 22.8, 411

CHAPTER 9

9.1 (a) $K_p = \infty$, $K_v = \dfrac{K_1}{4400}$, $K_a = 0$

9.2 $\varepsilon_s = 0$, $\varepsilon_v = \frac{4}{30}$, $\varepsilon_a = \infty$

9.4 $\varepsilon_s = 0$, $\varepsilon_v = 0$, $\varepsilon_a = \frac{1}{7.5}$

CHAPTER 10

10.2 $s = -5.76, -104.2$

10.3 $K = 900$

10.4 (a) $K = 308$, $\omega = 5.3$ radians/sec; (c) 545, 6.8

10.5 $s = -1.04, -7.09, -2.4 \pm j8.2$

10.6 (a) $C/R(s) = \dfrac{3400}{(s + 34)(s^2 + 6s + 100)}$

10.11 (a) 1.71; (b) $C/R(s) = \dfrac{1.71(s - 3)(s + 7)}{s[(s + 6.36)^2 + 1.56^2]}$

10.12 (c) $\dfrac{C}{R}(s) = \dfrac{1000(s + 11)(s + 16)(s + 26)}{(s + 5.8)(s + 15.7)[(s + 0.76)^2 + 10.3^2][(s + 32)^2 + 10.5^2]}$

10.13 (a) $s = -0.36 \pm j1.22, -6.13 \pm j3.43$
   (b) $s = 1.05 \pm j2.03, -1.92 \pm j1.77, -30.3$
   (c) $s = -1.33 \pm j1.06, 4.43 \pm j2.54, -22.2$
   (d) $s = -3.95 \pm j.82, +.91 \pm j3.11, -.97 \pm j4.34$

10.14 (a) $1.12e^{j30°}, 3.3e^{j81°}$; (b) $2.5e^{-j2.5°}, 2.45e^{-j12.5°}$; (c) $1.68e^{j110°}, 1.25e^{j5°}$

10.16 $\tau = 0.22$

10.19 (a) $K = 6.23$; (b) $\dfrac{\theta_o}{\theta_i}(s) = \dfrac{6.23(s + 2)(s + 10)}{(s - 1)(s + 5.9)(s + 21.1)}$

CHAPTER 11

11.1 (a) stable; (b) stable; (c) stable; (d) unstable

11.2 (a) unstable; (b) unstable; (e) stable

11.3 (a) 0; (b) not possible; (g) 4

11.4 (a) stable; (c) unstable

11.6 yes

CHAPTER 12

12.1 (a) 1.67; (b) 1.37

12.2 2.08, 0.885

12.3 (a) I; (b) III; (c) 0; (d) IV

12.4 (a) 25°, 4.25 radians/sec

12.6 $\omega_{co} = 6.3, GM = \infty, \phi_M = 46.5°$

CHAPTER 13

13.2 $G(s) = \dfrac{8[(s/2) + 1][(s/4) + 1]}{s[(s/8) + 1][(s/24) + 1](s/36) + 1]}$

13.3 (b) $\omega_{co} = 5.9, GM = \infty, \phi_M = 36°$

13.4 (a) I; (b) III

13.6 (b) 6470

13.7 (b) 23.4

INDEX